DANIEL McNAUGHTON

HIS TRIAL AND THE AFTERMATH

Edited by

DONALD J. WEST and ALEXANDER WALK

GASKELL BOOKS

1977

ROYAL COLLEGE OF PSYCHIATRISTS

© 1977

ISBN 902241 01 X

Published for

The British Journal of Psychiatry

by

Headley Brothers Ltd, Ashford, Kent

CONTRIBUTORS

PATRICIA ALLDERIDGE — Archivist, Bethlem Royal and Maudsley Hospitals, London, England

B. L. DIAMOND — Professor of Law and of Health and Medical Sciences, University of California, Berkeley; Professor of Clinical Psychiatry, University of California, San Francisco, USA

A. S. GOLDSTEIN — Sterling Professor of Law, Yale Law School, New Haven, Connecticut, USA

E. H. HARE — Physician, Bethlem Royal and Maudsley Hospitals, London, England

SIR R. F. G. ORMROD — Lord Justice of Appeal, Royal Courts of Justice, London, England

M. MARCUS — Research Fellow, Yale Law School 1975/76, New Haven, Connecticut, USA

H. R. ROLLIN — Consultant Psychiatrist, Horton Hospital, Epsom, Surrey, England

A. WALK (*Editor*) — Late Physician Superintendent, Cane Hill Hospital, Coulsdon, Surrey, England; Past President, Royal Medico-Psychological Association

N. D. WALKER — Wolfson Professor of Criminology, University of Cambridge, England

L. WALLER — Sir Leo Cussen Professor of Law, Monash University, Victoria, Australia

D. J. WEST (*Editor*) — Reader in Clinical Criminology, University of Cambridge, England

CONTENTS

CONTENTS

Sketch portrait of Daniel McNaughton at the time of his trial. [*Illustrated London News*, March 1843. For the spelling see p 89 footnote].

EDITOR'S PREFACE

Every lawyer and psychiatrist knows the McNaughton Rules concerning mental responsibility in English law; relatively few are familiar with the details of the trial of 1843 which brought them about. The idea, as soon as it was put forward by Lord Justice Ormrod, of reproducing the original report of the trial from *State Trials* was immediately accepted as fulfilling an obvious need. Commentaries on the historic medico-legal consequences followed as a matter of course, and so this publication came into being.

On 20 January 1843, Daniel McNaughton, acting under the influence of delusions of persecution, and apparently under the impression that he was attacking the Prime Minister, Sir Robert Peel, fired at and mortally wounded Edward Drummond, who was Sir Robert's Private Secretary. In view of the medical evidence presented, the judge interrupted the trial and directed the jury to find McNaughton not guilty on the ground of insanity. The verdict provoked so much comment that the House of Lords resolved to ask the judges to give opinions on the several points of law involved. Their opinions, known as the McNaughton Rules, were destined to influence the law on insanity in English-speaking countries for more than a century. The opinions are summarized at the beginning of the report of the trial (although, of course, they were not formulated until afterwards) and a more extended version is given as a postscript. They incorporate the famous dictum that if an offender knew that what he was doing was wrong he was legally sane and subject to punishment.

The report of the case in *State Trials* is not the only account available. In his contribution to this volume, Dr E. H. Hare analyses the differences between this and the abbreviated version contained in the *Annual Register* for 1843. One of the differences, the spelling of McNaughton's name, is still a matter of active controversy and an editorial decision has had to be made. The *British Journal of Psychiatry* and its predecessor, the *Journal of Mental Science*, have for many years adhered to the spelling 'McNaughton', which is that of the Bethlem and Broadmoor case-notes, and there seemed no good reason to depart from this, especially as Professor Diamond's account of the controversy, which is reprinted in this collection, makes it clear that the use of the more widespread spelling 'M'Naghten', is more a matter of convention that of historical exactitude. In the report from *State Trials* the name has been left as Daniel M'Naughton (a printer's variant), and in quotes from other original sources the spelling, however varied, has generally been reproduced unchanged.

For readers who come relatively fresh to the topic the first contribution,

1

Sir Roger Ormrod's outline of the historical context of the trial, and his lucid explanation of the legal issues at stake, acts as an introduction and provides a key to the arguments contained in the trial report. Dr Henry Rollin's chapter analyses the evidence which emerges from the trial transcript as to the nature of McNaughton's mental condition, and then goes on to describe the course of the illness after the patient's committal to hospital. After this comes Patricia Allderidge's historical account of the development of provisions for the housing of offenders found insane. She explains why, following his trial, McNaughton was placed in Bethlem Hospital, and she describes what that institution was like at the time. The next contribution, by Dr Walk, brings together extracts from the *Lancet* and other periodicals to illustrate the reaction of contemporary medical authorities to the McNaughton trial decision and to the Rules that followed. The problems and injustices likely to arise from a definition of insanity based exclusively upon intellectual awareness were immediately appreciated. Although some medical men were sensitive to the possibility that even the mentally ill might on occasion be deterred from crime by the prospect of hanging, the general view then, as now, was that the execution of the mentally afflicted was morally indefensible. Quite soon a modern-sounding argument was being put forward to the effect that all offenders have a right to humane, rehabilitative treatment regardless of their mental state.

In the next chapter, extracted from the first volume of his book *Crime and Insanity in England* (Edinburgh University Press, 1968), Professor Walker traces the history of the application of the McNaughton Rules in English courts from 1843 to modern times. He shows that criticisms of the Rules by physicians, lawyers and by a Royal Commission, on the grounds that they were unduly restrictive in failing to recognize abnormal impulses deriving from deranged emotions, produced singularly little result. Appeal decisions continued to uphold strict interpretations. Juries might disregard the Rules for the sake of preventing the hanging of offenders whose condition aroused their sympathy, but the letter of the law remained stubbornly unreformed until the Homicide Act of 1957. This introduced a new concept of diminished responsibility in murder cases, rendering resort to the awkward Rules of insanity unnecessary. However, McNaughton's ghost is insecurely laid. The Rules still exist, and should a defendant to a lesser charge than murder be so mad as to avail himself of them successfully, he may avoid a possible prison sentence at the cost of automatic committal to hospital for an indefinite period.

Professor Goldstein and Martin Marcus, describing the application of the McNaughton principles in the United States, recount a different story. The McNaughton Rules, or variations upon them, operate to this day in many States of the Union, but generally speaking American judicial decision have not, as in England, sought to impose a restrictive interpretation of the fateful words 'know the nature and quality of the act'. If an offender is too sick to appreciate fully the consequences of his actions or the enormity of his crime it is arguable that he does not truly 'know' what he is doing. The authors blame American psychiatrists and lawyers for failing to exploit this to the full when

2

presenting an insanity defence, and for assuming without justification that the Rules prohibit consideration of anything other than gross cognitive defect.

The final contribution, Professor Waller's review of the continuing application of the Rules in Australia, and the difficulties that have resulted therefrom, leave no doubt that McNaughton's ghost still manifests in some parts of the world. The last three contributions demonstrate striking similarities and equally striking differences between America, Australia and England in the way the Rules have been interpreted, and in the parts of the wording which have received most emphasis or caused most controversy.

The difficulty of defining the legal criteria whereby a criminal may be excused punishment on account of his mental condition has never been overcome. Where modifications or extensions of the Rules are in force, these have in turn led to renewed controversy. A recent authoritative review of the position in England is to be found in the (Butler) *Report of the Committee on Mentally Abnormal Offenders*, London, HMSO, 1975. Although the special verdict of 'Not guilty by reason of insanity' is rarely used in England, the Committee recommend its retention, but with a change in nomenclature to 'Not guilty on evidence of mental disorder'. They suggest that the court should have discretion instead of being obliged to commit every such offender to indefinite detention in hospital. They recommend that in place of the McNaughton criteria it should suffice to show that an offender was suffering from severe mental illness or severe subnormality or from any mental disorder (within the meaning of S4 of the Mental Health Act, 1959) that negatives the intention, foresight or knowledge necessary to the commission of a crime in English law.

The steam has gone out of this controversy today, not so much because satisfactory solutions have emerged, but because attention has been diverted to other issues. Recent decisions by the Supreme Court in the United States threaten to reverse the situation, but the abolition or suspension of capital punishment has meant that the insanity issue in murder trials is no longer a matter of life or death. The question of what type of institution, prison or hospital should detain the abnormal offender does not arouse the same emotion. Even this lesser issue has lost some of its importance with the development of provisions for psychiatric treatment in prisons, or for the transfer from prison to hospital of needy cases. In England, the system of Hospital Orders, introduced by the Mental Health Act, 1959, gives discretion to courts (in all save murder cases) to act upon psychiatric recommendation and substitute admission to hospital for imprisonment without reference to rules of criminal responsibility. The exact nature or extent of an offender's illness at the time of the crime is of less concern today than such questions as how best or where best to treat him, how long to detain him, how to assess his potential dangerousness if set at liberty, and who should be responsible for deciding his date of release. All of these matters have received detailed examination in the Butler Report.

D. J. WEST

THE McNAUGHTON CASE AND ITS PREDECESSORS[1]

SIR ROGER ORMROD

The case of the *Queen* v. *Daniel McNaughton* was the latest of a group of three cases which, within the relatively short period of forty years between 1800 and 1843, very nearly succeeded in transforming the legal concept of insanity in criminal cases from mediaeval notions to something approximating to contemporary ideas.

The three cases were *Hadfield*[2] (1800), *Oxford*[3] (1840) and *McNaughton*[4] (1843). They have many features in common; in all three, the defence of insanity succeeded; in all three the preparation and conduct of the defence followed the same pattern, and the same or very similar legal submissions were made. At the same time they stand out as a group in striking contrast to earlier cases such as *Arnold*[5] (1724) and *Ferrers*[6] (1760) and to some contemporary with them such as *Bowler*[7] (1812) and *Bellingham*[8] (1812).

The history of insanity as a defence in serious criminal cases demonstrates the extraordinary difficulty that lawyers, at all periods until quite recently, seem to have experienced in comprehending the effects of mental disease and in relating these effects to the basic principles of the criminal law. Chief Justice Hale, writing in the middle of the seventeenth century struggled with the problem. He recognized 'ideocy' (severe subnormality); 'melancholy' (depression); 'total alienation of the mind or perfect madness'; and 'phrenesis' (lunacy, i.e. intermittent bouts of madness believed to be influenced by the moon). 'Ideots' and persons suffering from total alienation of the mind were excused from the guilt of felony. But the other groups presented the age-old dilemma to the lawyer which Hale expressed in simple and vivid language: 'It is very difficult to define the indivisible line which divides perfect and partial

---

[1] The spelling varies in contemporary accounts, e.g. in four State Trials it is spelt M'Naughton and there are other variants. McNaughton is presumably correct, because in the Metropolitan Police file, preserved in the Record Office, there is an original signature 'Daniel McNaughton' at the foot of a brief written statement made by the accused at the conclusion of the committal proceedings at Bow Street Magistrates Court. The content of the statement is similar to but, curiously, not identical with that set out on page 25 of the report of the trial.
[2] (1800) 27 St. Tr. 1282.
[3] (1840) 4 St. Tr. (new series) 498.
[4] (1843) 4 St. Tr. (new series) 847.
[5] (1724) 16 St. Tr. 695.
[6] (1760) 19 St. Tr. 885.
[7] Collinson 673 n. Collinson, G. D., *A treatise on the law of idiots, lunatics, and other persons 'non compotes mentis'.* London, 1812.
[8] Collinson 636.

4

insanity, but it must rest upon circumstances duly to be weighed and considered both by the judge and jury, lest on the one hand there be a kind of inhumanity towards the defects of human nature, or on the other side too great an indulgence given to great crimes.' The only solution he could suggest was 'the best measure that I can think of is this; such a person as labouring under melancholy distempers hath yet ordinarily as great understanding, as ordinarily a child of fourteen years hath, is such a person as may be guilty of treason or felony'.[9] Blackstone,[10] writing a hundred years later, in 1765, had nothing to add to this view, but in later cases a significant change can be discerned. Hale chose 14 years of age as his standard because the common law presumed that a child under that age could not distinguish between right and wrong, although the presumption could be rebutted if he or she were over 12 years. Judges now began to ask juries the specific question 'Do you think that the prisoner was capable of distinguishing right from wrong.' (It was put thus in both *Bowler* and *Bellingham* with fatal consequences to both prisoners, and it was to be re-stated and re-emphasized in the reaction which followed *McNaughton* and still forms an essential element in the defence of insanity, to the dismay and confusion of generations of psychiatrists.)

The great advance which was made in *Hadfield*'s case, and seemingly consolidated in *Oxford* and *McNaughton*, was the recognition by the judges of the power which paranoid delusions can exert over the behaviour of individuals who are subject to them. This was achieved very largely by the efforts of one man, Erskine, who in defending Hadfield succeeded in demonstrating to the judges who tried that case the knowledge and understanding of the effects of such delusions which had been acquired quite recently by doctors studying mental disease. Erskine was one of the most brilliant advocates the Bar has ever produced and was afterwards Lord Chancellor. It was a lucky chance that brought him into Hadfield's case, for Hadfield, who had shot at George III in Drury Lane Theatre, missed his aim, and so was charged, not with murder, but with treason. It was the long-established practice in treason cases (but not in others, including murder) for the judges to 'assign' counsel and solicitors for the defence, but leaving the prisoner to choose his own counsel. Hadfield or his solicitors chose Erskine. The background made the case an ideal one for the reformers. Hadfield was an ex-sergeant in the Army, with a fine war record; some years before, he had sustained severe head injuries in battle which had seriously affected his behaviour, and he had failed even to injure the King. Clearly, his case excited sympathy on all sides.

Erskine set out to establish his client's case in the greatest detail. He called a large number of ordinary witnesses who gave evidence of Hadfield's bizarre behaviour to prove the fact that he was deluded; he called a surgeon to prove the nature of the head injuries, which consisted of a wound on the temple which had not damaged the brain, a penetrating wound above the eyebrow which had damaged the brain, and two other penetrating wounds; and finally he called

[9] Pleas of the Crown 1736, p. 30 et seq.
[10] Blackstone, *Commentaries on the Laws of England*, Vol. IV, p. 24.

Dr Alexander Crichton, a psychiatrist, to give expert evidence of Hadfield's state of mind. Crichton affirmed that Hadfield was insane. The effect of this evidence and of Erskine's address to the court was so great that the presiding judge, Lord Kenyon, stopped the trial and ordered Hadfield to be detained. His address was a remarkable exposition of current medical knowledge about delusions and their effects, and contains perhaps the best formulation of what later came to be called the defence of 'irresistible impulse'. He summed up his argument in these words: 'I must convince you, not only that the unhappy prisoner was a lunatic, within my own definition of lunacy, but that the act in question was the immediate unqualified offspring of the disease.' Long extracts from this speech are to be found in the report of the McNaughton trial.

The same pattern was followed with success in Oxford's case. He shot at, and missed, Queen Victoria while she was driving up Constitution Hill. Witness after witness was called to speak not only of his peculiar behaviour but also of his father's and grandfather's madness. No less than four doctors were called to give expert evidence of his mental condition, including the famous Dr Conolly of Hanwell Asylum. Like Hadfield, Oxford was charged with treason and so had counsel and solicitors 'assigned' to him.

The defence of McNaughton followed closely the lines established by Erskine in Hadfield's case. He, however, was indicted for murder, and consequently was not entitled to have counsel assigned to him by the court. Nevertheless, not only was he represented by solicitors and counsel but a most elaborate defence was organized, and in an incredibly short time. He was a wood-turner from Glasgow in his early thirties, suffering from persistent, if vague, delusions of persecution by what he called 'the Tories'. Eventually he made his way to London, where he was friendless and unknown, and began to hang about the Government offices in Whitehall. It will be seen from the evidence of P.C. James Silver of 'A' Division that he fired the shot at Mr Drummond literally 'with a policeman at his elbow', close enough, in fact, to prevent him from firing his second pistol.

Thereafter, things moved very fast indeed. He was immediately arrested and brought before a magistrate at Bow Street police court. On the following day he was committed for trial at the Old Bailey and his case appeared in the list for trial on 2 February, only 13 days after the shooting and 8 days after Mr Drummond's death on 25 January. By 2 February he was represented by solicitors and counsel, Mr Clarkson, who applied for an adjournment to enable the defence to be prepared. He was given a month only, and the trial began on 3 March before Chief Justice Tindal, Mr Justice Williams and Mr Justice Coleridge and a jury. By then, McNaughton was represented by four eminent counsel, Alexander Cockburn, Q.C., Clarkson, Bodkin and Monteith. His solicitor was Mr W. C. Humphries, of No. 119 Newgate Street. As the report shows, by 3 March, only six weeks after the shooting, the defence were in a position to call no less than nine witnesses as to the accused's abnormal behaviour, including the Lord Provost of Glasgow and the Commissioner for Police at Glasgow, and eight medical witnesses, including Dr E. T. Monro and

Sir Alexander Morison, Physicians to Bethlem Hospital, and Dr W. Hutcheson of the Royal Lunatic Asylum, Glasgow. How this was organized and by whom is an intriguing question which can only be answered in part. Obviously the costs of such a defence must have been very heavy, and some person or persons must have been very strongly motivated to undertake and carry out so much work in so short a time. There are, however, a few, mostly tantalizing clues.

In the Appendix to a report[11] of the trial published by the shorthand-writers, there is a detailed account of the proceedings at the Old Bailey on 2 February, when the application for an adjournment was made, and this includes an affidavit sworn by the solicitor, Mr Humphries, in which he asked the court to release to him, as solicitor for the defence, a receipt for £750 standing to McNaughton's credit at the Glasgow & Shipping Bank. Although refusing to hand over the receipt, the Attorney-General agreed to make the money available to the defence. This probably explains, at least in part, how the defence was financed.

McNaughton himself was clearly incapable of instructing a solicitor, but in the Metropolitan Police file in the Public Record Office there is a letter dated 30 January from a Mr Thomas Deans, a solicitor, saying that he had been instructed by the father of Daniel McNaughton to 'take charge of his Defence', and that he had employed Mr Humphries to act as his agent.

In the Appendix referred to above there is also a letter from Mr Humphries to the Treasury Solicitor, Mr G. Maule, dated 31 January, which refers to the fact that McNaughton had been provided by the police with numerous depositions taken, presumably by the police, in London and in Glasgow. This is to some extent confirmed by a long report, also contained in the Record Office file, of enquiries made in Glasgow about McNaughton by a Mr George Stephens, a police officer, dated 22 January, i.e. within 48 hours of the shooting.

But the intensity of the interest and concern of those involved in the case seems to suggest that they were activated by something more than the fate of an obscure Scotsman who had murdered an innocent victim by mistake. There are some interesting coincidences. Of the four counsel for the defence, one, Bodkin, had successfully defended Oxford three years earlier. Dr E. T. Monro, as appears from an answer which he gave at the trial, had been asked to examine Oxford on behalf of the prosecution but was not called as a witness at his trial. Bodkin, who was afterwards a judge at the Middlesex Sessions, seems to have had a special interest in social problems, for he was secretary of a body called 'The Society for the Suppression of Mendicity'. Curiously, Hadfield's solicitor, forty-three years earlier, had also been a Mr Humphries although with different Christian names. Cockburn himself, from the whole tenor of his speech and the immense effort entailed, obviously took the most intense personal interest in the case. He was just at the beginning of a very distinguished legal career, having been appointed Q.C. in 1841. He was afterwards Solicitor-General, Attorney-General, and Lord Chief Justice of England for 20 years. There is no doubt about the widespread concern at this period in the medical profession about the law's attitude to insanity as a defence to serious crimes, most of which at that

---

[11] Bonsfield and Merrett. London, 1843.

period were capital offences. All the circumstances of the McNaughton case suggest that this most ably conducted defence was organized by what today would be called a 'pressure group' of people, seriously concerned to bring about a much-needed reform of the law on insanity in criminal cases.

There is some reason to think that the situation was also troubling some of the judges. The alacrity with which Lord Kenyon accepted Erskine's novel argument in Hadfield's case was closely paralleled by Chief Justice Tindal's reaction to Cockburn's submissions in McNaughton's case. In both cases the judges, in effect, stopped the trial, by instructing the jury to find the prisoner not guilty on the ground of insanity. On the other hand, there had been two cases between Hadfield and McNaughton in which obviously deluded killers had been tried according to the older conception of insanity and had been hanged. These were the cases of Bowler (1812) and Bellingham (1812), but both were adversely criticized in the Oxford trial. Of Bowler's case, Baron Alderson remarked 'Bowler, I believe, was executed and very barbarous it was', while the Attorney-General (then Sir John Campbell) declined to support the Bellingham decision, conceding that the trial had not been properly conducted. Campbell was, in fact, Lord Chief Justice at the time of the McNaughton case.

The essence of Cockburn Q.C.'s argument is contained in this passage in his speech: 'The question is . . . whether under that delusion of mind he did an act which he would not have done under any other circumstances, save under the impulse of the delusion which he could not control and out of which delusion alone the act itself arose' (see later, p. 11). The evidence of the doctors, particularly that of Dr Monro and Sir Alexander Morison, directly supported this submission. The judges were so impressed by this and the other medical evidence that they, in effect, stopped the case, although Tindall C.J. in a brief summing-up to the jury avoided the issue by suggesting to them that if they thought the prisoner capable of distinguishing right from wrong then he was subject to all the penalties the law imposes (the old test), but 'If not so, and if in your judgment the subject should appear involved in very great difficulty, then you will probably not take upon yourselves to find the prisoner guilty.'

To those concerned to mitigate the rigour of the law in these cases it must have seemed that they had now achieved their aim. Certainly the law on insanity seemed to be evolving in accordance with the normal process by which the law is slowly adapted to take account of new knowledge and social change. But in this respect the evolutionary process in England and, in consequence, in most of the Common Law countries, such as the United States and the countries of the Commonwealth (but not in Scotland where English law does not apply), was brought to an abrupt and complete halt.

The decision in the McNaughton case provoked an immediate and intense reaction in the press and in Parliament. *The Times* published the following irritated letter (6 March 1843):

Sir,

If the result of McNaughton's trial satisfies the end of justice, by proving the moral irresponsibility of the murderer, it undoubtedly leaves the security of Her Majesty's subjects from similar murderous attacks in a very unsatisfactory state. McNaughton is not the only dangerous lunatic at large—nay, his case is so common, that a term has been invented to designate it, and was employed by his counsel, viz, 'homicidal monomania', in plain English, an irresistible impulse on the part of the maniac for blood—to put someone to death. The question then is, is the law sufficient for the protection of the public? Is there no responsibility on the part of the relatives in leaving such dangerous lunatics at large? It appears in evidence that the father was twice warned as to the state of his son's mind—once by the Provost of Glasgow, whose station ought to have given weight to his opinion; but to neither was any attention paid, and it is to be regretted that such culpable neglect and recklessness of consequences cannot be resisted by the law. We read in Dr. Monro's evidence that the assassin said that at one time he would have shot Mr. Sheriff Bell dead in his seat in the court of justice, if he had a pistol, and no one can doubt that Mr. Bell might have been the victim. Again, it appears that one of his illusions was that he had been attacked by paragraphs in *The Times* and the *Glasgow Herald*: it is quite as probable that McNaughton should have carried out his revenge on his fancied persecutors, and exercised his 'homicidal monomania' by waiting at the office of your journal, Sir, and shooting the first man who came out of the door, as that he should have taken the life of Mr. Drummond.

One word on the affected sentimentality of the day. A perusal of the second day's proceedings in the Central Criminal Court would almost persuade us to give our sympathy to the murderer, and not to the murdered. No words applicable to such a deed of horror are used, though our forcible Anglo-Saxon idiom supplies them in abundance. The prisoner is 'unfortunate'—'is in an unhappy situation, and all must regret the fate of the victim'. Such is the dainty language in vogue which tends to foster the false morality of the morbid humanitarians of the day.

Justus.

The Times also published these satirical verses:

On a Late Acquittal

Ye people of England exult and be glad
For ye're now at the will of the merciless mad
Why say ye that but three authorities reign
Crown, Commons and Lords?—You omit the insane.
They're a privileged class whom no statute controls,
And their murderous charter exists in their souls.
Do they wish to spill blood—they have only to play
A few pranks—get asylum'd a month and a day
Then Heigh! to escape from the mad doctor's keys
And to pistol or stab whomsoever they please.

Now the dog has a human-like wit in creation
He resembles most nearly our own generation
Then if madmen for murder escape with impunity
Why deny a poor dog the same noble immunity
So if a dog or man bite you beware being nettled
For crime is no crime—when the mind is unsettled.

Even the *Lancet* protested, and Queen Victoria wrote to Sir Robert Peel:[12]

'We have seen the trials of Oxford and M'Naughton conducted by the ablest lawyers of the day—and they *allow* and *advise* the Jury to pronounce the verdict of *Not Guilty*

12 Benson, A. C., *The Letters of Queen Victoria*. London, 1907.

9

on account of *Insanity* when everybody is morally convinced that both malefactors were perfectly conscious and aware of what they did . . . could not the legislation lay down the rule which . . . Chief Justice Mansfield did in the case of Bellingham: and why could not the judges be bound to interpret the law in this and in no other sense in their charges to the Juries.'

The issue was raised immediately in the House of Lords. *Hansard*, for 6 March 1843: reports:

Lord *Brougham* said, that in the event of his noble and learned Friend on the Woolsack, or his noble and learned Friend, the Lord Chief Justice of the Queen's Bench, not agreeing that it was necessary to bring in a measure, or to make any proposal relative to the state of the law relating to the crimes of persons alleged to be labouring under partial insanity, he should feel it his bounden duty to call the attention of their Lordships to the subject. He would do so with the more reluctance, because any such proposition would come with much better grace from either of his noble and learned Friends. It was only the present emergency of the case which induced him to take it up. But if either of the noble and learned Lords would take the matter in hand, he would be most deeply anxious to render them the best assistance in his power.

The *Lord Chancellor* said, he was happy his noble and learned Friend had mentioned the subject. He (the Lord Chancellor) had already turned his attention to it with a view of discovering if anything could be done to remedy the evil. He was about to enter into communication with those persons who were most likely to afford correct information upon the subject. Whether the course he had commenced would be productive of any practical effect or not, he could not then say, but he would take an early opportunity of again adverting to the subject. Meanwhile, he should be happy to co-operate with his noble and learned Friend.

Lord *Brougham* said, that nothing could be more satisfactory to the country than the statement just made by his noble and learned Friend.

The angry debate in the House of Lords put such pressure on the Government that the Lord Chancellor (Lord Lyndhurst), to calm the storm, suggested that the Lords might revive an obsolete piece of constitutional machinery which enabled the House to take opinion of the judges as to the law of England on any particular topic, in the form of answers to specific questions. This was accepted, and five questions were formulated. On 19 June 1843, the judges attended the House and gave their answers, which thenceforth came to be called the 'McNaughton Rules'. But one of the judges, Mr Justice Maule (who had been on the court in Oxford's case), protested vigorously, objecting to the judges being asked to give answers to abstract questions and particularly without hearing argument on the subject. He went on to say that he feared that the answers to such questions by the judges might 'embarrass the administration of justice when they are cited in criminal trials'. The other judges all agreed with the opinion of Chief Justice Tindal, as formulated in the famous Rules, which represented a major retreat from the position reached in the McNaughton case itself. In fact, it is difficult to see how McNaughton could have been found not guilty on the ground of insanity, if Chief Justice Tindal had applied the law as contained in his answers to the House of Lords. Mr Justice Maule's apprehensions of embarrassment were more than justified, because the form and manner in which the judges were obliged to express their view of the law gave it such a degree of authority that subsequent judicial modification or adaptation to fit new requirements became completely impossible. For over 100 years this effectively prevented English and American law from developing or accepting the concept of diminished responsibility which in Scotland was evolved as early as 1867 by Lord Deas, in *R. v. Dingwall*.[13] English law had to wait until the Homicide Act 1957 introduced the concept to our law; U.S. law had to wait until 1956, when Judge Bazelon, in his famous judgment in the Durham case,[14] held that an accused person was not responsible 'if his unlawful act was the product of mental disease or defect', echoing and accepting, almost in the same words, Erskine's submission in Hadfield's case and Cockburn's in McNaughton's case.

[13] *The Times*, Wednesday, 8 March 1843.
[14] Durham v. U.S., 1956. 94 App. D.C. 228.

11

THE STATE TRIALS REPORT

THE QUEEN AGAINST DANIEL M'NAUGHTON, 1843

Central Criminal Court, Old Bailey

Friday, March 3, 1843.

THE QUEEN *against* DANIEL M'NAUGHTON, for the wilful Murder of
MR. DRUMMOND.

Before TINDAL, C.J., WILLIAMS, J., and COLERIDGE, J.

Counsel for the prosecution: The *Solicitor General* (Sir *William Webb
Follett*),(*a*) *Adolphus Waddington*, and *Russell Gurney*.(*b*)
Counsel for the prisoner: *Cockburn*, Q.C.,(*c*) *Clarkson, Bodkin*, and *Monteith*.
The prisoner, on being placed at the bar, pleaded "Not guilty."(*d*)

Gurney opened the indictment, which alleged that the prisoner—

"on the 20th of January, at the parish of St. Martin-in-the-Fields, did feloniously
assault Mr. Edward Drummond with a certain pistol, which he then and there held in
his right hand, loaded with gunpowder and a leaden bullet, and which he, of his malice
aforethought, discharged at and against the said Edward Drummond, thereby giving
him a certain mortal wound, in and upon the left side of the back of the said Drummond,

(*a*) Afterwards Attorney General.
(*b*)   ,,   Recorder of London.
(*c*)   ,,   Lord Chief Justice of England.
(*d*) The prisoner had been placed on his trial at the previous session, February 2, and called
upon to plead.
    Straight: How say you, prisoner, are you guilty or not guilty?
    The prisoner, who kept his eyes steadily fixed towards the Bench, made no reply to the
question.
    Straight: Prisoner, you must answer the question, whether you are guilty or not?
    The prisoner, after again hesitating for some time said, "I was driven to desperation by
persecution."
    Lord ABINGER: Will you answer the question? You must say either guilty or not guilty.
    Prisoner, after another pause: I am guilty of firing.
    Lord ABINGER: By that, do you mean to say you are not guilty of the remainder of the
charge; that is, of intending to murder Mr. Drummond?
    Prisoner: Yes.
    Lord ABINGER: That certainly amounts to a plea of "Not guilty"; therefore, such a plea
must be recorded.
    The prisoner was then charged upon the coroner's inquisition with the like offence.
    To the inquisition also, a plea of "Not guilty" was entered.
    Clarkson then applied to postpone the trial to the next session, to allow of evidence as to the

a little below the blade-bone of his left shoulder, of the breadth of half an inch, and of the depth of twelve inches, and of which wound the said Edward Drummond did languish until the 25th of January, and languishing did live, on which 25th of January he, of the said mortal wounds so given in manner aforesaid by him, the said Daniel M'Naughton, died; and that he did wilfully kill and murder the said Edward Drummond."

OPENING SPEECH FOR THE CROWN

The *Solicitor General:* May it please you, my Lord, Gentlemen of the jury, You are assembled here to-day to discharge a most solemn and important duty. You will have to decide whether the prisoner at the bar be guilty or not guilty of the awful crime with which he stands charged; and I feel, gentlemen, that I shall best discharge my duty to the Crown and to the public, on whose behalf I appear here to-day, if I proceed at once to state, as calmly and dispassionately as I can, all the facts and circumstances connected with the melancholy case. Mr. *Drummond*, whose death we are to inquire into this day, was, as you all know probably, the private secretary of Sir *R. Peel*, and was on terms of friendship and intimacy with him. By virtue of his office he occupied apartments in the official residence of the Prime Minister of this country. He was in the constant habit of passing from those rooms to the private residence of Sir *R. Peel*, in Whitehall Gardens; and it will be proved to you that the prisoner at the bar, for many days before the fatal occurrence took place, was seen loitering about those spots, and watching the persons who went in and out of the public offices and the houses in Whitehall Gardens. This conduct had attracted attention, and he was spoken to by some soldiers, who had observed him, as well as by the police; but, unfortunately, no steps were taken to remove him. On Friday, January 20, Mr. *Drummond* left his apartments in Downing Street, and went to the Treasury, and thence to the Admiralty, in company with Lord *Haddington*, whom he left at the Admiralty, and proceeded alone to *Drummond's* banking-house, at Charing Cross; on his return from which, when near the "Salopian" coffee-house, the prisoner at the bar—for there can be no doubt of his identity—came behind him, and discharged a pistol almost close to him. After discharging that pistol, the prisoner drew another from his breast, presented it at Mr. *Drummond*, and was in the act of firing it at him, when a policeman, who had observed him from the opposite side of the street, ran across the road and threw his arms about him; and other persons also assisted the policeman to secure the prisoner, who, in struggling with them, discharged the second pistol, but luckily without doing any mischief. The prisoner was then seized and taken to the police station-house, in Gardner's

prisoner's state of mind being procured from Scotland and possibly from France; he also read affidavits in support of the motion.

The *Attorney General* (Sir *Frederick Pollock*), for the Crown, said that he had read the depositions taken at Glasgow and alluded to in the affidavits, and that they contained matter which it would be very proper to lay before the jury.

Lord ABINGER, C.B., ordered the trial to stand over, and also directed that sufficient funds should be supplied to the prisoner for the purposes of his defence out of the money found upon him at the time of his arrest.

Lane, where he was searched, and there were found on his person two five-pound notes, four sovereigns, and a deposit receipt for 745*l.* from the Glasgow Bank. Among some other trifling articles that were found in his pockets, were ten copper percussion caps, which fitted the nipples of the pistols he had discharged in the manner I have described; and afterwards, upon searching his lodgings, bullets were also found to match the barrels of those very pistols. Mr. *Drummond*, after the pistol which wounded him was fired, staggered from the effect of the shot, but did not fall. He walked, I believe, almost without assistance, back to the banking-house. A medical gentleman in the neighbourhood was sent for, and after a short time Mr. *Drummond* was removed in his own carriage to his private residence. For some time hopes were entertained of his recovery, and that the wound would not prove fatal; but, unfortunately, those hopes were abortive. He lingered in great pain for some days, and died on Wednesday, January 25.

Gentlemen, his death is deeply, and I may say permanently, regretted; for he was beloved, esteemed, and valued by all who knew him. He was of a disposition so amiable that it was impossible he could have had any personal enemies. You will naturally ask, then, gentlemen, who was the prisoner at the bar, and what could induce him to deprive of life a being so unoffending? Mr. *Drummond* was not only without any personal enemies, but he did not fill any prominent situation before the public. He did not hold that situation in public life which would render him obnoxious to political enemies, but he was the private secretary of the principal Minister of the Crown, often an inmate of his house, and constantly passing therefore to the public offices in Downing Street and the neighbourhood, about which the prisoner was observed to be loitering and watching. You will be satisfied, from the facts of the case, from the threats used by the prisoner before he committed his crime, and his declarations afterwards, that it was not the life of Mr. *Drummond* that he sought. You will be satisfied that it was the life of Sir *Robert Peel* that he desired to take, and that it was his life that he believed he was destroying when he discharged the fatal pistol against the person of Mr. *Drummond*.

Gentlemen, the nature of his crime is not altered by this circumstance, but it affords a reason for it. I need not tell you that he is guilty of murder, although he might have mistaken the person against whom he discharged the pistol. Of the guilt of the prisoner—of the fact of his having deprived Mr. *Drummond* of life—it is impossible I can suggest a doubt; it is impossible that any doubt can be suggested that the crime was committed, and that that crime was murder. But I cannot conceal from you, because I know, from applications which have been made to this Court, and the depositions which have been made on behalf of the prisoner, that it is intended to rest the defence on the plea that he was insane at the time he committed the crime; and, gentlemen, it will be your painful duty—for painful it must be—to decide whether he was in that degree of insanity at the time he committed that crime which would render him not a responsible agent, and not answerable to the laws of his country for the offence of which he has been guilty. This defence is a difficult one at all times; for while, on the one hand, everyone must be anxious that an unconscious being should not suffer, yet, on the other hand, the public safety requires that this defence should not be too readily listened to; and, above all, the public safety requires that the atrocious nature of the act itself, and the circumstances under which it was committed, should not form any ingredient in that defence. There are few crimes that are committed, and, above all, crimes of an atrocious nature like this, that are not committed by persons labouring under some morbid affection of the mind; and it is difficult for well-regulated minds to understand the motives which lead to such offences in the absence of that morbid affection of the mind. I believe that the truth of this remark will be more especially proved when attacks are directed to persons holding high and important stations in the nation. If you look back upon the page of history, and consider the facts connected with the death of persons whose lives have been destroyed by the hands of assassins, you will be satisfied in one moment of the truth of that proposition. But we need not look far back; occurrences of our own times furnish us with sufficient instances for illustration. If you look at a neighbouring country, you will see there that persons in broad day, in the crowded streets of the metropolis of France, without any precaution for their own safety, without any attempt to escape, in the midst of the people, close to the armed guards of the King, have discharged their weapons at the person of the sovereign of the country. What motive had they? We know of none but that of an ill-regulated mind, worked upon by morbid political feeling. We have seen other instances in France of parties, having laid plans to assist themselves in their escape, discharging infernal instruments in the streets of Paris, regardless of how many and what lives they destroyed, provided they could reach the person of the sovereign.(a) I refer to these things, gentlemen, to show that the circumstances attendant upon the crime itself afford no grounds for holding that the parties committing it are not responsible to the laws of their country.

But I know that in this case the defence on the part of the prisoner will not rest upon this, but that evidence will be offered to show that the prisoner was not in a sane state of mind at the time he committed the crime; and knowing that, I feel that I ought, in this stage of the case, to refer to some authorities, and state my view of the principles of the English law. It will be open to my learned friend, whose powerful assistance I am happy to see the prisoner will have, to comment upon that, and to differ from me if he thinks I am wrong. It has been the custom in these cases to refer to proceedings of authority, and to the *dicta* of judges who have tried similar questions; not that I mean to say for one moment that it is a question of law; on the contrary, the question to be decided by you is a question of fact, a question of common sense and belief. The whole question will turn upon this: if you believe the prisoner at the bar at the time he committed this act was not a responsible agent; if you believe that when he fired the pistol he was incapable of distinguishing between right and wrong; if you believe that he was under the influence and control of some disease of the mind which prevented him from being conscious that he was

(a) Fieschi attempted the life of Louis Philippe in this way July 28, 1835.

committing a crime; if you believe that he did not know he was violating the law both of God and man: then, undoubtedly, he is entitled to your acquittal. But it is my duty, subject to the correction of my Lord and to the observations of my learned friend, to tell you that nothing short of that will excuse him upon the principle of the English law. To excuse him it will not be sufficient that he laboured under partial insanity upon some subjects—that he had a morbid delusion of mind upon some subjects, which could not exist in a wholly sane person; that is not enough, if he had that degree of intellect which enabled him to know and distinguish between right and wrong, if he knew what would be the effects of his crime, and consciously committed it, and if with that consciousness he wilfully committed it. I shall be able to show you, gentlemen, with regard to the authorities upon this point, that observations have been made to the effect that they have attempted to define the law too strictly; but such observations were made without regard to the object of those authorities. It is impossible beforehand to lay down any definition of the kind of madness which will excuse the crime of murder; the disease assumes such different forms and such various shapes, and acts in such opposite ways, that you cannot define it. But you may lay down the principles of law which are applicable to it; and they are laid down, and uniformly laid down in the same way, that it is a question for the jury to take into their consideration whether the party was a responsible agent when he committed the crime, whether he then knew right from wrong, whether he was conscious that he was offending against the law of his country and nature, and whether he did it wilfully. Gentlemen, the public safety is the object of all law; the public safety is intrusted solely to the protection of courts of criminal judicature, and to juries who administer justice under the law; and it is with a view to the public safety that the law is laid down by legal authorities principally for the guidance of juries who have to decide upon questions of this nature.

[Counsel cited *Hale*,(a) and the following passage from the speech of the *Solicitor General*(b) in Lord *Ferrers'* case:—]

"If there be a total permanent want of reason, it will acquit the prisoner; if there be a total temporary want of it when the offence was committed, it will acquit the prisoner; but if there be only a partial degree of insanity mixed with a partial degree of reason—not a full and complete use of reason, but (as Lord Hale carefully and emphatically expresses himself) a competent use of it sufficient to have restrained those passions which produced crime—if there be thought and design, a faculty to distinguish the nature of actions, to discern the difference between moral good and evil; then, upon the fact of the offence proved, the judgment of the law must take place."

Counsel also quoted the direction of *Tracy*, J., in *Arnold's* case,(c) and of *Le Blanc*, J., in *Bowler's* case.(d)

There is, certainly, one other case to which I should refer. It is not the authority of a judge; but it is one of the most celebrated cases of the kind. I allude to the

(a) 1 P.C. 30; above, p. 507.
(b) Charles Yorke, 19 St. Tr. 886.
(c) 19 St. Tr. 886; and above, p. 508.
(d) Collinson, 673n; and above, p. 508.

16

trial of *Hadfield*,(*a*) on a charge of high treason, for firing at King *George* 3. He was defended by Lord *Erskine*, who made one of the most eloquent and able speeches, probably, that was ever delivered at the bar; and he entered at that time much into the law of insanity, and the nature of the insanity that would excuse the prisoner. In that case, I believe, no doubt could be entertained of the insanity of the prisoner, and the Court upon that ground, stopped the trial. But in the course of that trial Lord *Erskine* said the prisoner must be shown to labour under some delusion, and it must also be shown that he committed the act in consequence of that delusion. That was the ground upon which Lord *Erskine* put the defence. But, as was remarked by the present Lord Chief Justice of the Court of Queen's Bench,(*b*) the counsel for the prisoner would only state so much of the law as was applicable to the defence of the prisoner; and I cannot help thinking that there may be many cases in which the prisoner may be excused from the consequences of a crime that would not fall under the description of Lord *Erskine*. A party may have that state of mind which would render him wholly unconscious of right and wrong; he may have that state of mind which makes him not aware that he is committing a crime, and yet the crime may not be the offspring of any delusion he labours under; nor do I think it is right in another point of view. I think that parties may be liable to be punished under the law, although they did labour under a delusion, and although the act may have been committed under that delusion. I think, therefore, the doctrine of Lord *Erskine* is not true in either way to its fullest extent. I will put one case, that which Lord *Erskine* refers to in that celebrated speech. He speaks of two brothers —one of whom laboured under the morbid delusion that the other was his enemy, and conspiring against him; and in consequence of that delusion he made a will, in which he disinherited that brother. The question arose as to whether that will could be set aside; and it was held that the will was made under circumstances which rendered it invalid. Now, I cannot help thinking that, upon the principles of the English laws, if that brother was aware of the consequences of what he did; if he knew the difference between right and wrong, and with that knowledge and consciousness had deprived his brother of life, he would have been guilty of murder. I own that in that case the ground laid down does not appear satisfactory either in favour of or against the principle.

The next case, gentlemen, is that which took place here in the year 1812, when *Bellingham* was tried for the murder of Mr. *Perceval*, and convicted of that offence. He was tried in this Court before Lord Chief Justice *Mansfield*, Sir *James Mansfield*, who laid down the law in this way:

"In another part of the prisoner's defence, which was not, however, urged by himself, it was attempted to be proved that at the time of the commission of the crime he was insane. With respect to this the law was extremely clear. If a man were deprived of all power of reasoning, so as not to be able to distinguish whether it was right or wrong to commit the most wicked transaction, he could not do an act against the law. Such a man, so destitute of all power of judgment, could have no intention at all. In order to

(*a*) 27 St. Tr. 1314.
(*b*) In *Oxford's* case, above, p. 508.

17

support this defence, however, it ought to be proved, by the most distinct and unquestionable evidence, that the criminal was incapable of judging between right and wrong. It must, in fact, be proved beyond all doubt that, at the time he committed the atrocious act with which he stood charged, he did not consider that murder was a crime against the laws of God and nature. There was no other proof of insanity which would excuse murder or any other crime. There were various species of insanity. Some human creatures were void of all power of reasoning from their birth; such could not be guilty of any crime. There was another species of madness, in which persons were subject to temporary paroxysms, in which they were guilty of acts of extravagance; this was called lunacy. If these persons were to commit a crime when they were not affected with the malady, they would be, to all intents and purposes, amenable to justice. So long as they could distinguish good from evil, so long would they be answerable for their conduct. There was a third species of insanity, in which the patient fancied the existence of injury, and sought an opportunity of gratifying revenge by some hostile act. If such a person were capable in other respects of distinguishing right from wrong, there was no excuse for any act of atrocity which he might commit under the description of insanity."(a)

Now from the last observation of the learned judge who tried that cause, it appears to me, gentlemen, that a party may labour under the delusion of having received injury, but if he be able to distinguish between right and wrong, and if he be conscious of the nature of the crime, the delusion will not excuse him from punishment for that crime. [Counsel also referred to *R. v. Offord*,(b) in which Lord *Lyndhurst* approved of the direction in *Bellingham's* case, and told the jury that—

"they must be satisfied, before they could acquit the prisoner on the ground of insanity, that he did not know, when he committed the act, what the effect of it, if fatal, would be, with reference to the crime of murder. The question was, Did he know that he was committing an offence against the laws of God and nature?"]

I have referred to these authorities for the purpose of enabling you, gentlemen of the jury, to judge of the evidence which will, beyond doubt, be produced on behalf of the prisoner, that you may compare the circumstances and consider whether the prisoner at the bar was in that state of mind which rendered him not responsible for the crime he committed. But, knowing the nature and object of that evidence, I think I should not discharge my duty to the public or to the Crown, if I did not lay before you on my part what is known respecting the history of the prisoner and what is known of his conduct directly before his apprehension. It is right I should tell you, at least, that I do not mean to go into any observations which persons may have particularly directed to the state of mind of individuals in similar circumstances, but to show in what way the prisoner has conducted himself in his past life, the way in which he managed his business, the mode and manner of his living, what care he took of himself, and how he was left by all his connections to manage his own affairs, and continued to do so down to the very hour of his defence. It appears that he has carried on the business of a wood-turner in Glasgow, and that his father had

(a) Collinson, 636–674.
(b) 5 C. & P. 168.

18

carried on the same business before him. They did work together, but he left his father in consequence of some dispute between them, and set up on his own account as a wood-turner in Glasgow. He continued carrying on that business down to the end of the year 1840. He then left that business, and went and took lodgings in Glasgow with a person of the name of *Pattieson*. He seems to have been of very sober, prudent, and saving habits, and had, during the time he was in business in Glasgow, saved a considerable sum of money by the time he retired at the close of the year 1840. He afterwards occasionally came to London, and it appears that he has been upon the continent. While in London he resided with a Mrs. *Dutton*, who lives at No. 7, Poplar Row, Newington, and he was residing there when he committed the crime with which he now stands charged. While at Glasgow he attended lectures on natural philosophy at the Mechanics' Institution in that city, and he took an active part in various alterations which were made in the rules of that institution, and also in the arrangement of the rooms and the conveniences of the building. He was in the habit of getting books from the library; he was known to all the persons who frequented that institution, and, moreover, he afterwards attended lectures on anatomy, and made considerable progress in that science. I shall call one of the persons whose lectures he attended. He came first to London in July 1841, when he went to the house of Mrs. *Dutton* and lodged there continually, therefore she has had an opportunity of seeing him and noticing his habits for the last year and a half. He had been ill in her house, and she attended him, and she will be examined as a witness. She will tell you, gentlemen, that, as far as she could see, there was nothing extraordinary in his conduct. On the morning of the day on which the crime was committed she spoke to him, and assisted him in putting on part of his dress, but neither then nor when he left the house did she observe anything extraordinary in his manner or demeanor, and she had no reason at any time to consider him insane. Gentlemen, I stated that he came here in July 1841. Before that he had opened an account with the Bank of Glasgow, upon what is called a deposit receipt. He afterwards shifted that to the London Joint Stock Bank, and he had applied to the persons in London to give him 5*l.* on the deposit, which was for about 750*l.* They said it was contrary to usage to do it, and he then drew out the 750*l.*, and obtained the 5*l.* he wanted, and then, when he got that sum of money, he paid the other back. But on the 23rd May, desiring to transfer his account to the Glasgow Bank again, he wrote this letter:

"Sir,   Glasgow, May 23, 1842.

"I HEREBY intimate to you that I will require the money, ten days from this date, which I deposited in the London Joint Stock Bank, through you. The account is for 745*l.*; the account is dated August 28, 1841, but is not numbered. As it would put me to some inconvenience to give personal intimation, and then remain in London till the eleven days' notice agreed upon had expired, I trust this will be considered sufficient.

"Yours, &c.

"DANIEL M'NAUGHTON."

Well, upon that, gentlemen, the account was transferred to the Bank of Glasgow, and he received a deposit receipt from the Bank of Glasgow for the larger sum, specified in the deposit receipt found upon him at the time of his apprehension. Another letter was written by him in July 1842, which will be read to you, as it will be proved that he went to the shop of a gunsmith in the neighbourhood of Glasgow, where he bought the pistols, and bargained with the man for them, expressing a wish to have them of the same size, and desiring the man, if he had not them himself, to get them for him. In that month, he bought the pistols, and in that month he came to London, and again in the September following. But on the 19th of July he wrote the letter relating to his entering into some business or partnership in London, in consequence of an advertisement published in a London newspaper—the *Spectator*—of the 16th of that month as follows:—

"OPTIONAL PARTNERSHIP.—Any gentleman having 1,000*l*. may invest them, on the most advantageous terms, in a very genteel business in London, attended with no risk, with the option, within a given period, of becoming a partner, and of ultimately succeeding to the whole business. In the meantime, security and liberal interest will be given for the money.—Apply by letter to 'B.B.,' Mr. Hilton's, bookseller, Penton Street, Pentonville."

On the 21st of July the advertiser received from the prisoner the following letter:—

"SIR,   Glasgow, 19th July 1842.
"My attention has been attracted to your advertisement in the *Spectator* newspaper, and as I am unemployed at present, and very anxious to obtain some, I have been induced to write, requesting you to state some particulars regarding the nature of the business which you are engaged. If immediate employment can be given or otherwise, what sort of security will be given for the money, and how much interest? I may mention that I have been engaged in business on my own account for a few years, am under 30 years of age, and of very active and sober habits.
"The capital which I possess has been acquired by the most vigilant industry, but unfortunately does not amount to the exact sum specified in your advertisement. If nothing less will do, I will be sorry for it, but cannot help it; if otherwise, have the goodness to write me at your earliest convenience, and address 'D.M.M.,' 90, Clyde Street, Anderton's frontland, top flat."

He then came to London in that same month, and I shall call before you some of his friends and acquaintances who had known him in Glasgow, and who met with him and had various conversations with him, and with whom he walked by the house of Sir *Robert Peel*; particularly, evidence will be given with regard to a conversation with the prisoner in the month of November 1842. He remained in London from that time down to the time when he committed the offence, in the month of January, and still lodged in Mrs. *Dutton's* house. Other persons at that time were acquainted with the prisoner; these persons I will put into the witness-box—persons conversant with his manners and habits, as well as his landlady, in order that you may form an opinion whether or not the prisoner was a responsible agent at the time he committed the offence. On the other side, no doubt evidence will be offered to prove his insanity; and certainly it is some consolation to me, in the discharge of a painful duty, to know that the interests of the prisoner will be most ably and powerfully attended to; but it will be your duty, and no doubt your desire also, to most attentively listen to the evidence on both sides, and to weigh the one against the other. What the precise nature or the details of the evidence on the part of the prisoner may be, I cannot say. I know not the exact nature of it, nor its extent; but when it is adduced, you will say, upon that evidence, are you or are you not satisfied that the prisoner was, at the time he committed this crime, a responsible agent, that he did know right from wrong, and that he was aware of the consequences of the act which he committed? If you think he was not, he ought to be acquitted. If that should be the result of the evidence he will be entitled to your acquittal. But if it fall short of that, if you think he was a responsible agent, I need not say to you that public justice requires a different verdict. It is a painful duty, gentlemen, but it is a duty which must be faithfully discharged; and I am perfectly satisfied that when you have heard the witnesses, when you have maturely deliberated upon and considered the evidence, your verdict will be one of justice between the public and the prisoner.

EVIDENCE FOR THE CROWN.

James Silver.—Examined by *Waddington.*

I am a police constable of the A Division. On Friday, January 20, I was on duty at Charing Cross, twenty minutes before four o'clock in the afternoon. I was on the right side of the street from Whitehall. I heard a report of a pistol on the opposite side of the street. I look over and saw a gentleman stagger, with his hand pressed against the left side of his back. I also saw the prisoner returning a pistol with his right hand into the left side of his breast. He was behind the gentleman. When I saw him put the pistol into his bosom, I perceived that he drew another pistol from his right breast, with his left hand, and changed it into his right hand. I ran across the street and seized his right arm, and tripped his feet from under him. He struggled very violently, and the pistol went off upon the pavement. When I seized him he tried to raise his right arm and turn upon me, but I secured him so that he could not. I then took the pistol from his right hand, and also the other from his left breast. On the way to the station-house he said either "he" or "she" (I cannot recollect which) shall not break my peace of mind any longer. That was all he said. At the station-house I found ten pistol caps on him, three 5l. Bank of England notes, a receipt for 750l. of the Glasgow and Shipping Bank, four sovereigns, four half-crowns, one shilling and fourpence, a knife, a key, and a small coin. I also found upon him an address, "Daniel M'Naughton, 7, Poplar Row, New Kent Road," which was found to be correct. From being frequently on duty in the neighbourhood of Whitehall and Downing Street, I had often seen Mr. *Drummond.* I knew his person well, and he it was whom the prisoner shot. I had often seen Mr. *Drummond* coming out of Sir *Robert Peel's* house, and the Treasury, and the Privy Council offices. I produce the pistols and other articles found upon the prisoner. The date of the receipt from the Glasgow Bank is June 2, 1842, for 750*l.* (*The receipt was put in and read.*) I also produce a pistol ball which I received from Colonel *Drummond,* the brother of the deceased gentleman.

Cross-examined by *Cockburn.*

A few seconds only elapsed between the firing of the first pistol and my seizing the arm of the prisoner. When I seized him his right hand was elevated.

Benjamin Weston.—Examined by *Gurney.*

I am an office porter. On the afternoon of the 20th of January, shortly before four o'clock, I was in the neighbourhood of Charing Cross when I heard the report of a pistol; on turning round I saw a gentleman pointing to the prisoner, who was standing about three paces behind him. I then observed the prisoner draw back a pace or two and draw a pistol from his breast; he then placed the barrel of his pistol in his left hand and cocked it; I then observed that the gentleman was reeling, and the prisoner was pointing the pistol at him. At that moment the witness *Silver* ran up and sprung upon him, seizing him by the arms. A scuffle then took place, and in the scuffle the second pistol was discharged.

Cross-examined by *Clarkson.*

The prisoner drew the pistol very deliberately, but at the same time very quickly. As far as I can judge, it was a very cool, deliberate act. I was about eight paces distant, and did not hear the cocking of the pistol, but from his motion I could distinctly discern what he was doing. There was no one between the gentleman and the prisoner.

Richard Jackson.—Examined by the *Solicitor General.*

I am an apothecary in Charles Street, St. James', Westminster. I knew the deceased, Mr. *Drummond.* On the afternoon of the 20th of January I was sent for to attend him at the banking house, Charing Cross. I satisfied myself that he had been wounded. I recommended his immediate removal to his own residence, and accompanied him there in his carriage. Mr. *Guthrie,* Mr. *Bransby Cooper,* and other medical gentlemen, were soon in attendance upon him, and the ball was extracted the same day within an hour after the injury was received, and I was present at the time. Mr. *Drummond* lingered till the following Wednesday, when he died.

George James Guthrie, surgeon, spoke to the nature of the wound. The ball passed through the body, but not in a direct line. It wounded the diaphragm, and that is a wound which never heals under such circumstances.

George Walter Shaw, a policeman, spoke to searching the prisoner's lodgings at No. 7, Poplar Row, Kent Road, and finding a powder flask, percussion caps, five leaden bullets, and a pistol key. The bullets fitted the pistols used by the prisoner.

John Massey Tierney.—Examined by the *Solicitor General.*

I am an inspector of the A Division of police. On the evening of the 20th of January I went to the station-house in Gardener's Lane, where I found the prisoner in custody. Between the hours of five and eleven o'clock I visited the prisoner in his cell several times, and conversed with him. When I first went to him, I gave him a caution that in any conversation we might have together he should say nothing to criminate himself, as it might be used in evidence against him. I cautioned him in the same manner on other occasions, when he said I acted fairly towards him, and that fair play was the English character. He said that he had left Glasgow about three months; that he stayed at Liverpool seven days, and then came to London, where he had remained ever since; he then said that he was in business at Glasgow as a turner, but left that and was going into another business, but was prevented. I observed that he had a good share of money, to which he replied that he had wrought hard for it, and that he generally did the work of three ordinary men daily. I told him I had been in Glasgow three or four weeks before. He then asked the name of the ship I went in. I said I had forgotten, but thought it was the *British Queen.* He said I must have been mistaken, it must have been the *Princess Royal*, and I then recollected that was the name of the vessel. I then asked him whether he knew Mr. *Richardson*, the superintendent of the Gorbals police. He said he did, and added that he was considered a more clever man than *Miller* (another police officer). I then asked him whether he came over in the *Princess Royal*. He said he did not; he came over in the *Fire King*. I asked him whether there was a railway from Edinburgh to Glasgow? He told me there was, and, as far as I recollect, said they were thirty or forty miles apart. He also mentioned the fares. I told him that when I was going to Glasgow I went through Paisley. I asked him whether he had ever been there. He said he had. I remarked that it was a great place for shawls. He admitted that it was; that nearly all the inhabitants were weavers, but he was sorry to say there were a great many of them out of employ. I then asked him whether he would take any refreshment, when he expressed a wish to have some coffee, with which he was supplied. In the course of conversation I asked him whether *Drummond* was a Scotch name. He answered that it was; that it was the family name of the Earl of *Perth*, but the title had become extinct. On the following morning I again saw the prisoner, between eight and nine o'clock. On entering his cell I asked him whether he had had his breakfast. He replied in the affirmative, and asked to have some water to wash himself with. I then sent the constable, who had been sitting up with him, for some water, and when he had left the cell, I said to the prisoner—"I suppose you will assign some reason to the magistrate this morning for the crime you have committed?" He said, "I shall give a reason—a short one." I then said, "You might have

23

stated anything you thought proper to me last night after the caution I gave you." He then told me that he was an object of persecution by the Tories, that they followed him from place to place with their persecution. He seemed inclined to go on with his statement, when I said, "I suppose you are aware who the gentleman is you shot at?" He said, "It is Sir *Robert Peel*, is it not?" I at first said "No," but in a moment recollecting myself, said, "We do not exactly know who the gentleman is yet." Then turning round, I said, "Recollect the caution I gave you last night, not to say anything to criminate yourself, as it may be used in evidence against you;" to which he immediately replied, "But you will not use this against me?" I said, "I make you no promise; I gave you the caution." I then left the cell, and in the course of the same day took him to the police court, Bow Street.

Cross-examined by *Cockburn*.

It was my duty to visit all the cells in the course of the night.

Is it your duty to put questions to the prisoners?—As long as I do not interfere with the case in point I do not see any harm in putting questions to prisoners.

Did anyone direct you to put such questions?—Certainly not.

What was your object in putting them?—I wanted to get all the information I could about his former life.

In order to give it in evidence against him?—I never intended to give in evidence against him anything he told me till he mentioned the name of Sir *Robert Peel*.

What was your motive for wishing to get information respecting his former life?—Nothing that I know of but the anxiety of human nature, under such revolting circumstances, to know who and what he was.

Now, do you mean to swear that you ever intended to suppress the evidence you have given?—Not to suppress it, but I had no intention to mention it till he mentioned the name of Sir *Robert Peel*. I cannot give you the precise conversation which took place at each interview, but I have stated the substance of them all. A constable, of the name of *Edwards*, was present when the conversations took place, but he is not here to-day. As I did not intend to mention the conversations I did not make any notes of them, but I did make a memorandum of the conversation in which Sir *Robert Peel's* name was mentioned.

Why did you not have the morning conversation in the presence of the constable?—I wish he had been present. I had no motive for the conversation taking place in his absence. I first mentioned the conversation at Bow Street.

Do you mean to swear that you had no motive lurking in your mind when you asked him whether he intended to make any statement before the magistrate?—I had no particular motive, but I imagined the responsibility was off my shoulders after the caution I gave him on the previous night.

Was not the object of that interview to induce him to make that statement?—I did it for the purpose of letting him know that I was ready to receive any communication he thought proper to make.

When did you first mention these circumstances?—I first mentioned them to Mr. *Burnaby* at Bow Street on the morning of the prisoner's first examination, before the examination took place; and to Mr. *Hall*, the chief magistrate, afterwards; but I believe he was aware of it before the examination. I was not examined on the first occasion.

Did you mention the conversation to anyone else?—Yes; I mentioned it to the Commissioners of Police, but I cannot say whether I mentioned it to Colonel *Rowan*. I sent a private report in writing to the Commissioners.

Now, perhaps, you will tell me upon your solemn oath, whether, when you made that observation to him, you did not do so with the intention of extorting a confession from him?—The remark was thoughtlessly made. I wanted to turn the conversation, as I thought he was going to make a full confession, and I did not wish to hear it.

Re-examined by the *Solicitor General.*

I was subsequently examined at Bow Street, and I then heard the prisoner make a statement. That statement was taken in writing by the clerk and signed by the prisoner (*handing in a document*).

This is the statement?—It is.

The clerk of arraigns then read the statement as follows:—

"The Tories in my native city have compelled me to do this. They follow and persecute me wherever I go, and have entirely destroyed my peace of mind. They followed me to France, into Scotland, and all over England; in fact, they follow me wherever I go. I cannot get no rest for them night or day. I cannot sleep at night in consequence of the course they pursue towards me. I believe they have driven me into a consumption. I am sure I shall never be the man I formerly was. I used to have good health and strength, but I have not now. They have accused me of crimes of which I am not guilty; they do everything in their power to harass and persecute me; in fact, they wish to murder me. It can be proved by evidence. That's all I have to say."

Edward Howe.—Examined by *Waddington.*

I am office keeper at the office of the Board of Trade in Whitehall. I know the prisoner at the bar. I first saw him about a fortnight before the 20th January last. He was then standing at the top of the steps of the Council Office, which is at the corner of Downing Street. Sir *Robert Peel's* residence is in Privy Gardens, which is nearly opposite the end of Downing Street. Sir *Robert Peel*, at times, walks up Downing Street to his official residence. I saw him almost daily after that time, either on the Council Office steps or in the neighbourhood of the Treasury; sometimes I have seen him twice in one day. On the 20th of January, between three and four o'clock, I again observed the prisoner standing on the Council Office steps, when I said, "You will excuse my taking the liberty, sir, but I belong to the office next door; you are a police officer, are you not?" to which he replied, "Yes," and I said, "I suppose, then, it is all right." I then went

25

away, leaving him on the steps. In less than an hour afterwards I saw him in custody in Gardener's Lane station-house.

Not cross-examined.

James Partridge.—Examined by *Gurney*.

A police constable of the A Division, on duty at Whitehall, confirmed the last witness. I have frequently noticed the prisoner in the neighbourhood of the Council Office between the 5th and the 20th of January. On the 13th I spoke to him, and asked him whether he was waiting for any person, when he replied that he was waiting for a gentleman, and immediately walked away in the direction of the Horse Guards. On the 20th I again spoke to him, about ten o'clock in the morning; he was standing on the last step leading to the Council Office, where he remained for about twenty minutes. I asked him whether he had seen the gentleman he had previously told me he was waiting for? He quickly replied "No," and instantly walked away. He did not appear inclined to answer any questions. About twelve o'clock the same day I again saw the prisoner standing near Lady *Dover's*, eating a piece of bread. Lady *Dover's* is opposite Gwydyr House, at the back of which is the residence of Sir *Robert Peel*; but it cannot be seen from Lady *Dover's*.

Not cross-examined.

Richard Jones.—Examined by the *Solicitor General*.

A recruiting sergeant. Spoke to seeing the prisoner frequently in the neighbourhood of Whitehall, walking between Whitehall and Charing Cross. On one occasion I asked him to join Her Majesty's service, if he felt inclined to enlist, but he said he had something better in view. On a subsequent day I said, "Oh, what here again! is there any particular regiment you wish to join?" but his reply was, "I don't wish to enter the service, I am only waiting to see a gentleman." On the 20th I again saw the prisoner near Downing Street, about fifteen yards from the steps of the Privy Council Office, when I pointed him out to one of the police. The next time I saw him he was in custody.

Not cross-examined.

William Bale confirmed the last witness.

Not cross-examined.

John Drake.—Examined by *Gurney*.

A police constable. Spoke to seeing the prisoner near the corner of Downing Street, loitering about; on the 18th of January I said to him, "Some of the gentlemen inside have been speaking to me about your standing on the steps." He said, "Tell them it is a notion I have taken." I said, "If you are waiting for anyone you had better wait on the pavement, as they do not appear to like your standing on these steps, unless they know your business." He said, "You can tell them their property is quite safe." On that same day I spoke to him again, at the corner of Downing Street; he then asked me to take a glass of ale; I declined.

Not cross-examined.

Eliza Dutton.—Examined by the *Solicitor General.*

I live at No. 7, Poplar Row, Newington. The prisoner first came to lodge at my house about last July twelve months. He remained with me for three months; he generally went out between eight and nine in the morning, and sometimes later; sometimes he went out without having his breakfast; he returned home generally about eight or nine in the evening. I used to wash for him, and he always paid me punctually for it, and also my rent. When he left his lodging he was absent about a fortnight or three weeks, and I think he said he had been to France. I never thought him unsettled in his mind. He came back and then remained with me about three weeks, when he again quitted until the September following, when he returned. In the beginning of December he was poorly, but I never did anything for him in the house; he asked me to get him a little barley water, which I did; he had no medical man to attend him. He said he was suffering under a bad cold from neglect: he continued ill about a fortnight. I never had any conversation with him whatever about his friends. I recollect seeing the prisoner on the morning of the day Mr. *Drummond* was shot; I asked him if he had got the brushes for his boots, and he said he had. I gave him the clothes brush, but he did not use it. I saw him again on that day, about a quarter to ten o'clock, when he went out. I did not observe, on that morning, anything about his manner. When he came back to me in September last, he said he had been to Scotland. I asked him if he had seen the Queen when she visited there, and he said he had not, for he was not in that part. I asked him if he thought the Queen's visit had done trade good, and he said he thought it had. He was always very regular in his habits. I never knew him to stay out.

Cross-examined by *Clarkson.*

He appeared to me to be a man of very sober habits. He was very reserved in his manners. He avoided conversation with people. I never saw any companion with him. On the morning Mr. *Drummond* was shot he went out and returned; he ran up stairs, and then went out again. When he was ill, I observed that his head appeared to be bad, and that he had much fever. When I spoke to him about the Queen's visit to Scotland, he seemed to wish to avoid my questions. He was not in the habit of looking people in the face, but always hung his head down. He spoke quickly. His habits appeared to me to be very penurious; he had but one change of linen. I had no idea whatever that he was possessed of such a large sum of money as 700*l.* No person ever called upon the prisoner while he lodged at my house. Whenever he came home at night he went to bed immediately. He never had a fire in his bedroom. He had no sitting-room. I always considered the prisoner very sullen and reserved. There were five other lodgers

27

in my house. I sleep in the room adjoining the prisoner's. I have heard him get out of his bed at night, moan repeatedly, but it did not attract my attention, as I had observed nothing peculiar about him. I never heard him pacing the room of a night, but I have known him get out of bed and smoke a pipe. I thought the prisoner was a person out of a situation with very small means. I attributed his sullenness to his difficulty in obtaining a situation.

Re-examined by the *Solicitor General*.

The prisoner used to go out and stay out all day until the evening. He has returned occasionally during the day. He did not take his meals in my house. He breakfasted out, except when he was ill. His room was never locked; there were three table drawers in his room which had no locks. I saw the police find the powder flask and bullets in the table drawer; but I never knew that he had such things.

TINDAL, C.J.: When he came to lodge with me first he brought a portmanteau with him, which he kept in his bedroom. He took it away when he left me the second time, but did not bring it back on coming to lodge with me the third time. He then had nothing but what was about his person. The change of linen must have been in his pockets. He had no books lying about his room. I gave him one religious book—"Extracts from the Bible." I gave it him because he asked me for it. His habits were just the same on Sundays as on other days.

William Henry Stevenson.—Examined by the *Solicitor General*.

I am private secretary to Sir *Robert Peel*. The late Mr. *Edward Drummond* was also private secretary to Sir *Robert Peel*. Both Mr. *Drummond* and Sir *Robert Peel* were very much in the habit of going from the private residence of the premier, in Privy Gardens, to the house in Downing Street. In doing so you pass by the steps leading to the Council Office; you may also go through the Treasury.

John Gordon.—Examined by *Waddington*.

I have known *M'Naughton* about six years. I never saw anything particular about his conduct on any occasion. I came to London in November last, when I met the prisoner in St. Martin's Lane. Prisoner said, "I am in search of employment." He asked me where I was going, and I told him to Mr. *Hedge's*, in Great Peter Street. We then walked on together and passed by the Horse Guards and down Parliament Street. I know Sir *Robert Peel's* house. I mentioned to him that that (pointing to the house) was where Sir *Robert Peel* stopped. He said, "D——n him, sink him," or something like that. When we passed the Treasury, he said, "Look across the street, there is where all the treasure and worth of the world is," or something like that. When we got to Westminster Hall, we entered some of the courts, and afterwards we went to the Abbey. He said, "You see how time has affected that massive building," or something like that. We then went to Great Peter Street.

I have known the prisoner many years. He appeared to me to be carrying on a prosperous business in Glasgow. So far as my intercourse with him allowed me to judge, he appeared to be a particularly mild and inoffensive person. He would sometimes speak roughly. His manner did not appear changed when I met him in St. Martin's Lane. I did not have any idea that his mind was disordered.

John Caldwell and *James Thompson*, from whom the prisoner had rented workshops, deposed that they had not noticed anything strange in his manner.

Alexander Martin, gunmaker of Paisley, proved selling the two pistols produced, to the prisoner in the previous July, also a flask, powder, and balls.

William Ambrose, writer to the signet, and *William Swanstead*, curator of the Mechanics' Institution, Glasgow, spoke to seeing the prisoner frequently at the institution. *Swanstead* said he spoke tolerably fair, and made as respectable an appearance as the rest. Witness never observed anything remarkable in his conversation or manner.

James Douglas, M.D.—Examined by the *Solicitor General*.

I am a surgeon, residing at Glasgow. I am in the habit of giving lectures on anatomy. I recognise the prisoner as having been a student of mine last summer. I had opportunities of speaking to him almost every day; I merely spoke to him on the subject of anatomy. He seemed to understand it. I scarcely had any opportunity of judging of his knowledge, because he did not attend the examinations. He attended in the dissecting room an hour a day. He used to be reading there. I never observed anything to lead me to suppose his mind was disordered. I am in the habit of explaining in a familiar manner to the students the different parts of the body, independently of the lectures; I did so to *M'Naughton* as well as others. I had not seen him until he was in custody since the last day of July. When I saw him in custody he knew me. I expressed my surprise at seeing him there. He made some monosyllabic reply, but I could not tell what.

Cross-examined by *Cockburn*.

I went to the gaol to see the prisoner by the direction of Mr. *Maule*, the solicitor, simply for the purpose of identifying him. I observed nothing particular about him, except his being a man of little education. There was a want of polish about him. I think he was capable of understanding what was said to him.

Now, sir, do you mean to say you had an opportunity of forming a judgment as to the man's sanity or insanity?—No; I merely came to say that he appeared to understand what he heard of my lectures.

Joseph Forrester.—Examined by *Waddington*.

I am a hair dresser in Glasgow. I have known the prisoner for the last eighteen months. I never saw anything in his manner which led me to think he was not in his right senses, or that he was wrong in his intellect. I used to stay with him sometimes half an hour, sometimes two hours.

Cross-examined by *Clarkson*.

I never suspected there was anything wrong in the prisoner's mind. It never occurred to me that I should like to come to London as a witness. I am not aware how the attorneys for the prosecution found me out. I never offered myself as a witness to anyone else. I never told Mrs. *Patterson* that I wished to come as a witness for the prisoner, neither did I ever tell *Wilson*, the baker, that *M'Naughton* was a "daft" man. I have spoken to Mrs. *Patterson* on several occasions respecting the prisoner. One night she told me she wondered I said he was right, as I had once said he was wrong, but I denied having said anything of the sort. She then said that I was tipsy. I am quite sober now.

[Other witnesses proved the letters read by the *Solicitor General.*]

Solicitor General: That, my Lord, is the case on behalf of the Crown.

Cockburn applied to the Court to be allowed till the next morning before he entered upon the defence. He was himself labouring under very severe indisposition; and from the length to which the evidence on behalf of the prisoner would run, it would be impossible to close the proceedings that night.

TINDAL, C.J., inquired whether, if they adjourned at once, it was quite certain the remainder of the case would come within the compass of to-morrow.

Cockburn replied that he hoped it would, but that would depend mainly upon the course pursued by the counsel for the Crown.

TINDAL, C.J., said, if there was a probability of its being concluded to-morrow, the Court would at once accede to the learned counsel's request.

Cockburn said, that rather than make any statement which might mislead the Court he would go on till a late hour to-night.

TINDAL, C.J., said, that whatever might be the consequences, the Court would at once adjourn the proceedings, as the learned counsel had intimated that he did not feel he could in his present state do justice to the prisoner.

Cockburn assured the Court, that he not only spoke with great pain, but he felt that if he proceeded he should not be able to address the jury at the length the importance of the case required.

Saturday, March 4, 1843.

SPEECH FOR THE DEFENCE.

Cockburn: May it please your Lordships, Gentlemen of the Jury,—I rise to address you on behalf of the unfortunate prisoner at the bar, who stands charged with the awful crime of murder, under a feeling of anxiety so intense—of responsibility so overwhelming, that I feel almost borne down by the weight of my solemn and difficult task. Gentlemen, believe me when I assure you that I say this, not by way of idle or common-place exordium, but as expressing the deep emotions by which my mind is agitated. I believe that you—I know that the numerous professional brethren by whom I see myself surrounded—will understand me when I say that of all the positions in which, in the discharge of our various duties in the different relations of life, a man may be placed, none can be more painful or more paralysing to the energies of the mind than that of an advocate to whom is committed the defence of a fellow being in a matter involving life and death, and who, while deeply convinced that the defence which he has to offer is founded in truth and justice, yet sees in the circumstances by which the case is surrounded, that which makes him look forward with apprehension and trembling to the result. Gentlemen, if this were an ordinary case—if you had heard of it for the first time since you entered into that box—if the individual who has fallen a victim had been some obscure and unknown person, instead of one whose character, whose excellence, and whose fate had commanded the approbation, the love, and the sympathy of all, I should feel no anxiety as to the issue of this trial. But alas! can I dare to hope that even among you, who are to pass in judgment on the accused, there can be one who has not brought to the judgment-seat a mind imbued with preconceived notions on the case which is the subject of this important inquiry? In all classes of this great community—in every corner of this vast metropolis—from end to end, even to the remotest confines of this extensive empire—has this case been already canvassed, discussed, determined—and that, with reference only to the worth of the victim, and the nature of the crime—not with reference to the state or condition of him by whom that crime has been committed; and hence there has arisen in men's minds an insatiate desire of vengeance—there has gone forth a wild and merciless cry for blood, to which you are called upon this day to minister! Yet do I not complain. When I bear in mind how deeply the horror of assassination is stamped on the hearts of men, above all, on the characters of Englishmen—and believe me, there breathes no one on God's earth by whom that crime is more abhorred than by him who now addresses you, and who, deeply deploring the loss, and acknowledging the goodness—dwelt upon with such touching eloquence by my learned friend—of him who in this instance has been its victim, would fain add, if it may be permitted, an humble tribute to the memory of him who has been taken from us—when I bear in mind, I say, these things—I will not give way to one single feeling, I will not breathe one single murmur of complaint or surprise at the passionate excitement which has pervaded the public mind on this unfortunate occasion. But I shall, I trust, be forgiven if I give utterance to the feelings of fear and dread by which, on approaching this case, I find my mind borne down, lest the fierce and passionate resentment to which this event has given rise may interfere with the due performance of those sacred functions which you are now called upon to discharge. Yet, gentlemen, will I not give way to feelings of despair, or address you in the language of despondency. I am not unmindful of the presence in which I am to

31

plead for the life of my client. I have before me British judges, to whom I pay no idle compliment when I say that they are possessed of all the qualities which can adorn their exalted station, or ensure to the accused, a fair, a patient, and an impartial hearing—I am addressing a British jury, a tribunal to which truth has seldom been a suppliant in vain—I stand in a British court, where Justice, with Mercy for her handmaid, sits enthroned on the noblest of her altars, dispelling by the brightness of her presence the clouds which occasionally gather over human intelligence, and awing into silence by the holiness of her eternal majesty the angry passions which at times intrude beyond the threshold of her sanctuary, and force their way even to the very steps of her throne. In the name of that eternal justice—in the name of that God, whose great attribute we are taught that justice is, I call upon you to enter upon the consideration of this case with minds divested of every prejudice, of every passion, of every feeling of excitement. In the name of all that is sacred and holy, I call upon you calmly to weigh the evidence which will be brought before you, and to give your judgment according to that evidence. And if this appeal be not, as I know it will not be, made to you in vain, then, gentlemen, I know the result, and I shall look to the issue without fear or apprehension.

Gentlemen, my learned friend the *Solicitor General*, in stating this case to you, anticipated, with his usual acuteness and accuracy, the nature of the defence which would be set up. The defence upon which I shall rely will turn, not upon the denial of the act with which the prisoner is charged, but upon the state of his mind at the time he committed the act. There is no doubt, gentlemen, that, according to the law of England, insanity absolves a man from responsibility and from the legal consequences which would otherwise attach to the violation of the law. And in this respect, indeed, the law of England goes no further than the law of every other civilised community on the face of the earth. It goes no further than what reason strictly prescribes; and, if it be not too presumptuous to scan the judgments of a higher tribunal, it may not be too much to believe and hope that Providence, when in its inscrutable wisdom and its unfathomable councils, it thinks fit to lay upon a human being the heaviest and most appalling of all calamities to which, in this world of trial and suffering, human nature can be subjected—the deprivation of that reason, which is man's only light and guide in the intricate and slippery paths of life—will absolve him from his responsibility to the laws of God as well as to those of man. The law, then, takes cognisance of that disease which obscures the intellect and poisons the very sources of thought and feeling in the human being—which deprives man of reason, and converts him into the similitude of the lower animal—which bears down all the motives which usually stand as barriers around his conduct, and bring him within the operation of the Divine and human law—leaving the unhappy sufferer to the wild impulses which his frantic imagination engenders, and which urge him on with ungovernable fury to the commission of acts which his better reason, when yet unclouded, would have abhorred. The law, therefore, holds that a human being in such a state is exempt from legal responsibility and legal punishment; to hold otherwise would be to violate every

32

principle of justice and humanity. The principle of the English law, therefore, as a general proposition, admits of no doubt whatsoever. But at the same time, it would be idle to contend that, in the practical application of this great principle, difficulties do not occur. And therefore it is that I claim your utmost attention whilst I lay before you the considerations which present themselves to my mind upon this most important subject. I have already stated to you that the defence of the accused will rest upon his mental condition at the time when the offence was committed. The evidence upon which that defence is founded will be deserving of your most serious attention. I will content myself in the present stage by briefly stating its general character. It will be of a two-fold description. It will not be such as that by which my learned friend the *Solicitor General* has sought to anticipate the defence, and to establish the sanity of the prisoner. It will not be of that naked, vague, indefinite, and uncertain character; it will be testimony positive and precise, and I say, from the bottom of my heart, that I believe it will carry conviction to the mind of everyone who shall hear it. It will be the evidence of persons who have known the prisoner from his infancy—of parties who have been brought into close and intimate contact with him—it will be the evidence of his relations, his friends, and his connexions; but as the evidence of near relations and connexions is always open to suspicion and distrust, I rejoice to say that it will consist also of the statements of persons whose testimony will be beyond the reach of all suspicion or dispute. Gentlemen, I will call before you the authorities of his native place, to one and all of whom this unfortunate calamity with which it has pleased Providence to afflict the prisoner at the bar was distinctly known—to all of whom he has from time to time, and again and again, applied for protection from the fancied miseries which his disordered imagination produced; all of them I will call, and their evidence will leave no doubt upon your minds that this man has been the victim of a fierce and fearful delusion, which, after the intellect had become diseased, the moral sense broken down, and self-control destroyed, has led him on to the perpetration of the crime with which he now stands charged. In addition to this evidence I shall call before you members of the medical profession—men of intelligence, experience, skill, and undoubted probity—who will tell you upon their oaths that it is their belief, their deliberate opinion, their deep conviction, that this man is mad, that he is the creature of delusion, and the victim of ungovernable impulses, which wholly take away from him the character of a reasonable and responsible being. I need not point out to you the great importance and value of the latter description of testimony. You will not, I am sure, think that what I say is with the view, in the slightest degree, of disparaging your capacity, or of doubting your judgment, when I venture to suggest to you that, of all the questions which can possibly come before a tribunal of this kind, the question of insanity is one which (except in those few glaring cases where its effects pervade the whole of a man's mind) is the most difficult upon which men not scientifically acquainted with the subject can be called upon to decide, and upon which the greatest deference should be paid to the opinions of those who have made the subject their peculiar study.

33

It is now, I believe, a matter placed beyond doubt that madness is a disease of the body operating upon the mind, a disease of the cerebral organisation; and that a precise and accurate knowledge of this disease can only be acquired by those who have made it the subject of attention and experience, of long reflection, and of diligent investigation. The very nature of the disease necessitates the seclusion of those who are its victims from the rest of the world. How can we, then, who in the ordinary course of life are brought into contact only with the sane, be competent to judge of the nice and shadowy distinctions which mark the boundary line between mental soundness and mental disease? I do not ask you, gentlemen, to place your judgment at the mercy, or to surrender your minds and understanding to the opinions, of any set of men—for after all, it must be left to your consciences to decide,—I only point out to you the value and importance of this testimony, and the necessity there is that you should listen with patient attention to the evidence of men of skill and science, who have made insanity the subject of their especial attention. My learned friend the *Solicitor General* has directed your attention to the legal authorities; and, perhaps, when those authorities shall have been minutely examined, no great difference will be found to exist between my learned friend and myself. But lest any confusion should be produced in your minds to the detriment of justice, you will forgive me if I pray your attention to the observations which I deem it my duty to make on this branch of the subject. I think it will be quite impossible for any person, who brings a sound judgment to bear upon this judgment, when viewed with the aid of the light which science has thrown upon it, to come to the opinion that the ancient maxims, which, in times gone by, have been laid down for our guidance, can be taken still to obtain in the full force of the terms in which they were laid down. It must not be forgotten that the knowledge of this disease in all its various forms is a matter of very recent growth. I feel that I may appeal to the many medical gentlemen I see around me, whether the knowledge and pathology of this disease has not within a few recent years first acquired the character of a science? It is known to all that it is but as yesterday that the system of treatment, which in past ages—to the eternal disgrace of those ages—was pursued towards those whom it had pleased Heaven to visit with the heaviest of all human afflictions, and who were therefore best entitled to the tenderest care and most watchful kindness of their Christian brethren—it is but as yesterday, I say, that that system has been changed for another, which, thank God, exists to our honour, and to the comfort and better prospect of recovery of the unfortunate diseased in mind! It is but as yesterday that darkness and solitude—cut off from the rest of mankind like the lepers of old—the dismal cell, the bed of straw, the iron chain, and the inhuman scourge, were the fearful lot of those who were best entitled to human pity and to human sympathy, as being the victims of the most dreadful of all mortal calamities. This state of things has passed, or is passing fast away. But in former times when it did exist, you will not wonder that these unhappy persons were looked upon with a different eye. Thank God, at last—though but at last—humanity and wisdom have penetrated, hand in hand, into the dreary abodes of these miserable beings, and whilst the one has poured the balm of consolation into the bosoms of the afflicted, the other has held the light of science over our hitherto imperfect knowledge of this dire disease, has ascertained its varying character, and marked its shadowy boundaries, and taught us how, in gentleness and mercy, best to minister to the relief and restoration of the sufferer! You can easily understand, gentlemen, that when it was the practice to separate these unhappy beings from the rest of mankind and to subject them to this cruel treatment, the person whose reason was but partially obscured would ultimately, and perhaps speedily, in most cases, be converted into a raving madman. You can easily understand, too, that when thus immured and shut up from the inspection of public inquiry, neglected, abandoned, overlooked—all the peculiar forms, and characteristics, and changes of this malady were lost sight of and unknown, and kept from the knowledge of mankind at large, and therefore how difficult it was to judge correctly concerning it. Thus I am enabled to understand how it was that crude maxims and singular propositions founded upon the hitherto partial knowledge of this disease, have been put forward and received as authority, although utterly inapplicable to many of the cases arising under the varied forms of insanity. Science is ever on the advance; and, no doubt, science of this kind, like all other, is in advance of the generality of mankind. It is a matter of science altogether; and we who have the ordinary duties of our several stations and the business of our respective avocations to occupy our full attention, cannot be so well informed upon it as those who have scientifically pursued the study and the treatment of the disease. I think, then, we shall be fully justified in turning to the doctrines of matured science rather than to the maxims put forth in times when neither knowledge, nor philanthropy, nor philosophy, nor common justice had their full operations in discussions of this nature. My learned friend the *Solicitor General* has read to you the authority of Lord *Hale* upon the subject-matter of this inquiry. I hold in my hand perhaps the most scientific treatise that the age has produced upon the subject of insanity in relation to jurisprudence—it is the work of Dr. *Ray*, an American writer on medical jurisprudence, and a professor in one of the great national establishments of that country.

[Counsel quoted the criticisms of Drs. *Ray*(a) and *Prichard*(b) on the test suggested by Lord *Hale* in cases of partial insanity(c):—

"Such a person as labouring under melancholy distempers hath yet ordinarily as great understanding as ordinarily a child of fourteen years hath, is such a person as may be guilty of treason or felony."

On this Dr. *Ray* observes:—

"In the time of this eminent jurist insanity was a much less frequent disease that it is now, and the popular notions concerning it were derived from the observation of those wretched inmates of the mad-houses whom chains and stripes, cold and filth,

(a) "A Treatise on the Medical Jurisprudence of Insanity, by I. Ray, M.D. Boston, 1838."
(b) "On the different Forms of Insanity in relation to Jurisprudence, by James Cowles Prichard, M.D. London, 1842."
(c) 1 Hale, P.C. 30.

had reduced to the stupidity of the idiot, or exasperated to the fury of a demon. Those nice shades of the disease in which the mind, without being wholly driven from its propriety, pertinaciously clings to some absurd delusion, were either regarded as something very different from real madness, or were too far removed from the common gaze, and too soon converted by bad management into the more active forms of the disease, to enter much into the general idea entertained of madness. Could Lord Hale have contemplated the scenes presented by the lunatic asylums of our own times, we should undoubtedly have received from him a very different doctrine for the regulation of the decisions of after generations."

This is not the first time, gentlemen, that this doctrine of Lord *Hale* has been discussed, with the view to ascertain its true interpretation. One of those master minds whose imperishable productions form part of the intellectual treasure and birthright of their country—the great Lord *Erskine*, whose brilliant mind never shone forth more conspicuously than upon the occasion to which I am about to allude, and whose sentiments it would be presumption and profanation to give in other than the language which fell from his own gifted lips at the celebrated trial to which allusion was made by my learned friend, put the true interpretation upon the doctrine of Lord *Hale*. I will read the passage, and I know you will pardon me the time I occupy, for who would not gladly spare the time to listen to observations coming from such a man on so momentous an inquiry?

[Counsel read a passage from *Erskine's* speech in defence of *Hadfield*, concluding as follows:—]

"Delusion, therefore, when there is no frenzy or raving madness, is the true character of insanity; and when it cannot be predicated of a man standing for life or death for a crime, he ought not, in my opinion, to be acquitted, and if courts of law were to be governed by any other principle, every departure from sober, rational conduct would be an emancipation from criminal justice. I shall place my claim to your verdict upon no such dangerous foundation. I must convince you, not only that the unhappy prisoner was a lunatic within my own definition of lunacy, but that the act in question was the immediate, unqualified offspring of the disease. You perceive, therefore, gentlemen, that the prisoner, in naming me for the counsel, has not obtained the assistance of a person who is disposed to carry the doctrine of insanity in his defence so far as even the books would warrant me in carrying it. He alone can be so emancipated whose disease (call it what you will) consists not merely in seeing with a prejudiced eye, or with odd and absurd particularities, differing, in many respects, from the contemplations of sober sense upon the actual existence of things; but he only whose whole reasoning and corresponding conduct, though governed by the ordinary dictates of reason, proceed upon something which has no foundation or existence.(a)

Such gentlemen, is the language of this great man, and in this doctrine is the true interpretation of the law to be found. Gentlemen, that argument prevailed with the Court and jury in the case of the person on behalf of whom it was urged. Upon that argument I take my stand this day. I will bring this case within the scope of the incontrovertible and unanswerable reasoning which it comprises, and I feel perfectly confident that upon you, gentlemen, this reason-

(a) 27 St. Tr. 1314.

ing will not be lost, but that the same result will follow in this as did in that memorable case. My learned friend, the *Solicitor General*, has cited to you one or two other cases which I will dispose of in a very few words. A prominent case in his list is that of Earl *Ferrers*. Here, too, I am glad that my learned friend has referred to the celebrated case of *Hadfield*, because that case furnishes me with some valuable observations of Lord *Erskine's*, made on *Hadfield's* trial, which will enable me to show how that great authority disposed of two of the cases relied on by my learned friend. I prefer to read to you gentlemen, those observations rather than trouble you with any of my own. After stating Lord *Ferrers'* case and drawing the distinction between the species of insane delusion which produces erratic acts, and that species of insanity which I trust I shall be able to prove to you possessed the prisoner now at the bar, Lord *Erskine* says:—

"I have now lying before me the case of Earl Ferrers. Unquestionably there could not be a shadow of doubt, and none appears to have been entertained, of his guilt. I wish, indeed, nothing more than to contrast the two cases; and so far am I from disputing either the principle of that condemnation, or the evidence that was the foundation of it, that I invite you to examine whether any two instances in the whole body of the criminal law are more diametrically opposite to each other than the case of Earl Ferrers and that now before you. Lord Ferrers was divorced from his wife by Act of Parliament; and the person of the name of Johnson, who had been his steward, had taken part with the lady in that proceeding, and had conducted the business in carrying the Act through the two Houses. Lord Ferrers consequently wished to turn him out of a farm which he occupied under him; but his estate being in trust, Johnson was supported by the trustees in his possession. There were also some differences respecting coal mines, and in consequence of both transactions Lord Ferrers took up the most violent resentment against him. Let me here observe,"

continues Lord *Erskine*,

"that this was not a resentment founded upon any illusion; not a resentment forced upon a distempered mind by fallacious images, but depending upon actual circumstances and real facts; and acting like any other man under the influence of malignant passions, he repeatedly declared that he would be revenged on Mr. Johnson, particularly for the part he had taken in depriving him of a contract respecting the mines. Now, suppose that Lord Ferrers could have showed that no difference with Mr. Johnson had ever existed regarding his wife at all, that Mr. Johnson had never been his steward, and that he had only, from delusion, believed so when his situation in life was quite different. Suppose, further, that an illusive imagination had alone suggested to him that he had been thwarted by Johnson in his contract with these coal mines, there never having been any contract at all for coal mines; in short, that the whole basis of his enmity was without any foundation in nature, and had been shown to have been a morbid image imperiously fastened upon his mind. Such a case as that would have exhibited a character of insanity in Lord Ferrers, extremely different from that in which it was presented by the evidence of his peers. Before them he only appeared as a man of turbulent passions, whose mind was disturbed by no fallacious images of things without existence, whose quarrel with Johnson was founded upon no illusions, but upon existing acts, and whose resentment proceeded to the fatal consummation with all the ordinary indications of mischief and malice, and who conducted his own defence with the greatest dexterity and skill. Who then could doubt that Lord Ferrers was a murderer? When the act was done, he said, 'I am glad I have done it. He was a villain, and I am

37

revenged'; but when he afterwards saw that the wound was probably mortal, and that it involved consequences fatal to himself, he desired the surgeon to take all possible care of his patient; and, conscious of his crime, kept at bay the men who came with arms to arrest him, showing, from the beginning to the end, nothing that does not generally accompany the crime for which he was condemned. He was proved, to be sure, to be a man subject to unreasonable prejudices, addicted to absurd practices, and agitated by violent passions; but the act was not done under the dominion of uncontrollable disease; and whether the mischief and malice were substantive or marked in the mind of man whose passions bordered upon, or even amounted to insanity, it did not convince the lords that, under all the circumstances of the case, he was not a fit object of criminal justice."

Thus gentlemen, Lord Erskine showed the greatest possible contrast between the two cases; and I shall, in the case now before you, do the same thing. [Counsel also quoted *Erskine's* reference to *Arnold's* case, and Dr. *Ray's* arguments, to show that *Arnold* was insane.(a) Though *Arnold* was convicted, Lord *Onslow*, at whom he fired, thought he was insane, and procured a reprieve.]

Gentlemen, I will now go on to another case cited by my learned friend the *Solicitor General*. I allude to the case of *Bowler*, which is reported in *Collinson* on Lunacy.(b) I trust, gentlemen, I shall not be considered open to the imputation of arrogance, or as travelling out of the line of my duty on the present occasion, if I say that I cannot bring myself to look upon that case without a deep and profound sense of shame and sorrow that such a decision as was there come to should ever have been resolved upon by a British jury, or sanctioned by a British judge. What, when I remember that in that case Mr. *Warburton*, the keeper of a lunatic asylum, was called and examined, and that he stated that the prisoner *Bowler* had, some months previously, been brought home apparently lifeless, since which time he had perceived a great alteration in his conduct and demeanour; that he would frequently dine at nine o'clock in the morning, eat his meat almost raw, and lie on the grass exposed to rain; that his spirits were so dejected that it was necessary to watch him lest he should destroy himself—when I remember that it was further proved in that case that it was characteristic of insanity occasioned by epilepsy for the patients to imbibe violent antipathies against particular individuals, even their dearest friends, and a desire of taking vengeance upon them, from causes wholly imaginary, which no persuasion could remove, and yet the patient might be rational and collected upon every other subject—when I also recollect that a commission of lunacy had been issued and an inquisition taken upon it, whereby the prisoner was found to have been insane from a period anterior to the offence—when all these recollections cross my mind, I cannot help looking upon that case with feelings bordering upon indignation. But, gentlemen, I rejoice to say—because it absolves me from the imputation of presumption or arrogance in thus differing from the doctrines laid down in that case by the learned judge and adopted by the jury—that in the view which I have taken of it I am borne out by the authority of an English judge now living amongst us—a judge who is, and I trust will long continue to

(a) Ray's Medical Jurisprudence of Insanity, s. 10, p. 18.
(b) 673n.

be, one of the brightest ornaments of a profession which has, through all times, furnished such shining examples to the world. I refer, gentlemen, to Mr. Baron *Alderson*, and the opinion that learned judge pronounced upon *Bowler's* case on the recent trial of *Oxford* in this Court(a); and I must say that I think, if the attention of my learned friend the *Solicitor General* had been drawn to that case, if he had heard or read the observations made by Mr. Baron *Alderson* on that occasion, he would not now have pressed *Bowler's* case upon your notice. The Attorney General of that day, the present Lord *Campbell*, in conducting the prosecution against *Oxford* for shooting at Her Majesty, had, in his address to the jury, cited the case of *Bowler*. When he came to the close of it, Mr. Baron *Alderson* interrupted him with this observation, "*Bowler*, I believe, was executed, and very barbarous it was!" Such was the expression of Mr. Baron *Alderson* upon the mention of *Bowler's* case, and I rejoice to be able to cite it. I reverence the strength of feeling which alone could have given rise to that strength of expression; and I am sure that if the attention of my learned friend had been directed to such an observation coming from so high an authority, I know my learned friend's discretion and sense of propriety too well to think he would have cited *Bowler's* case for your guidance. Gentlemen, you will therefore, I am sure, dismiss that case from your minds after so clear and decided an exposition of the fallacious views which led to that decision. Let the error in that case, I implore you, operate as a warning to you not to be carried away headlong by antiquated maxims or delusive doctrines. God grant that never in future times may any authority, judicial or otherwise, have reason in this case to deplore the consequences of a similar error; never may it be in the power of any man to say of you, gentlemen, that you agreed to a verdict which in itself, or in its execution, deserved to be designated as barbarous.

I pass now, gentlemen, to the next case cited by my learned friend the *Solicitor General*—the case of *Bellingham*. All I can say of that case is, that I believe, in the opinion of the most scientific men who have considered it, there now exists no doubt at all that *Bellingham* was a madman. Few, I believe, at this period, unbiassed by the political prejudices of the times, and examining the event as a matter of history, will read the report of *Bellingham's* trial without being forced to the conclusion that he was really mad, or, at the very least, that the little evidence which did appear relative to the state of his mind was strong enough to have entitled him to a deliberate and thorough investigation of his case. The eminent writer I have already quoted—I mean Dr. *Ray*—in speaking of *Bellingham's* case, says(b):—

"It appeared from the history of the accused, from his own account of the transactions that led to the fatal act, and from the testimony of several witnesses, that he laboured under many of those strange delusions that find a place only in the brains of a madman. His fixed belief that his own private grievances were national wrongs; that his country's diplomatic agents in a foreign land neglected to hear his complaints and assist him in his troubles, though they had in reality done more than could have

(a) Above, p. 508.
(b) Ray's Medical Jurisprudence, p. 29, s. 15.

39

reasonably been expected of them; his conviction, in which he was firm almost to the last, that his losses would be made good by the Government, even after he had been repeatedly told, in consequence of repeated applications in various quarters, that the Government would not interfere in his affairs; and his determination, on the failure of all other means to bring his affairs before the country, to effect this purpose by assassinating the head of the Government, by which he would have an opportunity of making a public statement of his grievances and obtaining a triumph, which he never doubted, over the Attorney General; these were all delusions, as wild and strange as those of seven-eighths of the inmates of any lunatic asylum in the land. And so obvious were they, that though they had not the aid of an Erskine to press them upon the attention of the jury, and though he himself denied the imputation of insanity, the Government, as if virtually acknowledging their existence, contended for his responsibility on very different grounds."

Gentlemen, it is a fact that *Bellingham* was hanged within one week after the commission of the fatal act, while persons were on their way to England who had known him for years, and who were prepared to give decisive evidence of his insanity. He was tried, he was executed, notwithstanding the earnest appeal of Mr. *Alley*, his counsel, that time might be afforded him to obtain evidence as to the nature and extent of the malady to which *Bellingham* was subject. Moreover, on the occasion of the trial of *Oxford* in this Court, the then Attorney General, Sir *John Campbell*, now Lord *Campbell*, after *Bowler's* case had been disposed of by the emphatic observation of Mr. Baron *Alderson*, expressed himself in these words:—

"I will not refer to *Bellingham's* case, as there are some doubts as to the correctness of the mode in which that case was conducted."

I would that my learned friend the *Solicitor General* had taken on this occasion the same course, and had exercised the same wise forbearance; because the doubts expressed by the late Attorney General as to the propriety of the conduct of that case are not confined to that learned person, it being notorious that very serious doubts as to the propriety of that trial are commonly entertained among the profession at large. Under such circumstances, gentlemen, I feel that it would have been much better if your attention had not been directed to that trial as it has been. I turn now to a very recent treatise on criminal law, which I am the more entitled to cite as an authority, because its learned author, Mr. *Roscoe*, has been snatched from us by the hand of death,(a) while his career was full of that promise which his great attainments and varied learning held out to us. Referring to the rule laid down in the case of *Bellingham*, and which you have been told was adopted by Lord *Lyndhurst* in *Rex* v. *Offord*, Mr. *Roscoe* says:—

"The direction does not appear to make a sufficient allowance for the incapacity of judging between right and wrong upon the very matter in question, as in all cases of monomania."(b)

(a) Mr. Roscoe died March 25, 1836, in his 37th year.
(b) Roscoe's Criminal Evidence, p. 876.

40

Mr. *Roscoe* quotes some remarks by an eminent writer on the criminal law of Scotland. Now I may here observe, that I have the authority of the present Lord *Campbell*, when Attorney General, in *Oxford's* case, for saying that there is no difference between the law of Scotland and that of England in this respect; so that all which I may have to cite with respect to the law of Scotland will be quite applicable to the case in hand. Gentlemen, Mr. *Roscoe* goes on to say:—

"The following observations of an eminent writer on the criminal law of Scotland (Mr. Alison) are applicable to the subject: 'Although a prisoner understands perfectly the distinction between right and wrong, yet if he labours, as is generally the case, under an illusion and deception in his own particular case, and is thereby incapable of applying it correctly to his own conduct, he is in that state of mental aberration which renders him not criminally answerable for his actions. For example, a mad person may be perfectly aware that murder is a crime, and will admit it, if pressed on the subject; still he may conceive that the homicide he has committed was nowise blamable, because the deceased had engaged in a conspiracy, with others, against his own life, or was his mortal enemy, who had wounded him in his dearest interests, or was the devil incarnate, whom it was the duty of every good Christian to meet with weapons of carnal warfare.' "

These observations of Mr. *Roscoe* and Mr. *Alison*, when applied to the cases of *Bellingham*, of *Arnold*, and of *Offord*, show that they are not cases to be relied upon as perfect—that the doctrine laid down in them cannot be taken as an unerring criterion by a jury. Unless you attend to all the circumstances of the particular case, you may be led into disastrous results, which it must be your most anxious wish to avoid. [Counsel next referred to *Offord's* case, and read the report(*a*) to the jury.]

The verdict was not guilty. I think my learned friend did not state to you the verdict.

Solicitor General: I beg your pardon; I did.

Cockburn: If so, I was in error, and on my learned friend's statement, I withdraw at once the observation I made. I am sorry that I made it; and here let me take the opportunity of expressing my sense—and I am sure my learned friend will not object to receive such a tribute from me—of the forbearance and merciful consideration with which he opened and has conducted this case. I am bound also to say, that whatever facilities could be afforded to the defence, have been readily granted to the prisoner's friends by those who represent the Crown on this occasion. But to resume. With respect, then, to *Offord's* case, I have only to remind you that *Offord* was acquitted on the ground of insanity. Here, gentlemen, I shall prove a much stronger case; and when I have done so, you will, I feel confident, have no hesitation in following the precedent set you by the jury in that case. So much, gentlemen, for the legal authorities cited by my learned friend the *Solicitor General*; but, after all, as was observed by him, this is not so much a question of law as of fact. That which you have to determine is, whether the prisoner at the bar is guilty of the crime of wilful murder. Now, by "wilful" must be understood, not the mere will that makes a man raise his

(*a*) 5 C. & P. 168; and see above, p. 547.

hand against another; not a blind instinct that leads to the commission of an irrational act, because the brute creation, the beasts of the field, have, in that sense, a will; but by will, with reference to human action, must be understood the necessary moral sense that guides and directs the volition, acting on it through the medium of reason. I quite agree with my learned friend, that it is a question—being, namely, whether this moral sense exists or not—of fact rather than of law. At the same time, whatever light legal authorities may afford on the one hand, or philosophy and science on the other, we ought to avail ourselves of either with grateful alacrity. This being premised, I will now take the liberty of making a few general observations upon what appears to me to be the true view of the nature of this disease with reference to the application of the important principle of criminal responsibility. To the most superficial observer who has contemplated the mind of man, it must be perfectly obvious that the functions of the mind are of a twofold nature—those of the intellect or faculty of thought alone—such as perception, judgment, reasoning—and again, those of the moral faculties—the sentiments, affections, propensities, and passions, which it has pleased Heaven, for its own wise purposes, to implant in the nature of man. It is now received as an admitted principle by all inquirers, that the seat of the mental disease termed insanity is the cerebral organisation; that is to say, the brain of man. Whatever and wherever may be the seat of the immaterial man, one thing appears perfectly clear to human observation, namely—that the point which connects the immaterial and the material man—is the brain; and, furthermore, it is clear that all defects in the cerebral organisation, whether congenital—that is to say, born with a man—or supervening either by disease or by natural and gradual decay, have the effect of impairing and deranging the faculties and functions of the immaterial mind. The soul is there as when first the Maker breathed it into man; but the exercise of the intellectual and moral faculties is vitiated and disordered. Again, a further view of the subject is this—it is one which has only been perfectly understood and elucidated in its full extent by the inquiries of modern times. By any one of the legion of casualties by which the material organisation may be affected, any one or all of these various faculties of the mind may be disordered,—the perception, the judgment, the reason, the sentiments, the affections, the propensities, the passions—any one or all may become subject to insanity; and the mistake existing in ancient times, which the light of modern science has dispelled, lay in supposing that in order that a man should be mad—incapable of judging between right and wrong, or of exercising that self-control and dominion, without which the knowledge of right and wrong would become vague and useless—it was necessary that he should exhibit these symptoms which would amount to total prostration of the intellect; whereas modern science has incontrovertibly established that any one of these intellectual and moral functions of the mind may be subject to separate disease, and thereby man may be rendered the victim of the most fearful delusions, the slave of uncontrollable impulses impelling or rather compelling him to the commission of acts such as that which has given rise to the case now under your consideration. This is the view of the subject on which all scientific authorities

42

are agreed—a view not only entertained by medical, but also by legal authorities. It is almost with a blush that I now turn from the authorities in our own books, to those which I find in the works of the Scottish writers on jurisprudence. I turn to the celebrated work of a profound and scientific jurist, I allude to Baron *Hume*. He treats on the very subject which is now, gentlemen, under your consideration —namely, the test of insanity as a defence with reference to criminal acts, and he says(*a*):—

"To serve the purpose, therefore, of an excuse in law, the disorder must amount to absolute alienation of reason, '*ut continua mentis alienatione, omni intellectu cureat*'— such a disease as deprives the patient of the knowledge of the true disposition of things about him, and of the discernment of friend from foe, and gives him up to the impulse of his own distempered fancy, divested of all self-government or control of his passions. Whether it should be added to the description that he must have lost all knowledge of good and evil, right and wrong, is a more delicate question, and fit, perhaps, to be resolved differently, according to the sense in which it is understood. If it be put in this sense in a case for instance, of murder—Did the panel(*b*) know that murder was a crime? Would he have answered on the question, that it is wrong to kill a neighbour? This is hardly to be reputed a just criterion of such a state of soundness as ought to make a man accountable in law for his acts. Because it may happen to a person, to answer in this way, who yet is so absolutely mad as to have lost all true observation of facts, all understanding of the good or bad intention of those who are about him, or even the knowledge of their persons. But if the question is put in this other and more special sense, as relative to the act done by the panel, and his understanding of the particular situation in which he conceived himself to stand. Did he at that moment understand the evil of what he did? Was he impressed with the consciousness of guilt and fear of punishment? it is then a pertinent and a material question, but which cannot, to any substantial purpose, be answered, without taking into consideration the whole circumstances of the situation. Every judgment in the matter of right and wrong supposes a case, or state of facts, to which it applies. And though the panel may have that vestige of reason which may enable him to answer in the general, that murder is a crime, yet if he cannot distinguish his friend from his enemy, or a benefit from an injury, but conceive everything about him to be the reverse of what it really is, and mistake the illusions of his fancy for realities in respect of his own condition and that of others, those remains of intellect are of no use to him towards the government of his actions, nor in enabling him to form a judgment on any particular situation or conjunction of what is right or wrong with regard to it; if he does not know the person of his friend or neighbour, or though he do know him, if he is possessed with the vain conceit that he is come there to destroy him, or that he has already done him the most cruel injuries, and that all about him are engaged in one foul conspiracy to abuse him, as well might he be utterly ignorant of the quality of murder. Proceeding as it does on a false case of conjuration of his own fancy, his judgment of right and wrong, as to any responsibility that should attend it, is truly the same as none at all. It is, therefore, only in this complete and appropriated sense as relative to the particular thing done, and the situation of the panel's feelings and consciousness on that occasion, that this inquiry concerning his intelligence of moral good or evil is material, and not in any other or larger sense."

This, gentlemen, I take to be the true interpretation and construction of the law. The question is not here, as my learned friend would have you think,

(*a*) Hume's Commentaries on the Law of Scotland, vol. i. 37.
(*b*) The prisoner.

whether this individual knew that he was killing another when he raised his hand to destroy him, although he might be under a delusion, but whether under that delusion of mind he did an act which he would not have done under any other circumstances, save under the impulse of the delusion which he could not control, and out of which delusion alone the act itself arose. Again, gentlemen, I must have recourse to the observations of that eminent man, Lord *Erskine*. I am anxious, most anxious on this difficult subject, feeling deeply my own incapacity, and that I am but as the blind leading the blind (you will forgive me the expression); I am, I repeat, anxious to avail myself as much as possible of the great light which others have thrown upon the subject, and to avoid any observations of my own by referring to the remarks of much greater minds. I turn again, therefore, to the remarks of Lord *Erskine* on the subject of delusion, in the case which has so often been mentioned. The case here is one of delusion —the act in question is connected with that delusion out of which, and out of which alone, it sprung.

"Delusions,"

says Lord *Erskine*,

"therefore, where there is no frenzy or raving madness, is the true character of insanity, and where it cannot be predicated of a man standing for life or death for a crime, he ought not, in my opinion, to be acquitted; and if the courts of law were to be governed by any other principle, every departure from sober rational conduct would be emancipation from criminal justice. I shall place my claim to your verdict upon no such dangerous foundation."

And, gentlemen, I following at an immeasurable distance that great man, I, too, will place my claim to your verdict on no such dangerous foundation.

"I must convince you,"

said Lord *Erskine*,

"not only that the unhappy prisoner was a lunatic within my own definition of lunacy, but that the act in question was the immediate unqualified offspring of this disease."

I accept this construction of the law: by that interpretation, coupled with and qualified by the conditions annexed to it, I will abide. I am bound to show that the prisoner was acting under a delusion, and that the act sprung out of that delusion, and I will show it. I will show it by evidence irresistibly strong; and when I have done so I shall be entitled to your verdict. On the other hand, my learned friend the *Solicitor General* told you yesterday that in the case before you the prisoner had some rationality, because in the ordinary relations of life he had manifested ordinary sagacity, and that on this account you must come to the conclusion that he was not insane on any point, and that the act with which he now stands charged was not the result of delusion. I had thought that the many occasions upon which this matter had been discussed would have

44

rendered such a doctrine as obsolete and exploded in a court of law as it is everywhere else. Let my learned friend ask any of the medical gentlemen who surround him, and whose assistance he has on this occasion, if they will come forward and pledge their professional reputation, as well as their moral character, to the assertion that shall deny the proposition that a man may be a frenzied lunatic on one point, and yet on all others be capable of all the operations of the human mind, possessed of a high degree of sagacity, in possession of full rational powers, undisturbed by evil or excessive passions. On this point Dr. Ray,(a) in the following observations (the result of his long experience), disposes of the very objection which my learned friend has put forward on the present occasion:—

"The purest minds cannot express greater horror and loathing of various crimes than madmen often do, and from precisely the same causes. Their abstract conceptions of crime, not being perverted by the influence of disease, present its hideous outlines as strongly defined as they ever were in the healthiest condition; and the disapprobation they express at the sight arises from sincere and honest convictions. The particular criminal act, however, becomes divorced in their minds from its relations to crime in the abstract; and being regarded only in connexion with some favourite object which it may help to obtain, and which they see no reason to refrain from pursuing, is viewed, in fact, as of a highly laudable and meritorious nature. Herein, then, consists their insanity, not in preferring vice to virtue, in applauding crime and ridiculing justice, but in being unable to discern the essential identity of nature between a particular crime and all other crimes, whereby they are led to approve what, in general terms, they have already condemned. It is a fact not calculated to increase our faith in the march of intellect, that the very trait peculiarly characteristic of insanity has been seized upon as conclusive proof of sanity in doubtful cases; and thus the infirmity that entitles one to protection, is tortured into a good and sufficient reason for completing his ruin."

I trust, gentlemen, that these observations, proceeding from a man of the most scientific observation, having all the facilities of studying everything connected with the subject, will not be lost upon you. I could mention case after case—I could continue till the sun should go down on my uncompleted task—I could cite case after case, in which the intellectual faculty was so impaired that the insanity upon one point was beyond all doubt, and yet where there was upon all others the utmost sagacity and intelligence. You will see that all the evidence of my learned friend the *Solicitor General* relates to the ordinary relations of a man's life. That does not affect the real question. It may be that this man understood the nature of right and wrong on general subjects—it may be that he was competent to manage his own affairs, that he could fulfil his part in the different relations of life, that he was capable of transacting all ordinary business. I grant it. But admitting all this, it does not follow that he was not subject to delusion, and insane. If I had represented this as a case of a man altogether subject to a total frenzy—that all traces of human reason were obliterated and gone—that his life was one perpetual series of paroxysms of rage and fury, my learned friend might well have met me with the evidence he

(a) Ray's Med. Jurisp. s. 17, p. 32.

45

has produced upon the present occasion; but when I put my case upon the other ground, that of partial delusion, my learned friend has been adducing evidence which is altogether beside the question. I can show you instances in which a man was, on some particular point, to all intents and purposes mad—where reason had lost its empire—where the moral sense was effaced and gone—where all control, all self-dominion, was lost for ever under one particular delusion; and yet where in all the moral and social relations of life there was, in all other respects, no neglect, no irrationality, where the man might have gone through life without his infirmity being known to any except those to whom a knowledge of the particular delusion had been communicated. My learned friend has also remarked upon the silent design and contrivance which the prisoner manifested upon the occasion in question, as well as upon his rationality in the ordinary transactions of life. But my friend forgets that it is an established fact in the history of this disease, perhaps one of its most striking phenomena, that a man may be mad, may be under the influence of a wild and insane delusion,—one who, all barriers of self-control being broken down, is driven by frenzied impulse into crime, and yet, in carrying out the fell purposes which a diseased mind has suggested, may show all the skill, subtlety, and cunning, which the most intelligent and sane would have exhibited. Just so in the case of *Hadfield*; it was urged against Lord *Erskine*, that *Hadfield* could not be mad, because he had shown so much cunning, subtlety, deliberation, and design, in the whole of the circumstances which led to the perpetration of the act with which he was charged. In the present case, my learned friend the *Solicitor General* has told you that the prisoner watched for his victim, haunted the neighbourhood of the Government offices, waited for the moment to strike the blow, and throughout exhibited a degree of design and deliberation inconsistent with insanity. The same in *Hadfield's* case; *Hadfield* went to the theatre, got his pistol loaded, and took his position in a place to command the situation in which he knew the King would sit; he raised the pistol, he took deliberate aim, and fired at the person of the King. All these circumstances were urged as evidence of design, and as inconsistent with the acts of a madman. What then, gentlemen, is the result of these observations? What is the practical conclusion of these investigations of modern science upon the subject of insanity? It is simply this: that a man, though his mind may be sane upon other points, may, by the effect of mental disease, be rendered wholly incompetent to see some one or more of the relations of subsisting things around him in their true light, and though possessed of moral perception and control in general, may become the creature and the victim of some impulse so irresistibly strong as to annihilate all possibility of self dominion or resistance in the particular instance; and this being so, it follows, that if, under such an impulse, a man commits an act which the law denounces and visits with punishment, he cannot be made subject to such punishment, because he is not under the restraint of those motives which could alone create human responsibility. If, then, you shall find in this case that the moral sense was impaired, that this act was the result of a morbid delusion, and necessarily connects itself with that delusion; if I can establish such a case by evidence, so as to bring myself within the interpretation which the highest authorities have said is the true principle of law as they have laid it down for the guidance of courts of law and juries in inquiries of this kind, I shall feel perfectly confident that your verdict must be in favour of the prisoner at the bar.

With these observations I shall now proceed to lay before you the facts of this extraordinary case. My learned friend the *Solicitor General* has already given you some account of the prisoner at the bar, and I will now fill up the outline which my learned friend has drawn. The prisoner, as you have been told, is a native of Glasgow. At an early age he was apprenticed to his father, who carried on the business of a turner in that city; at the end of the apprenticeship he became a journeyman to his father, having been disappointed in not being taken by him as a partner. The prisoner, I should observe, is a natural son, and probably did not meet with that full measure of kindness which is usually shown to legitimate offspring. Whatever might have been the predetermining cause, he appears to have been from the commencement a man of gloomy, reserved, and unsocial habits. He was, moreover, as you will hear, though gloomy and reserved in himself, a man of singularly sensitive mind—one who spent his days in incessant labour and toil, and at night gave himself up to the study of difficult and abstruse matters; but whose mind, notwithstanding, was tinctured with refinement. As one trait of his character, I would mention that he was extremely fond of watching children at play, and took infinite delight in their infantine and innocent ways. I will prove, also, that he was a man of particular humanity towards the brute creation, and that when he went out he was in the habit of carrying crumbs in his pocket to distribute to the birds. If in the course of their walks his companions discovered a bird's nest, he would interfere, and not allow them to approach it. These things are striking indications of character, and certainly do not accord with the ferocity of an assassin. I mention these things to show that, from the earliest period, the prisoner had a predisposition to insanity. I shall prove to you, gentlemen, that the man and his wife with whom he lodged in 1837, became so alarmed at his behaviour that they gave him notice to quit, and forced him to leave, despite his wish to remain, from an apprehension that all was not right within his mind. I shall next carry him on to the time when he relinquished his business. When he quitted his lodgings in 1837 he went to live in his own workshop, and there he lived alone, without friend or associate, without recreation or amusement, save that which was found in turning from severe toil to severer studies. He then began to believe that persons persecuted him; he then began to act more strangely than before. With these moral phenomena must be coupled certain physical accompaniments. The unhappy prisoner would complain of pain; he would sit for hours, aye, even for days, holding his head within his hands, and uttering ejaculations descriptive of the tortures he endured. Often has he been known to hasten out, under the influence of these agonies, and throw himself into the waters of the Clyde in order to seek some relief from the torturing fever by which his brain was consumed. These facts I shall prove to the court and jury. They do not amount to insanity, but they will show what was going on within. They will show his pre-

47

disposition to the disease which has since assumed so terrible a shape. It appears that in the beginning of 1841 he gave up his business from which he was deriving considerable gain. Why? Doubtless because at that time the fearful phantasms of his own imagination rendered his existence miserable. He was wretched, because he was constantly harassed by the terrible images his disordered mind conjured up. These terrifying delusions had become associated with the place of his abode, haunting him at all hours of the day and night. You will hear from one of the witnesses, to whom he explained himself, that he gave up business "on account of the persecution by which he was pursued." Yet it appears that all this time his business was prosperous and thriving, and, in addition, the great tendency of his mind seemed still to be a desire to earn money and to save it. That these phantasms long existed in that man's mind there is no doubt, before he at length sought relief by flight from this hideous nightmare, which everlastingly tortured his distracted senses. No doubt these delusions existed in his mind before, but it was not until he left his business that they were revealed to others in anything like a definite shape. And, gentlemen, you will learn from the medical authorities that it was natural for him, who became at last borne down by these delusions to struggle against them as long as he could; to resist their influence, and to conceal their existence; until, at last, the mind, overwrought and overturned, could contain itself no longer, and was obliged to give form, and shape, and expression, "a local habitation and a name," to the fantasies against which it had struggled at first, believing, it may be, for a time, that they were delusions, until their influence gradually prevailing above the declining judgment, they at last assumed all the appearance of reality, and the man became as firmly persuaded of the substantiality of these creations of his own fevered brain as of his very existence. Wherever he was, these creatures of his imagination still haunted him with eager enmity, for the purpose of destroying his happiness and his life. Nothing, then, could be more natural than that a man under such a persuasion should attempt to escape from the persecution which he erringly imagined to exist, and to seek in some change of place and clime a refuge from the tortures he endured. Alas! alas! in this man's case the question put by the poet of old received a melancholy response:—

"——Patriæ quis exul
Se quoque fugit?"
What exile from his country's shore can from himself escape?

When he left his own country he visited England, and then France; but nowhere was there a "resting-place for the sole of his foot." Wherever he went, his diseased mind carried with him the diseased productions of its own perverted nature. Wherever he was, there were his fancies; there were present to his mind his imaginary persecutors. When he planted his foot on the quay at Boulogne, there he found them. No sooner was he landed on a foreign soil than there were his visionary enemies around him. Again he fled from them, and again returned to his native land. Feeling the impossibility of escape from his tormentors, what course did he pursue? When he found it was impossible to go anywhere by night or by day to effect his escape from those beings which his disordered imagination kept hovering around him, what does he? What was the best test of the reality of the delusion? That he should act exactly as a sane man would have done, if they had been realities instead of delusions. And there is my answer to the fallacious test of my learned friend the *Solicitor General*. He did so act; he acted as a sane man would have done, but he manifested beyond all doubt the continued existence of the delusions. He goes to the authorities of his native place, to those who could afford him protection, and with clamours entreats and implores them to defend him from the conspiracy which, he told them, had been entered into against his happiness and his life. Are we to be told that a man acting under such delusions, on whose mind was fixed the impression of their existence, and who was goaded on by them into the commission of acts which but for them he never would have committed,—are we to be told that such a man is to be dealt with in the same way as one who had committed a crime under the influence of the views and motives which operate upon the minds and passions of men under ordinary circumstances? [Counsel proceeded to refer to the prisoner's applications for protection to his father, to Mr. *Wilson*, the Sheriff Substitute, to the Lord Provost of Glasgow, &c.] That these delusions afterwards took a political bias is possible; they may have done so. But such was not the first morbid impression of the prisoner's mind. The first was, according to his own complaint to Mr. *Wilson*, that the Catholic priests and Jesuits were engaged in persecuting him, and he stated that the annoyance he had experienced from them was such that he had been obliged to leave the country, and had gone to France, but that on landing at Boulogne he found he was watched by them still, and therefore it was useless to go further. Mr. *Wilson* endeavoured to soothe him and to disabuse his mind, and he went away, apparently somewhat quieted. At the end of three or four days he comes back and says that there are spies all around him, and that the Church of Rome and the police and all the world are against him. Here you have in addition to the Church of Rome, the "police" and "all the world." Mr. *Wilson* spoke to him of the folly of supposing the Church of Rome to be against him, and assured him that if the police did anything against him, he, Mr. *Wilson*, would find it out. He comes again in the course of a few days, and then, in addition to his former complaints, he says, "The Tories are now persecuting me on account of a vote I gave at a former election." You will at once comprehend, gentlemen, that the delusion arose not from any part he had individually taken in politics—it was the form which was assumed by a diseased mind, believing itself to be the victim of persecution by anybody and everybody. First it was the "Catholic priests," then it was "the Church of Rome, the police, and all the world," and then it was "the Tories." After that he called again upon Mr. *Wilson* to know what had been done for him, when Mr. *Wilson*, to soothe him, told him that he had made inquiries; and promised to speak to Captain *Miller*, a superintendent of police. Again he called, and was told that Captain *Miller* said there were no such persecutors, if there were, he should know of it. The prisoner said that Captain *Miller* was deceiving Mr. *Wilson*, as he knew that his persecutors were more active than

49

ever; that they gave him no rest day or night; that his health was suffering, and that the persecutions he endured would drive him into a consumption. Mark that statement, gentlemen; couple it with the declaration he made after he was apprehended, and it will enable you to judge of the state of the man's mind at the time he made that declaration. Again he goes away; he does not come back again for some months, when he returns to talk again of his persecutors. This was in the summer, and the time was drawing nigh to the period of this unhappy deed. Mr. *Wilson* will tell you, gentlemen, that when he saw him at that time his conduct had become more strange, and his conversation more incoherent; doubtless as time progressed his disorder was becoming worse. Having got rid of him, Mr. *Wilson* does that which affords the best test of the sincerity of the conviction he will express to you—namely, that he believed the man to be insane. He goes to the man's father and tells him that, in his opinion, it was unfitting for his son any longer to be left at large.

[The prisoner also applied to Mr. *Turner*, who gave the same advice to his father.] Would to God that advice had been listened to! Would to God that warning voice had produced the effect which was intended! Then this melancholy catastrophe might have been prevented! By judicious medical treatment the man might have been restored to reason, or, at all events, such means might have been resorted to as the law allows for the protection of society. Oh, then, what different results would have been produced! The unhappy prisoner might have been spared the horror of having imbrued his hand in the blood of a fellow creature; he would have been spared the having to stand to-day at that bar on his trial for having committed the worst crime of which human nature is capable; as it now is, his only trust must be in your good sense, judgment, and humanity, in the opinion of which you may form upon the evidence which those who come from a distant part to throw a light on the subject will give you, and in such aid as my humble capacity enables me to afford him. So much, gentlemen, for the evidence I shall give with respect to the origin of this wretched assassination.

[The evidence called by the *Solicitor General* does not in the slightest degree negative the case of insanity which the witnesses will clearly establish. It is that sort of negative testimony which can only spring either from the absence of all opportunity of observation, or from want of attention to the matter in question.]

I now come, gentlemen, to the act itself, with which the prisoner now stands charged. The *Solicitor General* has said that you are not from the nature of the act itself, to draw an inference as to the state of mind of the person committing it. My learned friend put the proposition rather vaguely, but I can scarcely suppose that he meant what I have just said to the full extent of the terms. He might have meant either that you were not necessarily to infer from the nature of the act, from its atrocity and the absence of all probable impelling motives, the insanity of the person committing it, that is to say, that you were not to infer it conclusively from those circumstances alone, or he might have meant that the nature of the act itself ought not all to be an ingredient in forming a judgment of the state of the party committing it. Now, if my learned friend

50

could have meant this last proposition, I must say, that with all my respect for him, I should be compelled boldly to differ from him, and to dissent altogether from a proposition so monstrous as that would seem to be. If it be found that an act is done, for which he who committed it was without any of those motives which usually actuate men in a state of sanity to wickedness and crime, if the whole circumstances connected with the perpetration of that act tend to show that it was one wholly inconsistent with the relation towards the surrounding world of the party committing it, am I, in such a case, to be told that I am to draw no inference at all from the nature of the act itself? I am sure, gentlemen, you will not allow your minds to be influenced and misled by any such proposition. You must look to the act, not conclusively, indeed, but in connexion with the other leading circumstances of the case. What is the act? In the broad face of day, in the presence of surrounding numbers, in one of the great and busy thoroughfares of this peopled metropolis, with the certainty of detection, and the impossibility of flight, with the inevitable certainty of the terrible punishment awarded to such a deed, a man takes away the life from one who (in any view of the case) had never, in thought, word, or deed, done to the perpetrator of that act the faintest vestige of an injury, from one who, as my learned friend yesterday described him, was of so mild a nature that he would not injure any being that had life, does this in the total absence of all motive, with the certainty of inevitable detection, and of equally inevitable punishment; yet you are told by my learned friend that you are not to let the nature and the circumstances of such an act enter into your judgment as to whether the person so committing it was sane or not. Who is there who, not having his judgment overclouded by the indignation which the very mention of such a deed is calculated to excite, could bring for a single moment his dispassionate reason to bear upon the nature of the case whose mind would not suggest that the act must be that of a frenzied lunatic and not of one possessed of his senses? My learned friend says that, nevertheless, you are not to look to the question of motive, and he appeals to history for instances where fanaticism and enthusiasm have operated on ill-regulated minds to induce them to commit similar crimes. I might possibly object that these instances are not strictly in evidence before you, but I will not adopt such a course. I admit that in order to understand the nature of insanity aright we must look beyond the evidence in the particular case. I will travel, therefore, with my learned friend beyond the facts now before you, and will turn to history in order to aid our judgment. I concede to him that fanaticism and enthusiasm operating on ill-regulated minds have produced similar disastrous results on former occasions. But look at the mode in which those motives operated on the minds of the criminals. The religious fanatic sharpened his steel against his sovereign's life, because he was told by a fanatical priesthood that he was doing a service to God, and to religion, that he was devoting himself by that act to the maintenance of God's religion, and that, while incurring an earthly martyrdom, he was also ensuring to himself an everlasting reward. Again, I admit that political enthusiasm has urged on others to similar crimes. Why? Because they acted under the belief that in some great emergency, while they were sacrificing the moral law, they were ensuring the welfare of their country. They were impelled by fanaticism in another form, by political enthusiasm, by misdirected and ill-guided notions of patriotism. Political enthusiasm! Where in this case is there a single trace of the existence of such a sentiment in the mind of the assassin? Where has the evidence for the prosecution furnished you with a single instance of political extravagance on the part of this man? Is he shown to have taken a strong and active part in political matters? Did he attend political meetings? Is he shown to have been a man of ill-guided, strong, and enthusiastic political sentiments? There is not a tittle of evidence on that subject. Many among us entertain strong political opinions. I do not disclaim them myself. I entertain them, and most strongly too; but if I believed that they would make me love, cherish, esteem, or honour any human being the less on account of his holding different opinions I would renounce politics for ever, for I would rather live under the most despotical and slavish government than forego aught of those feelings of humanity which are the charm of human life, and without which this world would be a wilderness. [The prisoner had no animosity against Sir *Robert Peel*, for whom he is said to have mistaken Mr. *Drummond.*] There is no evidence to show that he did intend to shoot Sir *R. Peel*, save that of the policeman. I hardly know whether I am not throwing away time in devoting a single observation to the evidence of a man whose own statement justifies me in saying that he was acting a thoroughly treacherous part; a man who now shows himself in his true colours, an inquisitor and a spy; but who then, in the garb of fairness and honesty, sought to worm himself into the secrets of the unhappy man at the bar. I allude to the statement made before the magistrate as to the conversation he had with the prisoner. Having gently insinuated himself into the man's confidence, he asks a question as to the identity of the individual who had been shot. The answers he says the prisoner gave may be true or false; the statement of that witness may be consistent with truth, or it may be a fabrication; I know not, care not. Sure I am of this, that whatever may be the nature of the crime with which a man may stand charged, a British jury will hesitate to admit any one single fact which is an essential ingredient in the proof of the case, on the unsupported testimony of an individual who has manifested so much black perfidy, which will remain indelibly stamped upon his character. If the statement were true, why should it rest upon the evidence of that policeman only, when it is clear that at part of the conversation at least there was also a constable present? But I really waste time upon this part of the case, and I will proceed at once to a more important point, namely, the conduct of the prisoner himself after he had been brought before the magistrates.

And this brings me to the question, whether or not the delusion under which the prisoner previously laboured existed in his mind at the time the act was done with which he now stands charged, and in truth was the cause of that act? I have already laid before you circumstances (and they will be proved in evidence) which establish beyond all controversy the existence of a delusion, exercising a blind and imperious influence over the man; and I have only further to establish, that the delusion led to the act, and was subsisting at the time that act was done.

But surely it would be most monstrous and unjust to say that the same degree of delusion which prevailed eighteen months or two years before, did not exist at the time of his committing the act. What was his statement before the magistrate! He said:—

"The Tories in my native city have compelled me to do this. They follow and persecute me wherever I go, and have entirely destroyed my peace of mind. They followed me to France, into Scotland, and all over England; in fact, they follow me wherever I go. I can get no rest for them night or day. I cannot sleep at night in consequence of the course they pursue towards me. I believe they have driven me into a consumption. I am sure I shall never be the man I formerly was. I used to have good health and strength, but I have not now. They have accused me of crimes of which I am not guilty; they do everything in their power to harass and persecute me; in fact, they wish to murder me. It can be proved by evidence; that's all I have to say."

Save only that the enemies he spoke of and their persecution were the phantoms of a disordered mind, his statement was true. True it was that he was a different man, in health of body, and in health of mind, quite different in the regulation of his passions and propensities; he that at home had been a quiet, calm, inoffensive man, one who never raised his hand against a human being or created thing, had been converted by the pressure of imaginary evils into a shedder of human blood. This statement of the prisoner, which doubtless, at first, was received with suspicion, shows, when coupled with his previous history, in a totally different light, and now cannot be regarded otherwise than as the true and genuine expression of the feelings which were alive in his breast. No wonder that in the first excitement of popular feeling such a statement should be unfavourably received; the people had seen an innocent and unoffending man perish by the hand of an assassin; they were justified in viewing with distrust manifestations of insanity, which might be only assumed; but now, when the fearful delusions under which this man has so long laboured are made clearly known to you, the whole matter will, I am sure, be regarded by you under a totally different aspect. But then the *Solicitor General* speciously asks, whether this is not the case of a man feigning and simulating insanity in order to avoid the consequences of his crime? It is not so; it is the case of a man who manifested, after the deed was done, the same delusion, which will be proved to have been present in his mind for months, nay, years before the act was committed. But I shall not leave this part of the case upon the prisoner's statement alone, for I am enabled to lay before you evidence that will satisfy your minds of the prisoner's insanity since he has been confined within the walls of a prison. He has been visited by members of the medical profession, of the highest intelligence and the greatest skill, not chosen by the prisoner himself, but some of them selected by his friends, and others deputed by the Government which my honourable and learned friend the *Solicitor General* represents on the present occasion. They visited the prisoner together several times; they together heard the questions put to him, and noted the answers he gave. My learned friend has accurately told you the nature of the defence I have to offer; he has sought to anticipate it by evidence to establish the prisoner's sanity. How is it, then, that

53

the medical men employed by the Crown have not been called? Why, my learned friend has now beside him, within his arm's reach, two of the medical gentlemen sent by the Government, and he has not dared to call them. My learned friend knew (because their opinions have been communicated to the Government and to my learned friend) that the man was mad, and in justice to the public and to the prisoner those gentlemen ought to have been brought forward. I was astonished when the case for the prosecution was closed without those two witnesses being called. They sat within my learned friend's call, and yet my learned friend, in the exercise of the discretion which is his characteristic, dared not put them in the witness-box. Their testimony is, however, upon record; it requires not their delivery by their own mouths of the opinions I know them to entertain; their absence from the witness-box speaks trumpet-tongued as to the opinions they were ready to pronounce; and when I call before you the medical gentlemen who have attended at the request of the friends of the prisoner, and have communicated with this poor deluded maniac, and it is found that their opinions correspond in all particulars, there will not be left a shadow of doubt that this was no simulated insanity, but a real delusion, by which the prisoner was deprived of all possibility of self-control, and which left him a prey to violent passions and frenzied impulses.

I know there has been much said of the danger of admitting a defence of this kind. I do not dispute it; it is a defence of what it is the province of a court and jury to look with care. True, it is a defence easily made, but it is a defence which the sagacity of courts and juries prevents being too easily established. If an offender should first suggest insanity as a defence after the perpetration of a crime, the eye of suspicion would naturally rest upon such a defence. Here, however, there can be no pretence for saying there is the slightest reason to believe that this was a case of feigning and simulation, when I shall have proved the existence of the delusion for the space of two long years before, as well as its continuance since, the act was committed. When I have proved this, my learned friend will not dream of contending that this is a case of simulation. Again, I ask, is there no distinction between the manner in which the common murderer who acts under the impulse of ordinary motives executes his purpose, and that of the unhappy maniac who, in self-defence as he thinks, slays one who in his delusion he fancies is attacking him? There is every distinction. The ordinary murderer not only lays plans for the execution of his designs; not only selects time and place best suited to his purpose; but when successful he either flies from the scene of his enormities, or makes every effort to avoid discovery. The maniac, on the contrary, for the most part, consults none of the usual conveniences of crime; he falls upon his victim with a blind fury, perhaps in the presence of a multitude, as if expressly to court observation, and without a thought of escape or flight; not unfrequently he voluntarily surrenders himself to the constituted authorities. When, as is sometimes the case, he prepares the means, and calmly and deliberately executes his project, his subsequent conduct is still the same as in the former instance. The criminal often has accomplices, and always vicious associates; the maniac has neither. What was the case in the present instance? The prisoner does not attempt to escape; he acts coolly and deliberately; he shows himself to be a maniac seeking only the gratification of his involuntary impulse; he made no attempt to secure his own safety by flight or escape, though he knew that the noise of his first pistol must have attracted attention to the spot; though he saw Mr. *Drummond's* coat in flames, and his victim staggering under the shot, though he must have known that his purpose was effected, instead of thinking of himself, he drew forth the other pistol, with a deliberate intent he passed it from one hand to the other, he levelled it at his victim, and when the policeman had even seized him, still the struggle was not to escape, but to raise his arm and to carry out the raging impulse of his burning and fevered brain. A common murderer would have acted in a different manner; he would have chosen a different time, a different place; he would have sought safety by escape. Gentlemen, I have mentioned that I shall call medical men of the highest rank in the profession; men who have frequently been employed by the Government in cases of this nature, and upon whose characters the stamp of the highest approbation has thus been placed. They will state the result of their examinations of the prisoner, and their evidence upon the whole will be such as to leave no other than a firm conviction that he is insane. I shall also call the surgeon of the gaol, whose duty it has been to see him daily, and whose facilities of observation have therefore been such as to enable him to come to a sound conclusion, and who, besides, was directed to pay particular attention to the state of the prisoner's mind. My friend has not thought fit to call him. I will call him. You will hear from that gentleman the result of his deliberate and impartial judgment, which is that the prisoner is labouring under morbid insanity, which takes away from him all power of self-control, and that he is not responsible for his acts. When I have proved these things, I think the defence will be complete. I do not put this case forward as one of total insanity; it is a case of delusion, and I say so from sources upon which the light of science has thrown its holy beam. I have endeavoured to show the distinction between partial delusion and complete perversion and prostration of intellect. I may, however, perhaps be allowed to refer to one more author on this subject. I allude to M. *Marc*, physician to the King of the French, and one of the most profound investigators of this disease. I will translate the passage as I proceed. M. *Marc*, in his treatise "De la Folie," says(a):—

"Homicidal monomania is a partial delusion characterised by an impulse, more or less violent, to murder; just as suicidal monomania is a partial delusion characterised by a disposition, more or less voluntary, to destroy oneself. This monomania presents two very distinct forms. In some cases the murder is provoked by an internal but raving conviction, by the excitement of a wandering imagination, by a false reasoning, or by the passions in delirium. The monomaniac is impelled by some motive obvious but irrational; he always exhibits sufficient signs of partial delirium, of the intelligence or of the affections. Sometimes his conscience makes him turn with horror from the act which he is about to commit; but his will is overcome by the violence of his impulse; the man is deprived of his moral liberty; he is a prey to a partial delirium; he is a

(a) M. Marc, De la Folie, p. 25.

monomaniac; he is mad. In the other cases the homicidal monomaniac does not present any alteration of the intelligence or affections; he is carried away by a blind instinct, by something indefinable, which impels him to kill."

I think, gentlemen, I have sufficiently dwelt upon the authorities which can throw light upon this inquiry. I trust that I have satisfied you by these authorities, that the disease of partial insanity can exist—that it can lead to a partial or total aberration of the moral senses and affections, which may render the wretched patient incapable of resisting the delusion, and lead him to commit crimes for which morally he cannot be held to be responsible, and in respect of which, when such a case is established, he is withdrawn from the operation of human laws. I proceed now to lay the evidence before you. In doing so I shall give my learned friend the *Solicitor General* the opportunity of a reply. In this case it will be of considerable advantage, for he will have the opportunity of addressing you, and commenting on the evidence after it all shall have been given; whereas I can only anticipate what it may be. Many facts may be spoken to by the witnesses—many important observations may fall from them—on which I shall be deprived of all comment.(a) The arguments which my friend's profound experience and his great legal acquirements may suggest are yet within his own mind: I can but dimly anticipate them. If any advantage should exist in such a case, surely it should not be on the part of the prosecution, but of the prisoner. And my learned friend, moreover, will have the immense advantage resulting from that commanding talent before which we all bow down. But I know that he will prolong to the end of this eventful trial that calm and dispassionate bearing, that dignified and appropriate forbearance which sat so gracefully on him yesterday. Gentlemen, my task is at an end. I have received at your hands, and at the hands of the Court, a degree of considerate attention for which I owe you my most grateful acknowledgments. I ought to apologize to my lords and to you for the length of time that I have detained you; but you know the arduous and anxious duty which I have had to perform, and you will pardon me. From the beginning to the end I have felt my inadequacy to discharge it; but I have fulfilled it to the best of my poor ability. The rest is with you. I am sure that my observations in all that deserves consideration will be well weighed by you, and I am convinced that the facts of this case, and the evidence adduced in support of them, will be listened to by you with the most anxious and scrupulous attention. You can have but one object—to administer the law according to justice and to truth; and may that great Being from whom all truth proceeds guide you in this solemn inquiry, that when hereafter the proceedings of this memorable day, and their result shall be scanned by other minds, they may bear testimony that you have rightly done your duty; and, what to you is far more important, that when hereafter in the retirement of your own homes, and the secrecy of your own thoughts, you revert to the part you have taken in the business of this

(a) The right of summing up the evidence in cases of felony and misdemeanor was conferred on prisoners and their counsel in 1865 by 28 & 29 Vict. c. 18. s. 2 (Denman's Act). Similar provisions had already been enacted as regards civil trials by the Common Law Procedure Act, 1854, 17 & 18 Vict. c. 125. s. 18.

day, you may look back with satisfied consciences and tranquil breasts on the verdict you will this day have given. Gentlemen, the life of the prisoner is in your hands; it is for you to say whether you will visit one on whom God has been pleased to bring the heaviest of all human calamities—the most painful, the most appalling of all mortal ills—with the consequences of an act which most undoubtedly, but for this calamity, never would have been committed. It is for you to say whether you will consign a fellow being under such circumstances to a painful and ignominious death. May God protect both you and him from the consequences of erring reason and mistaken judgment! In conclusion, let me remind you, that though you do not punish the prisoner for an offence committed at a time when he was unconscious of wrong, you have, on the other hand, the power of causing him to be placed in an asylum provided by the mercy of the law, where he will be protected from the consequences of his own delusions, and society will be secured from the danger of his acts. With these observations I trust the case in your hands, with the full conviction that justice will be upheld in the verdict to which you shall come.

Daniel M'Naughton.—Examined by *Clarkson.*

I reside at Glasgow, and am a turner by business. The prisoner, who is a natural son of mine, was apprenticed to me, and after he had served about four years and a half became my journeyman, in which capacity he continued for about three years. When he left me he went into business as a turner on his own account, and was always a very steady, industrious young man, and exceedingly temperate in his habits. After he went into business I did not see him so often, although I saw him then frequently. He seemed to me more distant than formerly; but I knew of no reason for his being so. He would frequently pass me in the street and not speak to or notice me. About two years ago I recollect the prisoner calling at my house, and, upon seeing me, he expressed a wish to have an interview in private. We went into a room alone, and he then told me that various prosecutions had been raised against him, and begged that I would speak to the authorities of the town upon the subject, in order to have a stop put to them. He particularly mentioned the name of Mr. Sheriff *Alison* as one of the persons I was to speak to. I asked who the persons were that persecuted him, and he told me that Mr. Sheriff *Alison* knew all about it. I told him I was extremely sorry to hear that he was so persecuted, and endeavoured to persuade him that he was labouring under some mistake. I told him that I was not aware of any person being persecutive in Glasgow. Finding that he was labouring under some delusion, I said nothing more upon the subject, but tried to turn the conversation. We then talked upon other subjects, upon all of which he spoke rationally enough. He then asked me to get him a situation in some counting house in Glasgow. I promised him that I would endeavour to do so, but told him that I thought he had, in the first instance, better go to some respectable teacher, and learn writing and arithmetic. He said he would do so, and we then parted. About a week after that interview he again called upon me, and inquired whether I had, according to my promise caused the authorities to take any measures to prevent the persecution which was going on against him? I told him that I thought after our last interview he would have gone to school, and banished all such ideas from his mind. He then said that the persecution still continued, and that he was followed night and day by spies; wherever he went they followed him. I asked him who the spies were, whether he knew any of them, or whether he could point them out? To which he replied, that it would be quite useless to point them out, as they were always in his presence; wherever he might be, whenever he turned round, there they were. I asked him whether he ever spoke to them, or they to him? He said they never spoke to him, but whenever he looked at them they laughed at him, and shook their fists in his face, and those who had sticks shook them at him. He also said, that one of the men, whenever he looked at him, threw straws in his face. I asked him whether, if I went out with him, he could point out any of the spies to me? He said, "Oh, no; if they see anyone with me they will not follow at all; it is only when I am alone that they follow and annoy me." I then asked him what he thought they meant by showing him straws? To which he replied, he presumed it meant that he was to be reduced to a state of beggary by them. I told him that if he really saw a person with straws, in all probability it must be some person out of his mind. After some further conversation in the same strain, he begged of me, nay, insisted upon my calling on Mr. Sheriff *Bell*. I then promised him that I would see Sheriff *Bell* upon the subject. In about a week he called upon me a third time, and asked whether I had seen Sheriff *Bell*. I told him I had not. He then said the persecution still continued, and inquired why I had not seen Sheriff *Bell* according to my promise, as he knew all about the matter. I saw nothing more of him for a considerable time, and I then accidentally met him on the road, a short distance (about four miles) from Glasgow. We had a conversation for upwards of an hour, and the chief topic was the persecution he was enduring; he said he had left Glasgow, and had gone to England, and even to France, to get rid of the spies, but they still followed him; the moment he landed in France there they were also. After that interview he called upon me again, and requested that I would prevail upon the authorities, particularly Sheriffs *Alison* and *Bell*, to put an immediate stop to the persecution. On that occasion I reasoned with him for some time upon the folly and absurdity of supposing that such a conspiracy existed against him, and assured him that such was not the case; and I then thought that the impression was effaced. He again spoke to me about getting him a situation, and I promised I would do so. Between that interview and the month of September he called upon me several times, and always requested me to see the authorities upon the subject. I never saw any of the civil authorities, as I saw that he was labouring under some extraordinary delusion, and therefore considered it quite unnecessary.

Cross-examined by the *Solicitor General*.

The last interview I had with him was in August last, shortly before he came to London. When he was apprenticed to me he lived in my house, but whilst a

58

journeyman he went into lodgings. I do not know his reason for leaving my house, but it certainly was not on account of any quarrel. He did not go into business for himself before he left my house, nor till some time afterwards. I believe he went into business for himself because he felt dissatisfied at my not letting him have a share of my little business.

Did he ask you to take him into partnership?—Yes, he did; but I refused, because I had some younger children to provide for. After he went into business we very seldom spoke. For a long time I think he fancied that I was annoyed because he took some of my business from me, which was not the case. I know that his shop was in Stockwell Street, but I never went there. He carried on business in Stockwell Street for about five years, and disposed of it two years ago. We were not at all upon the terms that a father and son usually are. At times party politics run very high at Glasgow.

At the time the conversations you have been mentioning occurred, what was your opinion with respect to your son's mind?—It certainly was my impression that his intellects were impaired.

Did you consult any medical gentleman?—I did not, because I thought the delusions under which he was labouring would eventually pass away.

Then am I to understand that upon all other subjects he conversed rationally? —Yes, upon all subjects except the one I have mentioned.

Re-examined by *Clarkson*.

The prisoner continued to work at my shop after he left my house. He frequently passed me in the street without taking the slightest notice; it was his own act to do so, not mine. He was always a very harmless, inoffensive youth, and appeared harmless when labouring under these delusions. I never heard of his having evinced any disposition to do any injury either to himself or anyone else.

William Gilchrist.—Examined by *Bodkin*.

I am a printer in Glasgow. I have known the prisoner since the year 1834. I lodged with him at Gorbals. We slept in the same bed. The prisoner used frequently to get up in the night and walk about the room, uttering incoherent sentences, and making use of such ejaculations as "By Jove," "My God." He uttered them in a very serious manner, but not in a very loud tone. Sometimes he would walk about the room by the hour together whilst undressed, and then return to bed. Such conduct occurred from time to time during the whole period we lodged together. His conduct was always that of a mild, inoffensive, and humane man. I have frequently seen him, when we have been going out to take a walk, put crumbs of bread into his pocket to feed the birds with. He appeared to be very fond of children, and I have observed him watch the children at play for hours; he said he liked to see their innocence. The last time I saw the prisoner was in July 1842, when we walked together for a short distance. I thought he was altered, both in manner and appearance, for when I looked at him he always dropped down his head and looked on the ground. His conversation was not so connected as formerly. I have known the prisoner burst out into immoderate fits of laughter without any cause whatever; at other times he would moan. I never knew him to attend any political meetings, or express any extravagant political opinions. When I last saw him he told me, in the course of a conversation, that when he was in London he went one night to the House of Commons, and heard Sir *Robert Peel*, Lord *John Russell*, and Mr. *O'Connell* speak, and he expressed himself highly delighted. He said he thought Sir *Robert Peel* had arrived at what Lord *Byron* had said of him, "that he would be something great in the State"; he said he thought Lord *John Russell* was very inferior as a speaker to Sir *Robert Peel*, and that Mr. *O'Connell* was inferior to both.

Did you ever hear him, either on that or any other occasion, speak at all disrespectfully of Sir *Robert Peel*?—Certainly not.

Cross-examined by *Adolphus*.

The ejaculations which I have spoken of, and also the laughter, might have been caused by the recollection of something he had previously heard, and of which I was not aware.

Did you ever hear him speak about Sir *R. Peel's* political character?—Never. Or make use of any threat towards him?—No.

John Hughes.—Examined by *Monteith*.

A tailor at Glasgow, confirmed the evidence of the last witness. The prisoner lodged at my house during the year 1835. A person of the name of *M'Cordigan*, who slept in the same bed with the prisoner, made several complaints to me about the prisoner disturbing him during the night, and left me in consequence. The prisoner did not appear to be fond of society, and scarcely ever spoke unless first spoken to, and then his replies were quick and hurried, as if he wished to avoid conversation. I also noticed that when any person spoke to him, if their eye caught his he immediately looked down to the ground, as if ashamed; whenever he asked for anything he appeared confused. In consequence of his very strange manner I gave him notice to leave, but he was very unwilling to go away. Another reason I had for wishing him to leave was in consequence of the infidel doctrines he maintained, and the books of such a character which he was in the habit of reading. I always have family worship in my house every Sunday, and generally in the week days. The prisoner mostly attended on Sundays.

Cross-examined by the *Solicitor General*.

I did not tell him the true reason why I wished him to leave my house. I assigned as a reason that my wife could not wait upon him any longer.

Did you observe any particular difference in his behaviour whilst he was at your house?—Yes, I thought his appearance just before he left was more strange than when I first saw him.

COLERIDGE, J.: Have you any children living in your house?—I have, my Lord. Did the prisoner seem fond or take any notice of them?—He never used to take any notice of them.

William Carlo.—Examined by *Clarkson.*

I am a turner in Stockwell Street, Glasgow. I have known the prisoner for seven years, and was in his employ as journeyman for nearly three years, down to 1838. He had a very good business in 1840. I purchased it in 1841. Whilst I was in his employ he frequently complained of a pain in his head, and would often keep his hand to his head, as if in pain, the greater part of the evening. When in this state I have known him on several occasions go and bathe in the Clyde, which is near the premises, in order to get rid of it. I have very frequently seen him since 1841, but never observed anything particularly the matter with him till about six months ago. I had frequently heard it stated during the last eighteen months that there was something wrong about him, but I did not believe it. In consequence of those rumours, however, I went to see him whilst lodging at Mrs. *Patterson's.* We then walked out together, and he gave me a description of his visit to France; the only motive he assigned to me for going there was curiosity. He told me he was very much persecuted by certain parties, who always followed him about wherever he went, and that he could get no rest for them night or day. He said they were using all their influences against him, in order to prevent his getting a situation; whether he went to France, England, or Scotland, the spies were always about him. He told me it was immaterial in what country he was, for they were sure to send their emissaries before him, and he was known wherever he went. I asked him who the parties were, and he told me they were Scotchmen, and natives of Glasgow. I told him it was all imagination, and endeavoured to persuade him to think nothing more about it. I also told him that if any person ill-used him or slandered him I would have them punished, as I considered his character was very good. He said he would do so, and added that if he could once set his eyes upon them they should not be long in the land of the living. After the conversation had continued for some time he became very much excited; and, seeing that he was labouring under some extraordinary excitement, I considered it prudent to drop the subject. In consequence of that conversation I immediately came to the conclusion that he was not in his right mind.

Cross-examined by *Waddington.*

I never noticed anything extraordinary in his behaviour till the period I have just mentioned, although his habits were rather eccentric.

What do you mean by eccentric?—Why, that he was very hard-working and penurious; he was also eccentric in his dress. The last few times that I saw him, I noticed that he was not quite so cheerful as usual, though he was generally sullen and reserved, and always evinced a disposition to evade conversation.

COLERIDGE, J.: What did you pay him for his business?—18*l*.

Did that sum include the tools?—Yes; but there were very few, and most of them were worn out.

Jane Drummond Patterson.—Examined by Bodkin.

I know the prisoner. He lodged in my house two years ago. I observed something very peculiar in his manner. His eyes presented a very strange appearance; he looked wild, and very different from what he used to do. He was also very restless in his sleep. I frequently heard him moan and groan in his sleep, and sometimes he spoke as if disturbed. He went away twice, and told me he had been to France. I told him he had better stop away altogether; to which he replied that he could not stop either in London or in France, as he was constantly haunted by a parcel of devils following him, and they said they were persons from Glasgow. He appeared then rather angry. I at length began to be afraid of him, and expressed a wish for him to leave my house. He said he would leave as soon as possible; he could get situations anywhere, but it was of no use, as they were all haunted with devils. A few days before he left in September, I found some pistols in his room. I said, "What in the name of God are you doing with pistols there?" He said he was going to shoot birds with them. On one occasion, when I was speaking to him about getting a situation, he laid hold of me, made use of an oath, and looked very wild. When he went away he took nothing with him but the clothes on his back. I noticed when he went away that he looked very wild and frightsome-like.

Cross-examined by the Solicitor General.

I noticed the peculiarity when he first came to lodge with me, but he did not mention anything about being haunted by devils till three or four months afterwards.

Henry C. Bell.—Examined by Monteith.

I am one of the sheriffs depute of the county of Lanark, and reside at Glasgow. I believe the prisoner to be the person who called upon me about nine or ten months ago and complained that he was harassed to death by a system of persecution which had for some time been adopted towards him, and for which he could obtain no redress whatever. I told him I would render him any assistance in my power, and asked him the nature of the persecution he complained of. He made a long, rambling, unintelligible statement in reply, from which I gathered, as far as I can recollect, that he was constantly beset by spies, and that he considered his life and property in danger. I told him that I thought he must be labouring under some very erroneous impression, and advised him, if he had any criminal charge to make against any person, to go to the Procurator-Fiscal, or if his complaint was of a civil nature, to apply to some man of business.

He said it would be perfectly useless to make any such application, and appearing dissatisfied with my answer, he went away. He called upon me again about a fortnight or three weeks afterwards. I asked him whether he had seen the Procurator-Fiscal or a man of business, and he said he had not. He then made another statement of a precisely similar character, but I told him that I could not render him any assistance, and he then went away. I certainly concluded that he was not right in his intellects—that he was labouring under some very extraordinary delusion, and I made a remark to that effect to my clerk.

Not cross-examined.

Alexander Johnston, M.P.—Examined by *Clarkson*.

The prisoner called upon me about a twelvemonth ago and complained of being subjected to an extraordinary system of persecution, and wished for my advice as to the best method of getting rid of it. On subjects of general business he talked very rationally, but with respect to this particular business he said that he had for a considerable time been persecuted by the emissaries of a political party, whom he had offended by interfering in politics. He also complained of being attacked through the newspapers, and said the persons of whom he complained followed him night and day; that he could get no rest for them; that they had destroyed his peace of mind, and what to do he really did not know. I reasoned with him, and told him that I thought he must be mistaken; assured him that nobody followed him about, and advised him, if he received any annoyances, to apply to the captain of police. He then said that he thought his persecutors would be satisfied with nothing less than his life. When I told him that I thought he was mistaken, he said that he was quite certain that he was not. He assured me that he was perfectly sound in his mind, and in good bodily health. He then left me.

What was the impression left upon your mind by that interview?—I certainly thought that what he stated was his firm conviction. In about a week or ten days the prisoner again called upon me, and he then told me that his persecutors were still pursuing him, and wished me to take some steps in order to deter them from so doing. I again recommended him to go to the sheriff, and assured him that if he was in reality annoyed as he had described, he would be protected. I merely told him that in order to get rid of him, feeling assured that he was labouring under a delusion. About a month after the last interview, I came to London, and in a few days I received a letter from the prisoner, reiterating the same complaints, and begging of me to interfere in his behalf; to that communication I wrote the letter produced.

Have you the letter you received from the prisoner?—No, I have not.

Clarkson: We propose now, my Lord, to put in and read the letter this witness wrote to the prisoner.

TINDAL, C.J.: Be it so.

The clerk of arraigns then read the letter as follows:—

63

"Reform Club,

"SIR,   "May 5, 1842.

"I RECEIVED your letter of the 3rd of May, and am sorry I can do nothing for you. I fear you are labouring under an aberration of mind, and I think you have no reason to entertain such fears.

"I am, &c.

"ALEXANDER JOHNSTON.

"Mr. D. M'Naughton."

Cross-examined by the *Solicitor General*.

I had no knowledge of the prisoner previous to his calling upon me; neither had I any other conversations with him but those I have stated.

Sir James Campbell.—Examined by *Cockburn*.

I am Lord Provost of Glasgow, and was so in the year 1842. In the month of May in that year, the prisoner called upon me; he said he wanted my advice and protection. He said that he was the victim of an extraordinary persecution; that he was followed and beset by spies night and day, and that he could not get rid of them; they dogged him wherever he went, and he could not in consequence get any rest night or day; that he was afraid to go home, and had therefore been compelled to sleep in the fields in the suburbs of the town. I asked him who his persecutors were, and he told me they were persons who had an ill-feeling towards him, and that he considered his life in danger in consequence. I at once saw that he was labouring under a strange delusion, and told him that he was labouring under some hypochondriac affection, for which he ought to have advice, and asked him whether he had ever been treated as an insane person? He said he had not, and endeavoured to persuade me that he was in the enjoyment of sound mind and health. After some further conversation, I advised him to consult with his friends upon the subject, and suggested the propriety of seeing some medical gentleman. He did not appear to be satisfied with what I stated to him, and he then went away. I immediately sent for the prisoner's father, in order to let him know what had taken place, but he did not wait upon me, and I took no further steps in the affair. I felt no doubt at the time that the prisoner was labouring under some species of insanity.

Cross-examined by *Waddington*.

I did not notice anything particular in the prisoner's appearance, and I should not have observed there was anything wrong about him had it not been for what he stated. He was a total stranger to me, and I should think the conversation did not last more than five minutes.

[The Rev. *Alexander Turner* spoke to a similar interview with the prisoner, and to advising his father to put him under restraint.]

Hugh Wilson.—Examined by *Bodkin*.

Commissioner of police at Glasgow. I have known the prisoner for about ten or twelve years. I recollect his calling upon me, about eighteen months ago, to make a complaint. He said that he had come to consult me on a very delicate matter; and, after some hesitation, said that he was the object of some persecution, and added, that he thought it proceeded from the priests at the Catholic chapel in Clyde Street, who were assisted by a parcel of Jesuits. I asked him what they did to him, and his reply was, that they followed him wherever he went, and were never out of his sight, and when he went into his bedroom he still found them with him. He was perfectly calm and collected when he first came in, but when he began to talk about the persecution, he became very much excited; and I then thought he was daft. I saw that he was extremely anxious upon the subject, and therefore told him to call again on the following Tuesday, and I would see what could be done for him. A few days afterwards I again saw him, when I promised to speak to *Miller*, the superintendent, about it. When I again saw him, I told him that I had seen *Miller*, who said it was all nonsense and there was nothing in it; to which the prisoner replied that *Miller* was a bad one, that he saw it in his face, and he wanted to deceive both him and me. Having again run on about the Catholics and the Jesuits, he went away. In two or three days he again called, and on alluding to the subject, said, the Tories had joined with the Catholics, that he could get no rest either night or day, through their persecuting conduct, and he felt quite sure they would throw him into a consumption. At that interview I told him he had spoilt the scheme which I had planned for the purpose of finding out his persecutors, at which he appeared to be very much disappointed. I desired him not to look either to the right or to the left, and, if possible, let them see that he did not observe them. He said he would do so. After that interview, I did not see him for three or four months, when he again came to me and said he was worse than ever. I told him he should get out of their way. He said he had been to Boulogne, and asked me if I knew the watch-box on the Custom House Quay there? I told him I did. He then said that as soon as he landed, he saw one of his spies peep from behind it, and added, that it was no use going further into France, and spending his money, when he could get no relief. He appeared then worse than ever, and I advised him to go into the country and amuse himself by working, and not to think anything more about it; but he said it was no use going there, as they would be sure to follow him. I had several other interviews with him, and the last time I saw him was about the month of August last, when he made the same sort of complaint, and the delusion then appeared to be stronger in his mind than ever.

Cross-examined by the *Solicitor General*.

The office I hold is not one of a political character. I have not canvassed the prisoner for his vote within the last twelve months. I have solicited his vote, but that was three or four years ago. When I saw him in August last, he was very much excited. He said the police, the Jesuits, the Catholic priests, and Tories were all leagued against him.

Dr. *E. T. Monro.*—Examined by *Cockburn.*

I have devoted much attention to the subject of insanity, and have an experience of thirty years. I was requested by the friends of the prisoner to visit him in Newgate. I was accompanied by Sir *A. Morison*, Mr. *M'Clure*, and other professional gentlemen.

You met on that occasion some medical gentlemen, who were deputed on the part of the Crown to visit the prisoner?—I met Dr. *Sutherland*, jun., and Dr. *Bright.*

I believe you all saw the prisoner together?—Yes, we saw and examined the prisoner together.

How was the examination conducted?—We all asked the prisoner questions in turn.

Did you make at the time any note of the examination?—No; but I made some notes afterwards.

When did that examination take place?—On the 18th of February.

What did the prisoner say in answer to the questions put to him?—With the permission of the Court, I will state the substance of what he stated. In reply to the questions put to him, the prisoner said he was persecuted by a system or crew at Glasgow, Edinburgh, Liverpool, London, and Boulogne. That this crew preceded or followed him wherever he went; that he had no peace of mind, and he was sure it would kill him; that it was grinding of the mind. I asked him if he had availed himself of medical advice? He replied, that physicians could be of no service to him, for if he took a ton of drugs it would be of no service to him; that in Glasgow he observed people in the streets pointing at him, and speaking of him. They said that is the man, he is a murderer and the worst of characters. That everything was done to associate his name with the direst of crimes. He was tossed like a cork on the sea, and that wherever he went, in town or country, on sea or shore, he was perpetually watched and followed. At Edinburgh he saw a man on horseback watching him. That another person there nodded to him, and exclaimed, "That's he;" that he had applied to the authorities of Glasgow for protection and relief. His complaints had been sneered and scould at by Sheriff *Bell*, who had it in his power to put a stop to the persecution, if he had liked. If he had had a pistol in his possession, he would have shot Sheriff *Bell* dead as he sat in the court-house; that Mr. *Salmond*, the procurator-fiscal, Mr. Sheriff *Bell*, Sheriff *Alison*, and Sir *R. Peel* might have put a stop to this system of persecution if they would; that on coming out of the court-house he had seen a man frowning at him, with a bundle of straw under his arm; that he knew well enough what was meant; that everything was done by signs; that he was represented to be under a delusion; that the straw denoted that he should lie upon straw in an asylum; that whilst on board the steamboat on his way from Glasgow to Liverpool, he was watched, eyed, and examined closely by persons coming near

66

him; that they had followed him to Boulogne on two occasions; they would never allow him to learn French, and wanted to murder him—he was afraid of going out after dark, for fear of assassination—that individuals were made to appear before him, like those he had seen at Glasgow. He mentioned having applied to Mr. *A. Johnston*, M.P. for Kilmarnock, for protection; Mr. *Johnston* had told him that he (the prisoner) was labouring under a delusion, but that he was sure he was not. That he had seen paragraphs in the *Times* newspaper containing allusions which he was satisfied were directed at him; he had seen articles also in the *Glasgow Herald*, beastly and atrocious, insinuating things untrue and insufferable of him; that on one or two occasions something pernicious had been put into his food; that he had studied anatomy to obtain peace of mind, but he had not found it. That he imagined the person at whom he fired at Charing Cross to be one of the crew—a part of the system that was destroying his health.

When you referred to the person whom he had fired at at Charing Cross, how did you put your question?—I cannot recollect the exact question. I have no doubt I asked him who he thought the person was.

State, Dr. *Monro*, as correctly as you can, what the prisoner said on this point? —He observed that when he saw the person at Charing Cross at whom he fired, every feeling of suffering which he had endured for months and years rose up at once in his mind, and that he conceived that he should obtain peace by killing him.

I believe all the medical men heard the questions put to him and the answers? —Yes. Drs. *Bright* and *Sutherland* were present. I do not know if they saw the prisoner yesterday.

Do you think that your knowledge of insanity enables you to judge between the conduct of a man who feigns a delusion and one who feels it?—I do, certainly.

Do you consider, Dr. *Monro*, that the delusions were real or assumed?—I am quite satisfied that they were real. I have not a shadow of a doubt on the point.

Supposing you had heard nothing of the examination which took place in Newgate, but only the evidence which has been adduced in court for the last two days, would you then say that the prisoner was labouring under a delusion? —Most certainly. The act with which he is charged, coupled with the history of his past life, leaves not the remotest doubt on my mind of the presence of insanity sufficient to deprive the prisoner of all self-control. I consider the act of the prisoner in killing Mr. *Drummond* to have been committed whilst under a delusion; the act itself I look upon as the crowning act of the whole matter—as the climax—as a carrying out of the pre-existing idea which had haunted him for years.

It is consistent with the pathology of insanity, that a partial delusion may exist, depriving the person of all self-control, whilst the other faculties may be sound?—Certainly; monomania may exist with general sanity. I have frequently known a person insane upon one point exhibit great cleverness upon all others not immediately associated with his delusions. I have seen clever artists, arithmeticians, and architects, whose mind was disordered on one point. An insane person may commit an act similar to the one with which the prisoner is charged, and yet be aware of the consequences of such an act. The evidence which I have heard in Court has not induced me to alter my opinion of the case. Lunatics often manifest a high degree of cleverness and ingenuity, and exhibit occasionally great cunning in escaping from the consequences of such acts. I see a number of such cases every day.

Cross-examined by the *Solicitor General*.

You have stated that Drs. *Bright* and *Sutherland* were present at the examination. Did they hear your examination of the prisoner?—Yes, they were present and heard the examination. They were there on the part of the Crown. I asked all the questions.

Is it not the practice of the Crown to have medical gentlemen present at the examination of a person charged with such serious crimes as the prisoner is now accused of?—I believe it is.

I believe you attended in the case of *Oxford* on the part of the Crown?—I saw *Oxford* by myself; no other medical man was present.

Who were present when you examined *M'Naughton*?—Sir *A. Morison*, Mr. *M'Clure*, Drs. *Bright* and *Sutherland*. On the two last occasions on which I saw the prisoner, Mr. *Hutcheson* and Dr. *Crawford* were present at the request of the friends of the prisoner. They examined the prisoner almost exclusively on that occasion, and, in accordance with the usual practice, gentlemen in behalf of the Crown also attended.

I should like you to acquaint the Court with the exact form of the question you put to him which had a reference to his firing the pistol at Mr. *Drummond*, at Charing Cross?—I did not take any notes at the time.

Did you ask him if he knew whom he fired at?—I am not quite certain. I think I asked the prisoner whom he fired at.

Did anyone present ask the prisoner if he knew that it was Sir *Robert Peel* he shot at?—I think he was asked the question more than once. He hesitated and paused, and at length said he was not sure whether it was Sir *Robert Peel* or not. This was asked in my presence.

Please to refer to your notes, and tell me whether he did not say that if he thought it was not Sir *Robert Peel*, he would not have fired at all?—I have no notes to that effect. The notes that I have with me were made at home, and not at the time of the examination.

Did he not say he would not have fired if he had known that it was not Sir *Robert Peel*?—No, I think he did not. On this point he observed that the person at whom he fired gave him as he passed a scowling look. At that moment all the feelings of months and years rushed into his mind, and he thought that he could only obtain peace by shooting him. He stated this in answer to my questions. I avoided all leading questions. There was much repetition in the questions put to him. The gentlemen from Scotland also examined him.

What was the form of the question which related to his firing at Sir *Robert*

Peel?—I think the question was, "Did you known whom you were firing at?" In reply he observed, "He was one of the crew that had been following him."

Do you mean to say, Dr. *Monro*, that you could satisfy yourself as to a person's state of mind by merely going into a cell and putting questions to him? —In many instances I can; I will mention a case in point. A short time back I was called in to examine a man who was confined in Newgate under sentence of death. It was thought that he had feigned insanity. After an attentive examination, in conjunction with Mr. *M'Murdo*, I at once detected that his insanity was assumed, and such turned out to be the fact. I had the satisfaction afterwards of hearing that the man himself confessed prior to the execution that he had feigned insanity.

I wish to know whether your skill would enable you to ascertain the nature of the delusion under which the prisoner was labouring without seeing the depositions taken in his case?—Certainly. I have formed my opinion from an examination of the prisoner personally, in conjunction with the depositions.

Is it not necessary to examine the bodily symptoms in these cases; for instance, the pulse?—Yes, sometimes. I did not feel his pulse, neither did I lay much stress upon the appearance of his eye.

Do you always assume that the party tells you what is passing in his mind?— Not always.

What do you mean by insanity? Do you consider a person labouring under a morbid delusion of unsound mind?—I do.

Do you think insanity may exist without any morbid delusion?—Yes; a person may be imbecile; but there is generally some morbid delusion; there are various shades of insanity. A person may be of unsound mind, and yet be able to manage the usual affairs of life.

May insanity exist with a moral perception of right and wrong?—Yes; it is very common.

A person may have a delusion and know murder to be a crime?—If there existed antecedent symptoms I should consider the murder to be an overt act, the crowning piece of his insanity. But if he had stolen a 10*l*. note it would not have tallied with his delusion.

But suppose he had stolen the note from one of his persecutors?—

(Dr. *Monro's* answer was not heard owing to the laughter which followed the *Solicitor General's* observation.)

A delusion like *M'Naughton's* would carry him quite away. I think a person may be of unsound mind, labour under a morbid delusion, and yet know right from wrong.

Have you heard of what is called moral insanity? Have you read the works of M. *Marc*?—I understand what monomania means. It is attended by an irresistible propensity to thieve or burn, without being the result of particular motives.

Re-examined by *Cockburn*.

You said, Dr. *Monro*, that a person might labour under a particular form of insanity without having his moral perceptions deranged. For illustration—a man may fancy his legs made of glass. There is nothing in that which could affect his moral feelings?—Certainly not.

You have not the slightest doubt that *M'Naughton's* moral perceptions were impaired?—No.

Sir *A. Morison, M.D.*—Examined by *Clarkson.*

I believe, Dr. *Morison*, that you were one of the gentlemen who saw the prisoner in conjunction with Drs. *Monro, Sutherland,* and *Bright*?—I did.

You have been in Court during the whole of the day?—I have.

Were you not present during the whole of the examination of the prisoner in Newgate?—I was.

Did you arrive at any conclusion as to the prisoner's state of mind?—I did.

Please to state to the Court what your impression was?—That *M'Naughton* was insane.

After having heard the evidence adduced that day in Court, has your opinion undergone any alteration?—I am still of the same opinion, that the prisoner was insane at the time he committed the act with which he is charged.

The prisoner's morbid delusions consisted in his fancying himself subject to a system of persecutions?—Yes; that was the peculiar cause of his insanity.

What effect had this delusion upon his mind?—It deprived the prisoner of all restraint over his actions.

Do you speak with any doubt upon the point?—Not the slightest.

Cross-examined by the *Solicitor General.*

Had you formed your opinion in consequence of reading the depositions?—It is the result of reading the depositions and examining the prisoner. I had, however, arrived at a conclusion of his insanity before I read the depositions.

[Mr. *William M'Clure*, a surgeon living in Harley Street, confirmed the previous evidence.

I consider when he fired at Mr. *Drummond*, at Charing Cross, he (the prisoner) was suffering from an hallucination which deprived him of all ordinary restraint.

Dr. *W. Hutcheson*, physician to the Royal Lunatic Asylum at Glasgow, gave evidence to the same effect. The prisoner had lost all self-control at the moment he fired at Mr. *Drummond*. The act flowed immediately from the delusion.]

Cross-examined by the *Solicitor General.*

Do you mean to say that the delusion prevented the prisoner from exercising any control over his actions?—I said that the act was the consequence of the delusion, which was irresistible. The delusion was so strong that nothing but a physical impediment could have prevented him from committing the act. He might have done the same thing in Glasgow if the disease of the mind had reached the same point.

From what period do you date his insanity?—From the time when *M'Naughton* called upon the commissioner of police, Mr. *Wilson*, for protection.

Was he insane at that time?—Yes.

When was that?—Eighteen months back.

Cockburn: Supposing at that time the same morbid notion had seized him, do you think he would have committed a similar act?—I do not think he could have resisted any impulse springing from the morbid delusions under which he suffered.

Re-examined by *Cockburn*.

When patients exhibit symptoms similar to those which the prisoner manifested they are generally, I believe, placed under restraint?—Yes. Such symptoms often gradually develop themselves, whereas many have these delusions for some time and are harmless, and then they may suddenly impel them to the commission of crime. I have known cases of that kind.

[Dr. *P. J. Crawford*, of Glasgow, and Mr. *Aston Key*, of Guy's Hospital, confirmed the previous witnesses.]

Forbes Winslow.—Examined by *Clarkson*.

Mr. *Winslow*, you are a surgeon residing in Guildford Street?—I am.

You are the author of the "Plea of Insanity in Criminal Cases," and other works on the subject of insanity?—Yes.

I think, Mr. *Winslow*, that you have been in Court during the whole of the trial and have not been summoned on either side, and have heard all the evidence on the part of the Crown and for the defence?—I have.

Judging from the evidence which you have heard, what is your opinion as to the prisoner's state of mind?—I have not the slightest hesitation in saying that he is insane, and that he committed the offence in question whilst afflicted with a delusion, under which he appears to have been labouring for a considerable length of time.

TINDAL, C.J.: Mr. *Winslow*, will you repeat what you have just stated?—Witness again expressed an unqualified opinion of the prisoner's insanity.

Dr. *Philips*, surgeon and lecturer at the Westminster Hospital, was then called.

TINDAL, C.J.: Mr. *Solicitor General*, are you prepared, on the part of the Crown, with any evidence to combat this testimony of the medical witnesses who now have been examined, because we think if you have not, we must be under the necessity of stopping the case? Is there any medical evidence on the other side?

Solicitor General: No, my Lord.

TINDAL, C.J.: We feel the evidence, especially that of the last two medical gentlemen who have been examined, and who are strangers to both sides and only observers of the case, to be very strong, and sufficient to induce my learned brothers and myself to stop the case.

71

Solicitor General: Gentlemen of the jury, after the intimation I have received from the Bench I feel that I should not be properly discharging my duty to the Crown and to the public if I asked you to give your verdict in this case against the prisoner. The Lord Chief Justice has intimated to me the very strong opinion entertained by himself and the other learned judges who have presided here to-day, that the evidence on the part of the defendant, and more particularly the evidence of the medical witnesses, is sufficient to show that this unfortunate man at the time he committed the act was labouring under insanity; and, of course, if he were so, he would be entitled to his acquittal. I was anxious, however, to say, on the part of the Crown, that they have had no object whatever but the attainment of public justice, and I believe I am right in saying that, on the part of the prosecution, every facility has been given to the defence. There is no wish, there can be no wish on the part of the public prosecutor, but that the ends of public justice shall be attained; and, certainly, when in the streets of this metropolis a crime of this sort was committed, it was incumbent on those who have the care of the public peace and safety to have the case properly investigated. The safety of the lives and persons of all of us requires that there should be such an investigation. On the part of the Crown I felt it my duty to lay before you the evidence we possessed of the conduct of this young man. I cannot agree with the observations my learned friend has made on the doctrines and authorities that have been laid down in this case, because I think those doctrines and authorities are correct law; our object being to ascertain whether at the time the prisoner committed the crime he was at that time to be regarded as a responsible agent, or whether all control of himself was taken away? The Lord Chief Justice I understand, means to submit that question to you. I cannot press for a verdict against the prisoner. The learned judge will submit the case to you, and then it will be for you to come to your decision.

TINDAL, C.J.: Gentlemen of the jury, in this important case which has excited very great anxiety during the two preceding days, the point I shall have to submit to you is whether on the whole of the evidence you have heard, you are satisfied that at the time the act was committed, for the commission of which the prisoner now stands charged, he had that competent use of his understanding as that he knew that he was doing, by the very act itself, a wicked and a wrong thing. If he was not sensible at the time he committed that act, that it was a violation of the law of God or of man, undoubtedly he was not responsible for that act, or liable to any punishment whatever flowing from that act. Gentlemen, that is the precise point which I shall feel it my duty to leave to you. I have undoubtedly been very much struck, and so have my learned brethren, by the evidence we have heard during the evening from the medical persons who have been examined as to the state of the mind of the unhappy prisoner, for unhappy I must call him in reference to his state of mind. Now, gentlemen, I can go through the whole of the evidence, and particularly call back your attention to that part of it to which I at first adverted, but I cannot help remarking, in common with my learned brethren, that the whole of the medical evidence is on one side, and that there is no part of it which leaves any doubt on the mind.

72

It seems almost unnecessary that I should go through the evidence. I am, however, in your hands; but if on balancing the evidence in your minds you think the prisoner capable of distinguishing between right and wrong, then he was a responsible agent and liable to all the penalties the law imposes. If not so, and if in your judgment the subject should appear involved in very great difficulty, then you will probably not take upon yourselves to find the prisoner guilty. If that is your opinion then you will acquit the prisoner. If you think you ought to hear the evidence more fully, in that case I will state it to you, and leave the case in your hands. Probably, however, sufficient has now been laid before you, and you will say whether you want any further information.

Foreman of the Jury: We require no more, my Lord.

TINDAL, C.J.: If you find the prisoner not guilty, say on the ground of insanity, in which case proper care will be taken of him.

Foreman: We find the prisoner not guilty, on the ground of insanity.

The clerk of the arraigns, by order of the Court, directed the gaoler to keep the prisoner in safe custody till Her Majesty's pleasure be known.

The prisoner was then removed, and the jury were discharged.

On Wednesday, the 15th of March, the prisoner was removed by Mr. *Cope*, the governor of Newgate, to Bethlehem Hospital, St. George's Fields, under an order from the Right Hon. Sir *James Graham*, Her Majesty's Secretary of State for the Home Department.

NOTES

The footnotes to the *State Trials* report, which have been left as originally printed, include the following abbreviations:

Collinson: Collinson, G. D. (1812), *A treatise on the law of idiots, lunatics and other persons 'non compotes mentis'*.

Russ. Cri.: *Russell on Crime* (a standard textbook of English criminal law).

Hale P.C.: Hale, *Pleas of the Crown*.

Russ. & Ry.: Russell and Ryan, *Crown Cases Reserved*.

Marc, De la Folie: Marc, C. C., *De la folie considérée dans ses rapports avec les questions médicojudiciaires*. Paris, 1840.

The report of the trial has been abridged from the full report by *Richard M. Bonsfield* of Gray's Inn and *Richard Merrett* shorthand writer (London, 1843).

A few misprints in the text have been corrected.

THE HOUSE OF LORDS AND THE JUDGES' 'RULES'

THE QUESTIONS

HOUSE OF LORDS, May 26, 1843.

The House of Lords having resolved(*a*) in consequence of this verdict to take the opinion of the judges as to the law respecting crimes committed by persons afflicted with insane delusions, all the judges attended their Lordships, but no questions were then put.

June 19, 1843.—The judges again attended the House of Lords, when the following questions were put to them without argument:—

"1st.—What is the law respecting alleged crimes committed by persons afflicted with insane delusion in respect of one or more particular subjects or persons; as, for instance, where, at the time of the commission of the alleged crime, the accused knew he was acting contrary to law, but did the act complained of with a view, under the influence of insane delusion, of redressing or revenging some supposed grievance or injury, or of producing some supposed public benefit?

"2nd.—What are the proper questions to be submitted to the jury when a person, alleged to be afflicted with insane delusion respecting one or more particular subjects or persons, is charged with the commission of a crime (murder, for example), and insanity is set up as a defence?

"3rd.—In what terms ought the question to be left to the jury as to the prisoner's state of mind at the time when the act was committed?

"4th.—If a person under an insane delusion as to existing facts commits an offence in consequence thereof, is he thereby excused?

"5th.—Can a medical man, conversant with the disease of insanity, who never saw the prisoner previously to the trial, but who was present during the whole trial, and the examination of all the witnesses, be asked his opinion as to the state of the prisoner's mind at the time of the commission of the alleged crime, or his opinion whether the prisoner was conscious at the time of doing the act that he was acting contrary to law, or whether he was labouring under any and what delusion at the time?"

(*a*) See debate on March 6 and 13, 1843, Hansard, vol. 67, pp. 288, 714.

Sir Nicholas Tindal
1776–1846
Chief Justice of the Common
Pleas

[Portrait by T. Philips, R.A.,
National Portrait Gallery, London]

Sir Alexander Cockburn
1802–1880
as Lord Chief Justice of England
(from 1859)

[Portrait by A. D. Cooper,
National Portrait Gallery, London]

ce page 74]

Held by eleven of the judges—

1. *Criminal Responsibility of Persons labouring under partial Delusions.*

A person labouring under partial delusions only, and not otherwise insane, who did the act charged with a view, under the influence of insane delusion, of redressing or revenging some supposed grievance or wrong, or of producing some public benefit, is punishable, if he knew at the time that he was acting contrary to the law of the land.

If a party labouring under an insane delusion as to existing facts, and not otherwise insane, commits an offence, he must be considered in the same situation as if the facts in respect to which the delusion exists were real.

2. *Direction to the Jury in such Cases.*

To establish a defence on the ground of insanity it must be clearly proved that, at the time of committing the act, the party accused was labouring under such a defect of reason from disease of the mind, as not to know the nature and quality of the act he was doing, or if he did know it, that he did not know that what he was doing was wrong.

If the accused was conscious that the act was one which he ought not to do, and if that act was at the same time contrary to the law of the land, he is punishable.

3. *Evidence—Medical Witnesses present at the Trial.*

Where the defence of insanity is set up, a medical witness who never saw the prisoner before, but was present during the whole of the trial, cannot in strictness be asked his opinion as to the state of the prisoner's mind at the time of the commission of the alleged crime; or whether the prisoner was conscious at the time of doing the act that he was acting contrary to law; or whether he was labouring under any and what delusion at the time.

Such questions involve the determination of the truth of the facts deposed to, which it is for the jury to decide. But where the facts are admitted or not disputed, and the question becomes one of science only, such questions may be allowed to be put in that general form, though this cannot be insisted on as a matter of right.

4. *Right of the House of Lords to consult the Judges.*

The judges cannot be required by the House of Lords to give their opinion upon a Bill not yet passed into law, but they may be called on to assist the House by giving their opinions on abstract(a) questions of existing law.

(a) As to this limitation, see *London and Westminster Bank* case, 2 Cl. & F. 191; Macqueen's House of Lords, 47–57; also *Wensleydale Peerage* case, 5 H.L. 958; *Bright* v. *Hutton*, 3 H.L. 341; *Stephenson* v. *Higginson*, 3 H.L. 638; *Egerton* v. *Brownlow*, 4 H.L. 1.

Maule, J.: I feel great difficulty in answering the questions put by your Lordships on this occasion:—First, because they do not appear to arise out of, and are not put with reference to, a particular case, or for a particular purpose, which might explain or limit the generality of their terms, so that full answers to them ought to be applicable to every possible state of facts not inconsistent with those assumed in the questions; this difficulty is the greater, from the practical experience both of the Bar and the Court being confined to questions arising out of the facts of particular cases: secondly, because I have heard no argument at your Lordships' Bar or elsewhere on the subject of these questions, the want of which I feel the more the greater is the number and extent of questions which might be raised in argument: and, thirdly, from a fear, of which I cannot divest myself, that as these questions relate to matters of criminal law of great importance and frequent occurrence, the answers to them by the judges may embarrass the administration of justice when they are cited in criminal trials. For these reasons I should have been glad if my learned brethren would have joined me in praying your Lordships to excuse us from answering those questions, but as I do not think they ought to induce me to ask that indulgence for myself individually, I shall proceed to give such answers as I can, after the very short time which I have had to consider the questions, and under the difficulties I have mentioned, fearing that my answers may be as little satisfactory to others as they are to myself.

The first question, as I understand it, is, in effect, What is the law respecting alleged crime, when, at the time of the commission of it, the accused knew he was acting contrary to the law, but did the act with a view, under the influence of insane delusion, of redressing or revenging some supposed grievance of injury, or of producing some supposed public benefit? If I were to understand this question according to the strict meaning of its terms, it would require, in order to answer it, a solution of all questions of law which could arise on the circumstances stated in the question, either by explicitly stating and answering such questions, or by stating some principles or rules which would suffice for the solution. I am quite unable to do so, and, indeed, doubt whether it be possible to be done, and therefore request to be permitted to answer the question only so far as it comprehends the question whether a person, circumstanced as stated in the question, is for that reason only to be found not guilty of a crime respecting which the question of his guilt has been duly raised in a criminal proceeding; and I am of opinion that he is not. There is no law that I am aware of that makes persons in the state described in the question not responsible for their criminal acts. To render a person irresponsible for crime on account of unsoundness of mind, the unsoundness should, according to the law as it has long been understood and held, be such as to render him incapable of knowing right from wrong. The terms used in the question cannot be said (with reference only to the usage of language) to be equivalent to a description of this kind and degree of unsoundness of mind. If the state described in the question be one which involves, or is necessarily connected with, such an unsoundness, this is not a matter of law, but of physiology, and not of that obvious and familiar kind as to be inferred without proof.

Second, the questions necessarily to be submitted to the jury are those questions of fact which are raised on the record. In a criminal trial, the question commonly is, whether the accused be guilty, or not guilty; but in order to assist the jury in coming to a right conclusion on this necessary and ultimate question, it is usual and proper to submit such subordinate or intermediate questions as the course which the trial has taken may have made it convenient to direct their attention to. What those questions are, and the manner of submitting them, is a matter of discretion for the judge—a discretion to be guided by a consideration of all the circumstances attending the inquiry. In performing this duty, it is sometimes necessary or convenient to inform the jury as to the law; and if, on a trial, such as is suggested in the question, he should have occasion to state what kind and degree of insanity would amount to a defence, it should be stated conformably to what I have mentioned in my answer to the first question as being, in my opinion, the law on this subject.

Third, there are no terms which the judge is by law required to use. They should not be inconsistent with the law as above stated, but should be such as, in the discretion of the judge, are proper to assist the jury in coming to a right conclusion as to the guilt of the accused.

"Fourth, the answer which I have given to the first question is applicable to this.

Fifth, whether a question can be asked depends, not merely on the questions of fact raised on the record, but on the course of the cause at the time it is proposed to ask it; and the state of an inquiry as to the guilt of a person charged with a crime, and defended on the ground of insanity, may be such that such a question as either of those suggested is proper to be asked and answered, though the witness has never seen the person before the trial, and though he has been present and heard the witnesses; these circumstances, of his never having seen the person before and of his having been present at the trial, not being necessarily sufficient, as it seems to me, to exclude the lawfulness of a question which is otherwise lawful, though I will not say that an inquiry might not be in such a state as that these circumstances should have such an effect.

Supposing there is nothing else in the state of the trial to make the questions suggested proper to be asked and answered, except that the witness had been present and heard the evidence, it is to be considered whether that is enough to sustain the question. In principle it is open to this objection, that, as the opinion of the witness is founded on those conclusions of fact which he forms from the evidence, and as it does not appear what those conclusions are, it may be that the evidence he gives is on such an assumption of facts as makes it irrelevant to the inquiry. But such questions have been very frequently asked, and the evidence to which they are directed has been given, and has never, that I am aware of, been successfully objected to. Evidence, most clearly open to this objection, and on the admission of which the event of a most important trial probably turned, was received in the case of the *Queen* v. *M'Naughton,* tried at the Central

Criminal Court in March last, before the Lord Chief Justice, Mr. Justice *Williams*, and Mr. Justice *Coleridge*, in which counsel of the highest eminence was engaged on both sides; and I think the course and practice of receiving such evidence, confirmed by the very high authority of these judges, who not only received it, but left it, as I understand, to the jury without any remark derogating from its weight, ought to be held to warrant its reception, notwithstanding the objection in principle to which it may be open. In cases even where the course of practice in criminal law has been unfavourable to parties accused, it has been held that such practice constituted the law, and could not be altered without the authority of Parliament.

TINDAL, C.J.: My Lords, Her Majesty's judges, with the exception of Mr. Justice *Maule*, who has stated his opinion to your Lordships, in answering the questions proposed to them by your Lordships' House, think it right, in the first place, to state that they have forborne entering into any particular discussion upon these questions, from the extreme and almost insuperable difficulty of applying those answers to cases in which the facts are not brought judicially before them. The facts of each particular case must of necessity present themselves with endless variety, and with every shade of difference in each case; and as it is their duty to declare the law upon each particular case, on facts proved before them, and after hearing argument of counsel thereon, they deem it at once impracticable, and at the same time dangerous to the administration of justice if it were practicable, to attempt to make minute applications of the principles involved in the answers given by them to your Lordships' questions.

They have, therefore, confined their answers to the statement of that which they hold to be the law upon the abstract questions proposed by your Lordships; and as they deem it unnecessary, in this peculiar case, to deliver their opinions *seriatim*, and as all concur in the same opinion, they desire me to express such their unanimous opinion to your Lordships.

The first question proposed by your Lordships is this: "What is the law respecting alleged crimes committed by persons afflicted with insane delusion in respect of one or more particular subjects or persons; as, for instance, where at the time of the commission of the alleged crime, the accused knew he was acting contrary to law, but did the act complained of with a view, under the influence of insane delusion, of redressing or revenging some supposed grievance or injury, or of producing some supposed benefit?"

In answer to which question, assuming that your Lordships' inquiries are confined to those persons who labour under such partial delusions only, and are not in other respects insane, we are of opinion, that, notwithstanding the party accused did the act complained of with a view, under the influence of insane delusion, of redressing or revenging some supposed grievance or injury, or of producing some public benefit, he is nevertheless punishable, according to the nature of the crime committed, if he knew, at the time of committing such crime, that he was acting contrary to law, by which expression we understand your Lordships to mean the law of the land.

Your Lordships are pleased to inquire of us, secondly: "What are the proper questions to be submitted to the jury, where a person alleged to be afflicted with insane delusion respecting one or more particular subjects or persons is charged with the commission of a crime (murder, for example), and insanity is set up as a defence?" And thirdly: "In what terms ought the question to be left to the jury as to the prisoner's state of mind at the time when the act was committed?" And as these two questions appear to us to be more conveniently answered together, we have to submit our opinion to be, that the jury ought to be told in all cases that every man is to be presumed to be sane, and to possess a sufficient degree of reason to be responsible for his crimes, until the contrary be proved to their satisfaction; and that, to establish a defence on the ground of insanity, it must be clearly proved, that, at the time of the committing of the act, the party accused was labouring under such a defect of reason, from disease of the mind, as not to know the nature and quality of the act he was doing, or, if he did know it, that he did not know he was doing what was wrong. The mode of putting the latter part of the question to the jury on these occasions has generally been, whether the accused at the time of doing the act knew the difference between right and wrong; which mode, though rarely, if ever, leading to any mistake with the jury, is not, as we conceive, so accurate when put generally, and in the abstract, as when put with reference to the party's knowledge of right and wrong in respect to the very act with which he is charged. If the question were to be put as to the knowledge of the accused, solely and exclusively with reference to the law of the land, it might tend to confound the jury, by inducing them to believe that an actual knowledge of the law of the land was essential in order to lead to a conviction; whereas the law is administered upon the principle that every one must be taken conclusively to know it, without proof that he does know it. If the accused was conscious that the act was one which he ought not to do, and if that act was at the same time contrary to the law of the land, he in punishable; and the usual course, therefore, has been, to leave the question to the jury, whether the party accused had a sufficient degree of reason to know that he was doing an act that was wrong; and this course we think is correct, accompanied with such observations and explanations as the circumstances of each particular case may require.

The fourth question which your Lordships have proposed to us is this: "If a person under an insane delusion as to existing facts commits an offence in consequence thereof, is he thereby excused?" To which question the answer must of course depend on the nature of the delusion; but, making the same assumption as we did before, namely, that he labours under such partial delusion only, and is not in other respects insane, we think he must be considered in the same situation as to responsibility as if the facts with respect to which the delusion exists were real. For example, if, under the influence of his delusion, he supposes another man to be in the act of attempting to take away his life, and he kills that man, as he supposes, in self-defence, he would be exempt from punishment. If his delusion was that the deceased had inflicted a serious injury to his character and fortune, and he killed him in revenge for such supposed injury, he would be liable to punishment.

The question lastly proposed by your Lordships is: "Can a medical man, conversant with the disease of insanity, who never saw the prisoner previously to the trial, but who was present during the whole trial and the examination of all the witnesses, be asked his opinion as to the state of the prisoner's mind at the time of the commission of the alleged crime, or his opinion whether the prisoner was conscious at the time of doing the act that he was acting contrary to law, or whether he was labouring under any and what delusion at the time?" In answer thereto, we state to your Lordships, that we think the medical man, under the circumstances supposed, cannot in strictness be asked his opinion in the terms above stated, because each of those questions involves the determination of the truth of the facts deposed to, which it is for the jury to decide, and the questions are not mere questions upon a matter of science, in which case such evidence is admissible. But, where the facts are admitted, or not disputed, and the question becomes substantially one of science only, it may be convenient to allow the question to be put in that general form, though the same cannot be insisted on as a matter of right.(a)

The Lords Debate the Replies

Lord BROUGHAM: My Lords, the opinions of the learned judges, and the very able manner in which they have been presented to the House, deserve our best thanks. One of the learned judges has expressed his regret that these questions were not argued by counsel. Generally speaking, it is most important that in questions put for the consideration of the judges they should have all that assistance which is afforded by an argument of counsel; but, at the same time, there can be no doubt of your Lordships' right to put in this way abstract questions of law to the judges, the answer to which might be necessary to your Lordships in your legislative capacity. There is a precedent for this course in the memorable instance of Mr. *Fox's* Bill on the Law of Libel, where, before passing the Bill, this House called on the judges to give their opinion on what was the law as it then existed.(b)

Lord CAMPBELL: My Lords, I cannot avoid expressing my satisfaction that the noble and learned lord on the woolsack carried into effect his desire to put these questions to these judges. It was most fit that the opinions of the judges should be asked on these matters, the settling of which is not a mere matter of speculation, for your Lordships may be called on in your legislative capacity to change the law; and, before doing so, it is proper that you should be satisfied beyond doubt what the law really is. Your Lordships have been reminded of one precedent for this proceeding, but there is a still more recent instance, the judges having been summoned in the case of the Canada Reserves to express their

(a) As to these answers see Stephen's History of the Criminal Law of England, vol. 2, 152, &c.; also later cases collected in 1 Russ. Cri. 128 &c.
(b) See answers of the judges. 29 Parl. Hist. 1861.

opinions on what was then the law on that subject. The answers given by the judges are most highly satisfactory, and will be of the greatest use in the administration of justice.

Lord COTTENHAM: My Lords, I fully concur with the opinion now expressed as to the obligations we owe to the judges. It is true that they cannot be required to say what would be the construction of a Bill not in existence as a law at the moment at which the question is put to them; but they may be called on to assist your Lordships in declaring their opinions on abstract questions of existing law.

Lord WYNFORD: My Lords, I never doubted that your Lordships possess the power to call on the judges to give their opinions upon questions of existing law proposed to them as these questions have been. I myself recollect that when I had the honour to hold the office of Lord Chief Justice of the Court of Common Pleas, I communicated to the House the opinions of the judges on questions of this sort framed with reference to the usury laws. Upon the opinion of the judges thus delivered to the House by me, a Bill was founded and afterwards passed into a law.

Lord LYNDHURST, L.C.: My Lords, I entirely concur in the opinion given by my noble and learned friends, as to our right to have the opinions of the judges on abstract questions of existing law, and I agree that we owe our thanks to the judges for the attention and learning with which they have answered the questions now put to them.

A COMPARISON OF THE TRIAL REPORTS IN *STATE TRIALS* AND IN THE *ANNUAL REGISTER*

E. H. HARE

The State Trials (ST) Report is much fuller than that of the Annual Register (AR), being more than three times as long. It is also, in my judgement, a better report, AR showing some evidence of carelessness. With a few exceptions (detailed below) there is nothing in AR that is not also in ST.

The most interesting differences between ST and AR are those where AR gives a fuller account. Three of these merit notice. (1) The conclusions of the Solicitor General's opening speech (ST page 860, AR page 346). ST is rather fuller here (about 180 words as against 160): both Reports claim to be verbatim but are in fact quite differently worded. (2) The evidence of the surgeon George James Guthrie. ST (862) compresses this into six lines of reported speech but AR (348) gives nearly a column of quoted speech, and this (unlike ST) gives details of the post-mortem report. (3) In Cockburn's speech AR (end of 352) cites a case quoted by Erskine in his defence of Hadfield—a case bearing on the question of partial insanity; AR has 27 lines on this which is not mentioned at all in ST. We also learn from AR, but not from ST, that Cockburn's speech 'occupied upwards of four hours'. These three passages from the AR are worth quoting in full:

(1) *The conclusion of The Solicitor General's opening speech*

Of the prisoner's guilt, of the fact of his having deprived Mr. Drummond of life, it was impossible to suggest a doubt; he could not, however, be unaware that it was intended to rest the defence of the prisoner on the plea of insanity, and it would be the duty of the Jury to decide whether the prisoner, at the time he committed the act, was, or was not, a responsible agent. He (the Solicitor General) believed, indeed, that there were few crimes committed, and, above all, crimes of an atrocious nature like the present, in which the agent was not, at the time, labouring under some morbid affection of mind, and it was difficult for well regulated minds to understand the motives by which persons labouring under such morbid influences were actuated. Sir W. Follett then referred to the several attempts that had been made upon the life of the monarch of the French people, crimes for which it was difficult to assign any motive, but that of an ill-regulated mind, worked upon by political feeling. It was not, therefore, the absence of any adequate and assignable motive that was in itself to be taken as a proof of want of reason in the perpetrator. It would be necessary for the present purpose to refer to some of the established authorities of English law on the subject of criminal

82

responsibility in persons of unsound mind. Sir W. Follett referred to Hale's pleas of the Crown, and quoted passages from that learned writer. He then adverted to the case of Earl Ferrers, who was tried and executed for the murder of his servant, and read to the Jury part of the speech of the Solicitor-General (the Hon. Charles Yorke) on that occasion. He alluded also to the case of Arnold, who was tried for the murder of Lord Onslow; the case of Thomas Bowler, who was convicted of murder in 1812, after a defence set up on the ground of lunacy; to the trial of Hadfield for shooting at George III., and that of Bellingham for the murder of Mr. Perceval, and he deduced from these cases what was the established rule of English law with reference to the point in question, and he expressed the conclusion to the Jury in these terms:—"The whole question will turn upon this—if you believe the prisoner at the bar at the time he committed this act was not a responsible agent—if you believe that when he fired the pistol he was incapable of distinguishing between right and wrong—if you believe that he was under the influence and control of some disease of the mind, which prevented him from being conscious that he was committing a crime—if you believe that he did not know he was violating the law both of God and man, then, undoubtedly, he is entitled to your acquittal. But it is my duty, subject to the correction of my lord, and to the observations of my learned friend, to tell you that nothing short of that excuse can excuse him upon the principle of the English law. To excuse him, it will not be sufficient that he laboured at the time under partial insanity, that he had a morbid disposition of mind, which would not exist in a sane person; that is not enough, if he had that degree of intellect to enable him to know and distinguish right from wrong, if he knew what would be the effects of his crime, and consciously committed it, and if with that consciousness he wilfully committed it."—Sir W. Follett added that it would be his duty to call evidence in opposition to that which would be called on the prisoner's behalf, relating to the state of his mind, and he was convinced that, after hearing and duly weighing all the testimony which should be adduced, the verdict of the Jury would be that of justice between the prisoner and the public.

(2) *Evidence of the surgeon G. J. Guthrie*

Mr. George James Guthrie, examined by the Solicitor-General.—I saw Mr. Drummond about five o'clock on the evening of the 20th of January. Miss Drummond came in a carriage to my door, where I happened to be standing, and took me to his residence. I found Mr. Bransby Cooper there, who had examined the wound before my arrival; but as he had not found the bullet, we at once proceeded to make a further examination. We then turned Mr. Drummond upon his back, and found the ball in the front, about half an inch below the skin, which was taken out by a lancet, not at the time having other instruments at hand. I continued in attendance upon deceased to the time of his death, and was subsequently present at the *post mortem* examination. I have no hesitation whatever in saying that his death was occasioned by the wound. In my opinion it is quite impossible that any person could have survived such a wound; the ball passed through the body directly, but not in a straight line. It wounded the diaphragm, and that is a wound which never heals under such circumstances. It is certainly a mortal wound. I never knew a person to recover from such a wound made by a ball; but when occasioned by a lance, sword, or spear, I have seen them healed.

Mr. Bransby Blake Cooper, who had also attended the deceased, expressed his perfect concurrence with Mr. Guthrie respecting the cause of his death.

(3) *Extract from the speech by the prisoner's counsel, Alexander Cockburn, Q.C.*

The true nature of the delusion which exempted from crime had been admirably laid down by Lord Erskine; who said, in his defence of Hadfield, that insanity might prevail upon a particular point, and that monomania exculpated an individual from the guilt of crime committed under its influence. Mr. Ray likewise held that a man might be as sane as the rest of the world on all points but one, and yet that an act committed under that particular delusion was one for which the man was no more answerable than if *all* his mental faculties had been deranged. He cited cases in support of that proposition—One of these, which was quoted by Lord Erskine in his speech in defence of Hadfield, was the case of a lunatic who had brought an action against his own brother and a madhouse-keeper for false imprisonment. Lord Erskine, who was counsel for the defence, was unable in the course of the cross-examination to extract a single answer from the witness which could show that he laboured under the slightest delusion. Before the close of the proceedings, however, a medical gentleman in court informed him that the man believed he was Jesus Christ; this being, in fact, his sole delusion. Lord Erskine immediately begged the lunatic's pardon, for the disrespect of which he had been guilty, and having now obtained his clue, soon succeeded in bringing to light the real state of the lunatic's mind.

AR mentions some evidence from persons not so mentioned by ST. Thus AR (349 col. 1), included in the second extract cited, quotes the evidence from Mr Bransby Blake Cooper whose name occurs in ST only as being mentioned in the evidence of Richard Jackson (862). Evidence of Mr Robert Swanston, the clerk in the London Joint Stock Bank, occupies 20 lines in AR (end of 351) but receives no mention at all in ST:—

(4) *Evidence of Mr Robert Swanston*

Mr. Robert Swanston, a clerk in the London Joint Stock Bank, said, both the papers produced were written by me. The one dated the 7th of August is for 750*l.*, which was for the sum he deposited with us. He subsequently called and wished to draw out 5*l.*, but I told him that I could not let him have that sum, but he might have the whole amount if he pleased, and he gave notice of withdrawal; on the 28th of August he drew out the money, and having deducted 5*l.*, again deposited the remainder, to which the second paper referred, being a receipt for 745*l.* In June last, in consequence of a letter I received from the prisoner, I transferred the amount to the Glasgow and Shipping Bank.

The last person to give evidence for the defence is mentioned by AR (359 col. 1) as "Mr. McClure a surgeon"; but ST (end of 923) names this witness as "Dr. Philips, surgeon and lecturer at the Westminster Hospital". This difference is perhaps noteworthy in view of the Judge's remark, following very soon after, that the evidence from the last two medical men (i.e. Forbes Winslow and the last witness) "who are strangers to both sides and only observers of the case", was very strong. In ST Mr. McClure is one of the doctors who examined McNaughton along with Dr. Monro and others, and he gave evidence similar to theirs.

There are numerous places where AR and ST differ as to fact. Most of these are trivial, but some are worth noting if only because they suggest that AR's Report is less reliable than ST's. The differences can be classed under four headings. Thus (1) Spelling of the prisoner's name. AR gives MacNaghten in the title and the opening paragraph but thereafter M'Naghten; ST gives

M'Naughton throughout. (2) Names and addresses. The Christian name of Mrs. Dutton is given as Sarah by AR (350 col. 2) and as Eliza by ST (867). The Christian name of Gordon, the Glasgow brass-founder, is given as David by AR (351 col. 1) and as John by ST (869). AR (351 col. 2) gives the name of the Curator of the Glasgow Mechanics' Institution, as Mr. Swanston, ST (870) as William Swanstead; but here AR may be confusing the name with that of Mr. Robert Swanston (not mentioned by ST), the clerk in the London Joint Stock Bank who is mentioned in ST a few lines below. In AR (353 col. 2), the prisoner's father refers to the prisoner simply as his son whereas in ST (906) he describes the prisoner as his natural son: ST is probably correct here in view of the later statement by the father that he did not take the prisoner into partnership in his business because he had younger children to provide for. (3) Timing. AR states (352 col. 1) that the evidence for the prosecution occupied the entire day but ST indicates that the trial was adjourned early on that day at the request of Cockburn: and the detailed account of this given by ST makes its version much the more probable. (4) In general, AR gives more detail than ST on the physical aspects of the prisoner's health. AR has the long account of Guthrie's evidence (see above). In Mrs. Dutton's evidence, ST says (867) "in the beginning of December he was poorly but I never did anything for him in the house . . . he said he was suffering a bad cold from neglect: he continued ill for about a fortnight". AR's version (350 col. 2) runs "in the month of December he was very unwell for a fortnight during which time I attended upon him. He said he had taken cold in consequence of getting wet". In Cockburn's account of the prisoner's early life, AR (353 col. 1) has the passage "about the year 1834 he had a typhus fever, and he began to be restless and sleepless at night"; there is no equivalent passage in ST. AR also refers to "wracking pains in the head", "a glare with his eyes" (351 col. 2) and to his being "tossed like a cork on a sea" (end of 357), none of these being mentioned in ST.

ON THE SPELLING OF DANIEL M'NAGHTEN'S NAME*

BERNARD L. DIAMOND, M.D.

Having just participated in three years of argument and debate over the substance of the M'Naghten Rules,[1] the resultant emotional tensions impel me to attempt to put to rest, once and for all, at least one aspect, no matter how inconsequential of that most famous case: What is the correct spelling of *M'Naghten*? But, as the reader will discover, even that small comfort is denied me.

M'Naghten achieved immortality by lending his name to the famous (or infamous) rules which govern the criminal responsibility of the mentally ill throughout the English speaking world.[2] His intended victim, Sir Robert Peel, had accomplished his fame in perpetuity in a manner reserved for the very few: his name (or rather, his nickname) has become part of our language itself. "Bobby" as the designation of the English policeman is directly derived from Sir Robert.[3] The actual victim, Edward Drummond, assassinated solely because he was mistakenly identified (as the Prime Minister) by Daniel M'Naghten has remained forgotten. Perhaps it is Drummond's uneasy ghost, doomed to the limbo of the unremembered, who is really behind the unending *M'Naghten* controversies.

At any rate, when one tires of dispute over the substance of *M'Naghten*, one can continue endlessly over the form of *M'Naghten*, even to the spelling of his name.

M'Naghten is the customary spelling in both English and American law reports. I use it here only out of deference to the indexers who will wish to file this article in its appropriate alphabetical position among other medico-legal trivia. Of all possible spellings, it is probably the least correct. Yet, if one attempts a more accurate spelling, the critical reviewer will immediately spot it and accuse one of ignorance.

Clarence B. Farrar, the distinguished editor of the *American Journal of Psychiatry*, and a medico-legal authority on his own right, did just that in a

---

* Reprinted from *Ohio State Law Journal*, 1964, Volume 25, Number 1.
[1] California Special Commissions on Insanity and Criminal Offenders, First Report (July 7, 1962), Second Report (November 15, 1962).
[2] See Diamond, "Isaac Ray and the Trial of Daniel M'Naghten," 112 Am. J. Psychiatry 651 (1956).
[3] Webster, New International Dictionary 300 (2d unabridged ed. 1952).

review of Partridge's *Broadmoor: A History of Criminal Lunacy and its Problems*.[4] In a letter to the editor, I took issue with Dr. Farrar, who enlisted the aid of Dr. Winifred Overholser, then Superintendent of St. Elizabeth's Hospital, to defeat me and assert the superiority of the conventional spelling *M'Naghten*.[5] But I knew this could not settle the issue, for the hospital records of both Bethlem and Broadmoor, where M'Naghten was confined after his aquittal on the grounds of insanity, spelled the name sometimes *McNaughten* and sometimes *McNaughton*.[6] The original report of the trial spelled it *M'Naughton*.[7]

With this background of controversy, it was with pleasure and amusement that I received from Judge John Biggs, Jr. copies of the following correspondence between Justice Felix Frankfurter and Sir William J. Haley, Editor of *The Times*, of London.[8]

November 3, 1952

Dear Sir William:

That poor creature, Daniel M'Naghten, not only killed an innocent man, but also occasioned considerable conflict between law and medicine. But in so doing he gave his name to a leading case and thus obtained a permanent place in the history of the law. I am sure that *The Times* does not want to make inroads on his fame. A strange fatality has dogged the spelling of his name; too often it is incorrectly spelled. It is M'Naghten, not M'Naughten or any of the variants of its misspelling.

Or am I wrong in relying on the spelling given by Clark and Finnelly in their report of the case? See *Daniel M'Naghten's* case, 10 Cl. & Fin. 200.

Sincerely yours,
Felix Frankfurter

Sir William J. Haley

THE   TIMES
1785
The Times Publishing Company, Ltd.,
Printing House Square,
London, E. C. 4
Telephone: Central 2000

November 10, 1952

Dear Mr. Justice Frankfurter,

The strong leaven of Daniel M'Naghten still works on. He is a benefactor indeed to have occasioned a letter from you. The interesting thing about the point you raise is that all through the proof stage of the article M'Naghten had appeared as such, but so strong is the tradition of *The Times* that it was altered to M'Naughton just as it was going to press. One of the most powerful things which hits a newcomer to Printing House Square is the magnificent strength of tradition, and the fact is that that was how *The Times* spelt him in its report of the original trial.

The exact spelling has been a problem down the years. No doubt high authority must be given to Clark and Finnelly but there are other authorities, dare I say it, equally

---

[4] Farrar, Book Review, 110 Am. J. Psychiatry 399 (1953).
[5] Diamond, Correspondence, 110 Am. J. Psychiatry 705 (1954).
[6] Transcripts of the Bethlehem and Broadmoor hospital records of Daniel M'Naghten were obtained with the permission of, and the courteous cooperation of, the Secretary of State, Home Office, Whitehall, London.
[7] Bousfield & Merrett, Report of the Trial of Daniel M'Naughton (London, 1843).
[8] Permission for publication of this correspondence has been kindly granted by Justice Felix Frankfurter, Sir William Haley and Judge John Biggs, Jr.

high who disagree. It may amuse you to have the following list got out by the writer of the article when I told him you had raised the point. (Incidentally he is that kind of man.)

1. The original Gaelic—Mhicneachdain.
2. The lunatic himself, signing a letter produced at the trial—M'Naughten (as reported in *The Times*).
3. The State Trials—Macnaughton.
4. Clark and Finelly—M'Naghten.
5. Archbold, 1938 edition—Macnaughton
   1927 edition—Macnaughten
   Index   —Macnaghten
6. Stephen, earlier editions—Macnaughten
   later editions—Macnaghten
7. Halsbury, earlier editions—M'Naughton
   later editions—M'Naughten
8. Select Committee on Capital Punishment 1930—McNaughten, and several other spellings.
9. Encyclopaedia Britannica—different spellings in different articles.
10. Royal Commission on Capital Punishment, 1949, instructed by its Chairman, Sir Ernest Gowers—M'Naghten.

After all that I do not quite know what *The Times* can do if it is to desert its long standing tradition based, as you see, on a letter signed by the man himself. Perhaps it would be a nice tribute to the spirit of *The Times* if we went back to the original Gaelic.

Yours sincerely,
W. J. Haley

The Hon. Felix Frankfurter,
Supreme Court of the United States,
Washington 13, D.C.
U. S. A.

November 26, 1952

Dear Sir William:

Your kindness in sending me a variorum of Mhicneachdain afforded me another experience with the perplexities and exhilaration of scholarship. But you also raise what the lawyers like to call "a nice point." To what extent is a lunatic's spelling even of his own name to be deemed an authority?

And when you speak of "the magnificent strength of tradition" in Printing House Square, you stir in me the suspicion that the task of the Editor of *The Times* is not unlike one's job on this Court—namely, how to reconcile the conflicting demands of the needs of stability and of change. In expressing greater confidence in the ability of the Editor of *The Times* than in my own to square that circle, I speak with the bluntness that is supposed to be American.

Very sincerely yours,
Felix Frankfurter

Sir William J. Haley

As a collector of *M'Naghteniana* I have long searched for an autograph specimen of M'Naghten's signature. Dr. Leslie T. Morton, co-author of the bible of the medical bibliomaniac,[9] succeeded where I failed, and reproduced here is a photograph of M'Naghten's signature.[10] Morton obtained this rarest

[9] Garrison & Morton, Medical Bibliography (2d ed. 1954).
[10] Reproduced by permission of the British Medical Journal.

of rare autographs from a statement made before the Bow Street magistrate and signed by the prisoner on January 21, 1843.

[signature: Daniel McNaughtun]

As Morton regretfully states: "Unfortunately it fails to make clear just how McNaughton spelt his name."[11] So Justice Frankfurter has a point in asking: "To what extent is a lunatic's spelling of his own name to be deemed an authority?"[12]

At first glance, the signature would seem to read *McNaughtun* and Morton says that an authority at the British Museum reads it so. But he quotes other handwriting experts who dispute this, and his research into many British genealogical texts as well as the Glasgow registers of births and baptisms do not support the spelling *McNaughtun*. After reviewing evidence from a large number of other sources, Morton concludes in favor of the spelling *McNaughton*.

How does one reconcile Sir William Haley's contention that M'Naghten signed his name as *M'Naughten* in a letter produced in the trial and reported in *The Times* of that day?[13] It is, of course, possible, that an ignorant or illiterate man might spell his own name one way one time and another way another time. But M'Naghten was neither ignorant nor illiterate. Testimony at the trial elicited the information that he had attended lectures at the Mechanics Museum at Glasgow in anatomy, physiology and natural philosophy between 1838 and 1840. The Curator of the Museum testified that during that period M'Naghten took out 36 books from the Museum's library.[14]

M'Naghten was undoubtedly suffering from paranoid schizophrenia.[15] It has been my clinical experience that paranoid patients are unusually particular as to how they spell their names in their signatures. It would be very surprising for such a person to vary the spelling unless his delusions required it for some dark and mysterious reason.

Sir Ernest Gowers, chairman of the Royal Commission on Capital Punishment, attempts to solve the problem through dictatorial authority. Lord Justice Asquith in a letter to *The Times* of December 5, 1949 protests the spelling *M'Naghten*. Sir Ernest Gowers replied in a letter of December 16, 1949: "So for us [The Royal Commission] the Rules will be the M'Naghten Rules: any

[11] Morton, "Daniel McNaughton's Signature," British Medical Journal 107 (Jan. 14, 1956).
[12] Frankfurter, Letter to Sir William Haley (Nov. 26, 1952).
[13] I have verified this myself and found that *The Times* of March 4, 5 & 6, 1843 uses this spelling throughout its extensive reports of the trial. *The London Illustrated News* of March 4, 1843 spells the name the same way.
[14] *The Times* 6 (London, March 4, 1843).
[15] The hospital records of Daniel M'Naghten, *supra* note 6, describe typical behavior which would now be so diagnosed.

4

witness who spells the name differently will be treated as a deviationist, and forced into conformity by the printer."[16]

But I fear the controversy will proceed. It would not appear that anything about *M'Naghten* can ever be put to rest: form or substance.

Editors' Note

An authority on Scottish names states that 'in general, the spelling M' represents the lack of availability of a small letter "c" placed above the line in the printer's range of type. The apostrophe will mean, in fact, "Mc" '.

In fact, one should add, the sign in question is not an apostrophe at all—it is an apostrophe *reversed*, thus resembling and substituting for the small 'c'. Hence the name was *written McNaughton*, as in the signature and the Bethlem case-notes, but *printed M'Naughton*, as in the State Trials report.

The spelling with this reversed apostrophe has been gradually abandoned by those families who formerly used it. In *Who Was Who* for 1897–1916 there are 132 'Mc' or 'Mac' spellings and 54 'M' '. In the latest *Who's Who* there is one solitary 'M' '.

[16] Quoted by Morton, *op. cit. supra* note 11, at 109.

'McNAUGHTON'S MADNESS'

HENRY R. ROLLIN

Had the victim of Daniel McNaughton's murderous assault been a person of no importance, the event would have scarcely troubled the waters of medico-legal history. As it was, the fatal bullet lodged in a man of first class importance, Mr Edward Drummond, Private Secretary to Sir Robert Peel, Tory Prime Minister of the United Kingdom, for whom, it was confidently assumed, the bullet was really intended. The consequence of the murder, the subsequent trial, and the verdict, 'Not guilty on the ground of insanity', was to set up a veritable tidal wave of public alarm concerning the obvious defect in the Criminal Law which seemingly allowed madmen to commit murder and get away scot-free—if incarceration in a lunatic asylum for the rest of a man's natural life can be so construed. The 'McNaughton Rules' were the direct outcome of the consternation and are dealt with by other contributors.

Exceptional as the McNaughton case was in all its ramifications, the form of insanity from which the culprit suffered is relatively commonplace. There can be no doubt that he would be diagnosed today as suffering from schizophrenia, using that term as a shorthand way of describing a group of cases with similar but by no means identical symptoms. In McNaughton's case the psychosis was characterized by a host of paranoid delusions, although evidence of virtually all the other classical signs and symptoms of schizophrenia are not difficult to determine. The transcript of the trial is in itself a splendid case-history, thanks to the assiduity and perspicacity of the defence lawyers in the preparation of their case. The pity is that the doctors who had to do with McNaughton after he had been admitted to the Bethlem Royal Hospital, and later to Broadmoor Criminal Lunatic Asylum, did not exercise the same care in recording their observations.

Daniel McNaughton now aged 29 years, was the natural son of a Glasgow wood turner who bore the same name. (The mother, incidentally, receives no mention.) Alexander Cockburn, Q.C., counsel for the defences, notes with commendable insight in his opening speech that Daniel junior, 'probably did not meet with that full measure of kindness which is usually shown to legitimate offspring'. He could have added that this lack of affection in childhood might have been the genesis of his later feelings of rejection. He goes on to give an illuminating sketch of Daniel's pre-morbid personality: 'He appears to have been from the commencement a man of gloomy, reserved, and unsocial habits.

He was, moreover, as you will hear, though gloomy and reserved in himself, a man of singularly sensitive mind—one who spent his days in incessant labour and toil, and at night gave himself up to the study of difficult and abstruse matters; but whose mind, notwithstanding, was tinctured with refinement.' With an even more commendable degree of psychiatric awareness, Cockburn goes on: 'I mention these things to show that, from the earliest period, the prisoner had a predisposition to insanity.' There would, therefore, be ample justification for maintaining that McNaughton had what these days would be called a 'schizoid personality', a common precursor of schizophrenia.

The way in which the psychosis evolved is beautifully detailed in the evidence given at the trial. Of primary importance, of course, are McNaughton's own statements. After the assault, he was taken to Bow Street Police Court where on interrogation he said: 'The Tories in my native city have compelled me to do this. They follow and persecute me wherever I go, and have entirely destroyed my peace of mind. They followed me to France, into Scotland, and all over England; in fact, they follow me wherever I go. I cannot get no rest for them night or day. I cannot sleep at night in consequence of the course they pursue towards me. I believe they have driven me into a consumption. I am sure I shall never be the man I formerly was. I used to have good health and strength, but I have not now. They have accused me of crimes of which I am not guilty; they do everything in their power to harass and persecute me; in fact, they wish to murder me. It can be proved by evidence. That's all I have to say.' Again, at the time of the trial after a considerable degree of persuasion to plead to the indictment, McNaughton hesitatingly admits: 'I was driven to desperation by persecution.'

Almost all the witnesses in the case gave perfectly clear-cut evidence which would support the contention that McNaughton's delusional system, and therefore his psychosis, antedated the murder by some years, and that as time went on it had become increasingly severe. In this respect the father's evidence is obviously most pertinent. He describes how Daniel had been apprenticed to him and later became his journeyman. Eventually he left him and started in business on his own, after which he saw him less frequently. He makes the significant remark: 'He seemed to me more distant than formerly, but I knew of no reason for his being so. He would frequently pass me in the street and did not speak to or notice me.' Two years before the trial, the father became very concerned about his son because of the emergence of what he describes as Daniel's, 'extraordinary delusions'. Daniel, he related, complained with increasing bitterness of the persecution to which he was subject and of which, he alleged, various dignitaries in the City of Glasgow were fully aware. In this context he mentioned Sheriff Alison and Sheriff Bell. He implored his father to approach these gentlemen with a view to having the persecution stopped.

The intensity of the delusions and the misery which they occasioned the unfortunate Daniel are well documented. He himself alleges, as he did at Bow Street, that wherever he went he was followed night and day by spies. Wherever he might be, whenever he turned round, there they were. They laughed at him and shook their fists in his face, and those who had sticks shook them at him. So desperate did he become that he left Glasgow and went to England and even to France to get rid of the spies, but they still followed him; the moment he landed in France, there they were.

To return to Cockburn. In his elegant, early-Victorian Gothic prose, he describes the suffering of the mad Daniel. First in Latin, and then in English, he quotes a most appropriate text: 'What exile from his country's shore can from himself escape?' It was impossible, in other words, for McNaughton to shake off the man on his back.

Cockburn goes on: 'When he left his own country he (McNaughton) visited England, and then France; but nowhere was there a "resting-place for the sole of his foot". Wherever he went his diseased mind carried with him the diseased productions of its own perverted nature. Wherever he was, there were his fancies; there were present to his mind imaginary persecutors.'

As his psychosis deepened so his persecutory delusions became increasingly widespread. The first complaint he made in Glasgow to Sheriff Wilson was that Catholic priests and Jesuits were engaged in persecuting him. Shortly afterwards the delusions mushroomed and included the police and then 'all the world'. Seemingly the Tories were thrown in for good measure only latterly 'on account of a vote I gave at a former election', Daniel explained.

However, the Tories, for reasons not easily understandable, now become the focal point of his delusional system. He is determined to act against the leader of the Tory party, the Prime Minister himself. 'He (presumably Sir Robert Peel) shall break my peace of mind no longer,' McNaughton is alleged to have said to the police constable, James Silver, who disarmed him after the shooting. But the assassination plot had been laid long before. McNaughton purchased the pistols in Glasgow in July 1842 (the murder took place on 20 January 1843). Several witnesses at the trial attested to the fact that for some days previously McNaughton had been frequently seen in the vicinity of Downing Street and had in fact been questioned as to his business there. An eye witness of the assault said: 'The prisoner drew the pistol very deliberately, but at the same time very quickly. As far as I can judge, it was a very cool deliberate act.'

Despite his apparent coolness and deliberation McNaughton was at this time exceedingly mad, yet he was capable of formulating and carrying out a complicated plan of action. At various points in the transcript reference is made to the occasions when his written and spoken speech were quite rational. But the redoubtable Cockburn scents danger and boldly counter-attacks. He challenges the Solicitor General to ask any of the medical gentlemen in the case to: 'deny the proposition that a man may be a frenzied lunatic on one point, and yet on all others be capable of all the operations of the human mind, possessed of a high degree of sagacity, in possession of full rational powers, undisturbed by evil or excessive passions.'

It is apropos to recall that in 1786 Margaret Nicholson made an attempt to stab King George III. She was found to be insane and was confined to Bethlem Hospital for life. Dr Monro, one of the dynasty of Monro physicians to that hospital, is credited with the profound observation that in her case it was quite possible to be insane and still take a hand at whist.

Although his network of delusions are in themselves evidence enough of McNaughton's madness, there are other classical signs and symptoms of schizophrenia which in the aggregate add considerable weight to that diagnosis. For example, there is a strong likelihood that he was hallucinated for hearing: in his statement made at Bow Street he talks of hearing his persecutors accusing him of crimes of which he protests he was not guilty. Again, there are statements by witnesses which would indicate an obvious interference with his thought processes. One such, William Gilchrist, examined by Mr Bodkin, counsel for the defence, said: 'The prisoner used frequently to get up in the night and walk about the room, uttering incoherent sentences . . .'. Later in the same examination Gilchrist said: 'His conversation was not so connected as formerly.' The same witness highlights another significant symptom, that is, emotional incongruity. 'I have known the prisoner burst out into immoderate fits of laughter without any cause whatever; at other times he would moan,' he said. Furthermore, several witnesses attested to his much altered and very strange manner and appearance. John Hughes, with whom McNaughton at one time lodged, examined by Mr Monteith, counsel for the defence, stated: 'In consequence of his very strange manner I gave him notice to leave.' And a onetime landlady, Jane Drummond Pattison, examined by Mr Bodkin, said: 'I observed something very peculiar in his manner. His eyes presented a very strange appearance.'

The overall evidence gleaned from a host of witnesses would refute any suggestion that McNaughton's insanity was 'partial': the cancer of his psychosis had invaded every department of his mind, although some admittedly were more affected than others.

The defence counsel were having a field day. The prosecution's witnesses called to testify as to McNaughton's sanity had been singularly unconvincing. It only required the doctors to deliver the *coup de grâce*.

There was, in fact, a veritable army of medical gentlemen concerned in the case. Dr Edward Thomas Monro (Tom to his family), the last of the Monro dynasty associated with Bethlem, had examined McNaughton for the defence on the first occasion in Newgate prison. Also present at the examination were Sir Alexander Morison, Monro's colleague at Bethlem; Dr A. J. Sutherland, physician to St Luke's Hospital; and Mr William McClure, a surgeon living in Harley Street. During his last two examinations Dr Hutcheson, Physician to the Royal Asylum, Glasgow, and Dr Crawford, also of Glasgow, were present. Independently, Mr Aston Key of Guy's Hospital, and Dr Philips, surgeon and lecturer at the Westminster Hospital, had examined McNaughton and gave evidence at the trial.

Dr Forbes Winslow, who later became an established authority in trials where a defence of insanity was raised, was also called. He had not actually examined McNaughton, but had merely been present in court as a spectator throughout the trial—a circumstance which led to much controversy and was the subject of one of the questions put to the judges by the House of Lords.

The evidence of Dr Monro, speaking with the authority of thirty years' experience of the 'subject of insanity', was by far the most important and understandably his examination was reserved for Cockburn himself. The substance of what McNaughton told Dr Monro at the time of his examination, and which he in turn told the Court, is worth turning back to read in full (see p. 66) because, as the passage well illustrates, it condenses and substantiates a good deal of the evidence given by lay persons previously. The misinterpretations and ideas of self reference underlying his persecutory delusions, and his complete lack of insight into the fact of his illness, are clearly set out. Dr Monro reports McNaughton as saying: 'that on coming out of the court-house he had seen a man frowning at him, with a bundle of straw under his arm; that he knew well enough what was meant; that everything was done by signs; that he was represented to be under a delusion; that the straw denoted that he should lie upon straw in an asylum; that whilst on board the steamboat on his way from Glasgow to Liverpool he was watched, eyed, and examined closely by persons coming near him; that they had followed him to Boulogne on two occasions; they would never allow him to learn French, and wanted to murder him . . .'.

Later on in the examination, to the question put to him by Cockburn: 'Do you consider that the delusions were real or assumed?' Dr Monro replied categorically: 'I am quite satisfied that they were real. I have not a shadow of a doubt on the point.' Still later Dr Monro said: 'I consider the act of killing Mr. Drummond to have been committed whilst under a delusion; the act itself I look upon as the crowning act of the whole matter—as the climax—as a carrying out of the pre-existing idea which had haunted him for years.'

It is of interest that Dr Monro gives as the diagnosis the then fashionable one of Monomania. This term was invented by the distinguished French psychiatrist, J. E. D. Esquirol, and later adopted in England by Dr J. C. Prichard and others. The implication of the diagnosis is one of partial insanity, or insanity in respect of one subject or a series of subjects. Thus, Dr Monro was asked by counsel: 'Is it consistent with the pathology of insanity, that a partial delusion may exist depriving the person of all self-control whilst other faculties may be sound?' 'Certainly; monomania may exist with general sanity,' he replied.

The diagnosis of Monomania has long since been abandoned. Certainly in McNaughton's case all the clinical evidence which emerged in the trial is proof that his insanity was in no way partial. The rot had spread and involved all his mental processes in a way characteristic of schizophrenia in its more malignant form, so malignant, indeed, that even in these days of sophisticated pharmacotherapy McNaughton's own bitter reflection that 'a ton of drugs would be of no service to him', is as applicable as it was then.

All the other doctors called to give evidence confirmed absolutely that McNaughton was insane and that he was deluded. To quote Dr Hutcheson as an example: 'The delusion was so strong that nothing but a physical impediment could have prevented him from committing the act.'

The case for the prosecution finally collapsed after the evidence of Dr Forbes

Winslow and Dr Philips, who both appeared for the Crown, but both agreed unhesitatingly with the opinion of the other doctors. The Solicitor-General admitted defeat. The case was stopped. The foreman of the jury, without the jury retiring, returned the now famous verdict: 'We find the prisoner not guilty on the ground of insanity.'

As an epilogue to the drama the transcript of the trial ends: 'On Wednesday the 15th March, the prisoner was removed by Mr. Cope, the governor of Newgate to Bethlehem Hospital, St. George's Fields, under an order from the Right Hon. Sir James Graham, Her Majesty's Secretary of State for the Home Department.'

After the 'great commotion' created by his crime, and the high drama of his trial, McNaughton's subsequent career was a dull, pedestrian affair—an anticlimax if ever there was one. He was duly transferred to Bethlem Hospital and later to Broadmoor Asylum where, first in one and then in the other he sank unobtrusively into obscurity.

Most unfortunately the standard of clinical note-keeping in both hospitals was far from exemplary, so that the progress of McNaughton's mental illness is impossible to determine with any degree of precision. However, the entry in the Bethlem case paper for 21 March 1854, shines like a good deed in a naughty world and is well worth quoting in full:

'He is a man of so retiring a disposition and so averse to conversation or notice of any kind that it is very difficult even for his attendant to glean from him any information as to his state of mind or the character of his delusions, but one point has been made out that he imagines he is the subject of annoyance from some real or fanciful being or beings; but more than this is not known, for he studiously avoids entering into the subject with any one. If a stranger walks through the Gallery he at once hides in the water closet or in a bedroom and at other times he chooses some darkish corner where he reads or knits. His crime created great commotion at the time. In mistake for the late Sir Robert Peel he shot Mr. Drummond as he was going into the Treasury or some Government Office and that time imagined that the Tories were his enemies and annoyed him. He has refused food and been fed with the stomach pump.'

It would be unwise to read too much into this single anecdotal account. Nevertheless, there is obviously a change for the worse in McNaughton's mental state. From the little information that his attendant could glean from him it is evident that he still clings to some at least of his paranoid delusions; but the emotional concomitants that at one time were associated with them appear to have evaporated. He now appears to be emotionally flat. His withdrawal from the real world, even the microcosm of the asylum, is about complete: he hides himself away from all human contact. His refusal of food, necessitating feeding by a stomach tube, would indicate a degree of negativism or perhaps stupor. The whole clinical picture is therefore consonant with that of a severe, chronic schizophrenic illness affecting every department of the mind. The picture finally gives the lie to the diagnosis of Monomania: there is nothing at all 'partial' about his mental disintegration.

There are also in existence two independent references to McNaughton at

Bethlem, for which I am indebted to Miss P. Allderidge and Dr Alexander Walk respectively. The first is merely a brief sighting which appeared in the *Illustrated London News* for 25 March 1843, at the time of McNaughton's admission. It reads:

'We accompanied a party on Tuesday last, and passed through the criminals' exercising ground as the patients entered. Oxford was busily engaged, with three others, in playing at fives; and, as the recent regulation of the Governors of the hospital precludes the keepers from pointing out any individual among the criminals, he was observed only by those who had a previous knowledge of his person. McNaughton was also in the yard, but, probably from the novelty of his situation, he appeared ill at ease, and was seated alone, under a covered shed in the centre. As our party entered he purposely averted his face, seeming anxious to avoid observation, and, fortunately, none were curious enough to intrude upon him further.'

The second reference, an excellent description of McNaughton's parlous psychiatric condition some eight years later, is quoted in the *Journal of Psychological Medicine* for 1852 from an article published in *Blackwood's Magazine* the previous year. The article, which was 'said on good authority' to be by Mr Samuel Warren, a member of the legal profession, was an elaborate analysis of the first volume of *Modern State Trials*, by another lawyer, Mr Townsend:

"M'Naughten was standing in the courtyard, dressed in the costume of the place, (a pepper-and-salt jacket and corduroy trousers) with his hat on, knitting. He looks about forty years old, and in perfect health. His features are regular, and their expression is mild and prepossessing. His manner is tranquil. Usually he wears his hat somewhat slouched over his eyes, and sidles slowly away from any one approaching him, as if anxious to escape observation; but on this occasion he at once entered into conversation with our companion, calmly and cheerfully, and afforded us a full opportunity of watching him. Had we seen him casually elsewhere, and as a stranger, we should have thought his countenance indicative of a certain sort of cheerful quiet humour, especially while he was speaking; but to us it seemed certainly to exhibit a feeble intellect, shown chiefly by a faint flickering smile, even when he was speaking on the gravest subjects.—When asked what had brought him where he was, he replied, '*Fate*.' 'And what is fate?' 'The will of God, or perhaps'—he added quickly, 'of the devil—or it may be of both?' and he half closed his eyes and smiled.—When told that Sir Robert Peel was dead, he betrayed no emotion, nor exhibited the slightest interest. 'One should have thought that, considering what has happened, you would have felt some interest in that gentleman.' He looked rather quickly at the speaker, and said, calmly, with a faint smile, 'It is quite useless to talk to me on *that* subject: you know quite well I have long and long ago made up my mind never to say one word about it. I never have, and I never will; and so it would be quite childish to put any questions.' . . . . 'How are you, M'Naughten?'—He slightly sighed, and said, 'I am very uncomfortable. I am very ill-used here; there is somebody [or something] always using me ill here. It is really too bad! I have spoken about it many, many times; but it is quite useless. I wish I could get away from this place! If I could just get out of this place, and go back to Glasgow, my native place, it is all I would ask for: I should be quite well there! I shall never be well or happy *here*, for there is always some one ill-using me here.' 'Well, but what do they do to you?' 'Oh,' shaking his head, and smiling, 'they are always doing it; really it is too bad.'—'Who are they?' 'Oh, I am always being ill-used here! My only wish now is, to get away from this place! If I could only once get to Glasgow, my native place!' This is the continual burthen of his song. It is needless to say that his complaints are altogether unfounded; he is treated with the utmost kindness consistent with his situation; and, as he has never exhibited violence nor ill-behaviour, it has never been necessary to resort to personal coercion, with one exception. Two or three years ago, he took it into his head that, as he could not get away, he would starve himself; and he persevered for such a length of time in refusing all kind of food that he began to lose flesh fast. At length he was told by the physician that, since he would not eat voluntarily, he must be made to eat; and it was actually necessary to feed him for a considerable time mechanically, by means of the stomach-pump. Under this treatment he presently regained his flesh, in spite—as it were—of himself; and at length suffered himself to be laughed out of his obstinacy, and has ever since taken his food voluntarily. He seemed himself to be tickled by a sense of the absurdity of which he was guilty. Not a doubt of his complete insanity was entertained by my acute companion, who has devoted much observation to the case. Shortly after we had quitted him, and were out of his sight, he put away his knitting, placed his hands in his jacket-pockets, and walked very rapidly to and fro, his face bent on the ground; and he was apparently somewhat excited. Whatever may have been the state of M'Naughten at the time to which our inquiries have been directed in this article, we entertain little if any doubt, that he is now in an imbecile condition."

This description certainly confirms the picture of mental disintegration given in the 1854 Bethlem notes. Following that one illuminating record at Bethlem, there are no less than seventy-four entries in the case notes at about monthly intervals between 26 July 1854 and January 1863 in which, with monotonous regularity and exceedingly doubtful validity, the entry 'No change' is made. Then in January 1863 comes a dramatic statement: 'He complains very much of palpitation of the heart and at present is keeping his bed. Appetite is not good.'

On 26 March 1864, McNaughton, now aged 50, a dying man, and in all probability entirely harmless, is transferred to the newly established Broadmoor Criminal Lunatic Asylum, where he is entered as No. 75 in the register.

There are in all seven entries in his Broadmoor case-sheet. The only one having any bearing on his mental state is that of 28 March 1864:

'A native of Glasgow, an intelligent man, states that he must have done something very bad or they would not have sent him to Bethlem, gives distinctly the sentence of the Chief Justice—"Acquitted on the ground of Insanity to be confined during Her Majesty's pleasure." When asked whether he now thinks that he must have been out of his mind—he replies—"Such was the verdict—the opinion of the jury after hearing the Evidence." Has been suffering from rheumatism lately. Has an anaemic appearance, ancles [sic] swell a little. Appetite tolerably good, pulse 84, regular.'

The rest of the entries are concerned with his rapidly deteriorating physical health. On 3 May 1865, it is written: 'Gradually sank and died at 1.10 a.m.' He was aged 52.

The only psychiatric diagnosis made is that entered in the post-mortem report, which gives the cause of death as 'anaemia, brain disease and gradual failure of heart's action'. The Form of Insanity is given as: 'Chronic Mania and Dementia', a diagnosis which would not bear close scrutiny if modern criteria were applied. The term 'schizophrenia' had of course yet to be invented.

So ends this strange eventful history which began in 1843 quite literally with a bang, and expired 22 years later with such a pathetic whimper.

But the ghost of Daniel McNaughton still walks, although, if a mixed metaphor can be employed, its teeth have been drawn since the concept of Diminished Responsibility was introduced in the Homicide Act, 1957. British psychiatrists today can concern themselves with McNaughton's Madness rather than risk being stretched over a barrel in an attempt to interpret McNaughton's Rules.

REFERENCES

ALLDERIDGE, P. H. Criminal Insanity: Bethlem to Broadmoor. *Proceedings of the Royal Society of Medicine*, Vol 67. Sept. 1974.

BRITTAIN, R. P. (1963) Historic Autopsies. The Post-Mortem Examination of Daniel McNaughton. *Medicine, Science and the Law*, 3, 100–4.

HUNTER, R. A. and MACALPINE, I. (1963) *Three Hundred Years of Psychiatry 1535–1860*. London: Oxford University Press.

WHY WAS McNAUGHTON SENT TO BETHLEM?

PATRICIA ALLDERIDGE

In 1786, after her abortive attempt on the life of King George III, Margaret Nicholson was examined by the Privy Council, found to be insane, and sent to Bethlem Hospital. Though her offence was technically High Treason she was never brought to trial; she was admitted to an ordinary ward of the hospital, and the legal basis of the transaction seems to have been somewhat informal. Fifty-seven years later Daniel McNaughton was admitted to a department of Bethlem which had the official status of Government Criminal Lunatic Asylum, and his admission had the full backing of statute law. Between these two events a considerable amount of legislation had been passed, in an area in which no provision whatever had been made in English law before the beginning of the nineteenth century.

Two important features of Margaret Nicholson's assassination attempt, in influencing her subsequent treatment, were that it had been unsuccessful and that she was readily acknowledged to be insane. The King himself had said immediately after the incident, rather poignantly in view of his own subsequent history, '... do not hurt her, for she is mad'; the Privy Council had been assisted in their examination by the two current representatives of the Monro family (without whose opinion no aspirant to insanity might consider his case complete), and both had pronounced her to be mad: and her removal to Bethlem provoked comment chiefly on the grounds that she had been fortunate in being dealt with by so merciful an administration. No one seems to have been surprised that her confinement should have been ordered, under whatever kind of judicial procedure, in a hospital which existed for the care and cure of the sick poor.

The Governors of Bethlem can hardly have been surprised either, though they may have been a little resentful, for it was not the first time such a thing had happened. For over a century at least, the Privy Council had been sending deranged trouble-makers to the hospital; and while the Privy Council may have had the right to send anyone anywhere it chose, it seems unlikely that the Governors' obligation to receive them can ever have been dictated by any more compelling force than expediency.

Bethlem or 'Bedlam', founded in 1247 as the Priory of St Mary of Bethlehem, had been a hospital for the insane since the end of the fourteenth century, and after the dissolution of the religious houses under Henry VIII was taken over

100

Photograph of Daniel McNaughton taken about 1856.
[Bethlem Royal Hospital archives]

Reg: 75.

Schedule A.

STATEMENT RESPECTING CRIMINAL LUNATICS,

To be filled up and transmitted to the Medical Superintendent with every Criminal Lunatic.

Name - - - - - - -	Daniel McNaughton.
Age - - - - - - -	29 on admission.
Date of Admission - - - -	March 13th 1843
Former Occupation - - - -	Turner.
From whence brought - - -	Newgate.
Married, Single, or Widowed - -	Single
How many Children - - -	————
Age of Youngest - - - -	————
Whether First Attack - - -	————
When previous Attacks occurred -	————
Duration of existing Attack - -	
State of Bodily Health - - -	Moderate.
Whether Suicidal or Dangerous to others -	No. No.
Supposed Cause - - - -	
Chief delusions or Indications of Insanity -	Imagines the Tories are his enemies they'd altering in his manner —
Whether subject to Epilepsy - -	No.
Whether of temperate habits - -	Yes,
Degree of Education - - -	Fair.
Religious Persuasion - - -	Episcopalian.
Crime - - - - -	Murder —
When and where tried - - -	Central Crim'l Court. 1843
Verdict of Jury - - - -	Found to be Insane
Sentence - - - - -	Her Majesty's Pleasure —

London: SHAW & SONS, Fetter Lane.

Bethlem: McNaughton's Admission Statement.
[Bethlem Royal Hospital archives]

by the City of London as one of its five Royal Hospitals. Though no longer devoted solely to the City's own poor, it remained a charitable institution, and its Governors still had close links with and governed in the name of the Mayor, Commonalty and Citizens of London. Though a City hospital it was, however, until the second half of the eighteenth century the only public institution in the country devoted exclusively to the care of the insane (with the exception of the small hospital of Bethel at Norwich, founded 1713), and thus the most obvious resting place for people like Margaret Nicholson and her predecessors.

An early example of such cases is found in 1630, when the Privy Council required the Justices of the Peace for Westminster to send to Bedlam three 'certaine persons who run up and downe the streets and doe much harme, being either distracted or els counterfeites, and therefore not to be suffered to have their liberties to range, as now they doe . . . to which purpose wee sende you herewith a warrant directed to the Master and Matrone of Bedlame, for the receiving of them'.[1]

The precise details of Bethlem's admission procedure at this date, and also of the hospital's current relationship with the Crown, have yet to be clarified, but it may be significant that the warrant was directed to the Master and Matron and not to the Governors; for the appointment of a Master seems still to have been within the recommendation of the Crown, and the Governors had not yet taken the admission of patients fully into their own control. Certainly there is no record relating to this episode in the Minutes of the Court of Governors, who admittedly appear to have shown little interest in the affairs of Bethlem at the time, concentrating almost exclusively on the management of Bridewell Hospital (to whose administration that of Bethlem had been annexed by the City in 1557). It may be, therefore, that the practice of sending mentally disordered offenders to Bethlem Hospital was established at a period when the Crown still claimed and exercised in the hospital certain proprietary rights (albeit disputed since the medieval period), and when the reception of patients was in the hands of a royal nominee, factors which would undoubtedly have facilitated their admission.

The first cases recorded in the Bethlem archives date from the late seventeenth century, by which time the hospital had moved from the old monastic house in Bishopsgate to its first custom-built accommodation at Moorfields, and was developing a somewhat more organized admission system. Admission registers begin in 1683, and the first entry relating to a patient sent to the hospital by order of the Government dates from 1684. The record is a warrant for admission by way of a letter from the Board of Green Cloth.

The 'Green Cloth', which was presided over by the Lord Steward and was responsible for the financial affairs of the Royal Household, also functioned in one respect as a court with jurisdiction 'within the verge', that is within twelve miles of the sovereign's residence, and features prominently in many of the cases with which we are concerned. Though the details differ, this first entry is typical in form:

[1] Quoted in Nigel Walker and Sarah McCabe, *Crime and Insanity in England*, vol II, p 2.

'Gentlemen

By his Majestyes expresse Command wee herewith send you the Body of Captaine White Who yesterday being Sunday the seventeenth instant August did intrude himselfe into his Majestyes Castle and Pallaces of Windsor and without any Provocation in a Violent and rude Manner did Assault one George Huthwaite one of the Poore Knights, and Committed severall high misdemeanours. And finding him to be a Person much discomposed and disordered in his Braine: and having heretofore wounded Captaine Hull the Governour of the Poor Knights, and apprehending that he may doe other Mischiefes. For prevention whereof wee desire that you will recieve him into the Hospitall of Bethelem there to be treated in such manner as is most fitt and usuall for Persons in his Condition for which you shall have the usuall Allowance from us. Thus not doubting of your compliance herein wee rest Gent[lemen] Your very loving Friends

Wᵐ Meynard
Stephen Fox
Richard Mason
Board of Greenecloath at Windsor Castle 18ᵗʰ August 1684.'[2]

The assurance about 'the usual allowance' shows a delicate taste for irony, for the Governors had spent the years 1677/83 vigorously campaigning to induce the Board to pay anything at all for the maintenance of patients sent by itself and by the Privy Council, and had finally triumphed with a back payment of £373. At the rate of 5/- a week per patient, this suggests that there were on average four to five patients of this class in the hospital at any time over the period.

Fears of conspiracy and rebellion seem from time to time to have influenced the determination to remove people to Bethlem, as in the case of Richard Stafford, a rabid Jacobite pamphleteer who in 1691 arrived with a letter stating that he was distracted and 'hath been very troublesome to their Ma[jes]ties Court at Kensington, By Dispersing Books & Pamphletts full of Enthusiasme and Sedition . . .'. Over-enthusiasm at Royal palaces was a constant cause of what might be called the Bethlem/Green Cloth Syndrome.

Though there has been little research so far into what happened during the eighteenth century, it can be assumed for the present that the pattern remained much the same up to the time of Margaret Nicholson's admission. Her case, which seems unlikely to have differed greatly from those that went before except in the publicity attending it, achieves a nice compromise between official direction and institutional independence. She was admitted to the hospital by order of the Governors, after a letter from the Secretary of State had been read at the weekly sub-committee which by now controlled the admission and discharge of all patients. After twelve months patients were normally discharged even if uncured, though they might then be put on the waiting list for the limited number of places in the Incurable department if they were considered suitable (the criteria being chiefly poverty and unmanageability); and in special circumstances they might occasionally even be transferred directly, without leaving the building.

Accordingly, a year after Margaret Nicholson's admission an Under-Secretary of State attended the weekly sub-committee with a verbal message from the

² Bethlem Royal Hospital archives: Admission Book 1683–1701/2.

104

King himself, who, 'being highly sensible of the great care with which she had been treated and being informed that she was still distracted', wished 'that she might be still accommodated in the Hosp[l] in any manner consistently with the standing Rules and Regulat[ns] of the Hospital'; whereupon it was resolved unanimously 'That the said Margaret Nicholson be admitted as an Incurable Patient immediately upon the same Terms as other Incurable Patients have been heretofore admitted from The Public Offices.'[3] Concern for the rules and regulations of the hospital may or may not have been a novel feature of the case by this date: the Governors were not without influential members, and might at some stage have put down their corporate foot at Whitehall; but they were not without commonsense either, and it would be surprising to learn that any case sent by their very loving friends at the Board of Green Cloth should have turned out to be totally unsuitable for admission.

Margaret Nicholson had been in Bethlem for nearly fourteen years when, on 15 May 1800, the most notorious of all attempts on the King's life was made by James Hadfield; and, as his case was a key one in the development of the plea of insanity itself, so it had important repercussions on the still more immediate problem of the disposal of insane offenders. Arising directly from it came a new law providing for their special custody, and more indirectly and at some years' distance, a completely new department was added to Bethlem Hospital. Both events were later to figure prominently in the life of Daniel McNaughton.

The medico-legal implications of Hadfield's trial have already been mentioned by Sir Roger Ormrod, and it is only necessary here to consider the verdict and its aftermath. The verdict, after some specific direction by Lord Kenyon, was clear enough. 'The Jury at the Barr here say that the Prisoner is Not Guilty of the Treason whereof he is Indicted being under the Influence of Insanity at the Time when the several Overt Acts mentioned in the Indictment were Committed . . .'; what was, and is not, so clear, was what the Court then had the authority to do with him.

Earlier writers such as Coke, Hale and Bracton had attempted to clarify the doctrines of criminal insanity, but did little to indicate what should be done with the prisoner acquitted as a result of these doctrines, and it is often difficult to make out what actually happened in individual cases. The Court at the end of the Hadfield trial was thus in some discomfort over the discrepancy between the requirements of the circumstances and its own uncertain but apparently limited powers. As Lord Kenyon said, 'the prisoner for his own sake, and for the sake of society at large, must not be discharged': but he does not seem to have felt that a judge in this situation could do more than remand the prisoner back to the place he had come from, even though two Justices of the Peace would undoubtedly have had powers under the vagrancy legislation of 1744[4] to order his detention as a dangerous lunatic. Hadfield was therefore remanded back to custody in Newgate 'in order to be dealt with according to Law'.

---

[3] 'The Public Offices' here probably included the Admiralty and the War Office, both of which sent patients to Bethlem throughout the period which concerns us.
[4] *17 Geo. II c. 5.*

The law in question had not, in fact, yet been passed; but on 28 July 1800 *An Act for the Safe Custody of Insane Persons charged with Offences (39 & 40 Geo. III c. 94)* received the Royal Assent, and there is no doubt as to whom its retrospective powers were aimed at. 'Whereas persons charged with high treason, murder or felony *may have been* or may be of unsound mind at the time of committing the offence wherewith they *may have been* or shall be charged . . .' ran the preamble (my italics), 'and by reason of such insanity *may have been* or may be found not guilty of such offence, and it may be dangerous to permit persons so acquitted to go at large . . .', in such case the court must order the person 'to be kept in strict custody, in such place and in such manner as to the court shall seem fit, until His Majesty's Pleasure be known'.

In introducing the Bill the Attorney-General summarized the need for legislation (incidentally repeating his own view expressed at the trial, that a judge *did* have the power to order confinement in such circumstances): 'By the common law, when a person of this kind is acquitted, the court before which he is tried have full power to direct the safe custody of such a person; but then the law has so little regulated that custody, and is so silent as to the rules to be observed with regard to it, that it may be said to be defective in that particular.' Matters had now been regularized, and not only the powers but also the obligations of the courts were clearly set out. The only trouble was that the fit place envisaged in the Act did not actually exist, and the Governors of Bethlem must have braced themselves to await the inevitable, which on 10 October 1800 duly arrived in the shape of the Keeper of Newgate accompanied by James Hadfield and a letter from the Secretary of State.

If Hadfield's admission was better regulated than those which had gone before, it was followed two months later by one which, while closely linked with it, appears to have been made in an interesting manner under the old dispensation. Bannister Truelock, a deranged cobbler whose millenarianist fervour was suspected of having incited the already unbalanced Hadfield to commit his treasonable act, had been taken into custody the previous May; now, in December, he was transferred to Bethlem with a request that he be placed on the Incurable establishment if not 'thoroughly cured' at the time when the rules required his discharge.

The 1800 Act provided for the detention of people found by jury to be insane on arraignment, as well as those acquitted on grounds of insanity, and it made a highly specific provision for the Privy Council to dispose of persons appearing to be insane and endeavouring to gain admittance to His Majesty (the old 'Green Cloth' cases), but it does not seem possible that Truelock could have been held even notionally to come within any of these terms. Fears of conspiracy had featured prominently in the investigations immediately after Hadfield's assassination attempt, and the rounding up of Truelock (who spent the next thirty years in Bethlem breeding canaries and writing prophecies), makes an interesting parallel with the case already mentioned of Richard Stafford at the end of the seventeenth century. Amidst the tensions of post-French-

Revolution Europe, enthusiasm was still a state of mind to be treated with deep mistrust.[5]

Two years after his admission Hadfield demonstrated the continuing defects in the law regulating safe custody by escaping, and was returned to the rather stricter security of Newgate. Meanwhile the public, or at least the parliamentary conscience, had been sparked into life mainly by the efforts of Sir George Onesiphorus Paul of Gloucester, and in 1807 a Select Committee of the House of Commons was appointed to look into the whole question of the provisions for insane criminals and paupers. In fact, as the inquiry discovered, Nicholson and Hadfield were among the very small and fortunate minority, the great majority of insane criminals remaining in gaols and houses of correction in conditions frequently far worse than the worst that Bethlem could offer.

The immediate outcome of the Committe's Report was the *County Asylums Act* of 1808 (*48 Geo. III c. 96*), which empowered but did not oblige each county to provide an asylum for its own insane paupers and criminals or to join with an adjacent county in doing so, through the agency of its Court of Quarter Sessions (this was repealed and replaced in 1828 by *9 Geo. IV c. 40* containing similar powers). This meant that there was now at least a chance of there being somewhere other than a gaol to which a court could direct a person who had been acquitted on grounds of insanity, in such counties as chose to avail themselves of the Act (which the majority did not, until the compulsory legislation of 1845); but the matter of a separate Criminal Lunatic Asylum to serve the whole country, though recommended in the Report, appears to have been shelved for the time being. It is likely, however, that the Government had already laid its plan for getting such an asylum on the cheap.

All this time the rebuilding of Bethlem Hospital had been in prospect, though the search for a suitable site had continued unsuccessfully for some years; but in 1809 one was finally acquired at St George's Fields, Southwark. It was not long before the first shot in the ensuing action was fired from Whitehall, by way of a letter dated 25 August 1810: 'Mr Ryder [then Secretary of State for the Home Department] having understood that . . . the Governors of Bethlem Hospital . . . have become seized of a spacious piece of Ground in Saint George's Fields upon which it is their intention to erect a new Hospital for the Care and accommodation of Insane Persons; He is very desirous of ascertaining how far it may appear to the Governors to be practicable . . . that a portion of the ground in Saint George's Fields should be set apart for the erection of an additional Building for the special accommodation of Criminal Lunatics, which it is in contemplation to establish as soon as possible under an Act of the Legislature passed for that purpose.'

The Governors clearly hoped that it would be far from practicable, but contented themselves with expressing apprehension that the Act referred to, assuming it to be *48 Geo. III c. 96*, might interfere with their own management of the Hospital. Some months later another letter brought the assurance that the

[5] I am grateful to Professor John Harrison for drawing my attention to the political aspects of the Hadfield/Truelock association.

107

authority under which the erection of the new building was proposed was not this Act, but an Address to the King of 20 June 1808 with which His Majesty had been pleased to comply, under the terms of which 'Mr Ryder was of opinion that it would be perfectly competent to him to take measures for the establishment of a Criminal Lunatic Asylum . . .'. There was also enclosed, by way of reassurance, a copy of the opinion of the Law Officers of the Crown, to the effect that provided the Asylum was erected without the aid of the 1808 Act, the Act would not confer on it the visitatorial power and control of the County Magistrates—which was the Governors' chief dread.

After a further three years of negotiation a set of terms and conditions 'by which His Majesty's Government and the Governors of Bethlem Hospital are mutually engaged to each other' were finally agreed. These laid down that a separate place of confinement sufficient for the reception of 45 male and 15 female Criminal Lunatics should be erected by the Governors: that His Majesty's Government should defray the expense of the building provided it did not exceed £19,800: that the Government should be at the annual charge of maintaing the inmates at the rate of £48 per annum each, and also pay the funeral expenses of such as died there: that the control and management of all lunatics of the above description should be exercised under the superintendence of the Governors and that they should be attended by the medical and other officers of the establishment; and that for the extra trouble occasioned to the officers the Government would make an annual allowance of £200 to be distributed as the Governors should think fit.

The expense of erecting the buildings, which occupied another two years, did of course exceed the agreed estimate, by £5,344.15s. Lord Sidmouth (Henry Addington, by now Secretary of State) wrote expressing his surprise and concern at the additional expense and at the Governors' having suddenly changed the method of payment for maintenance (in order to be sure that they did not lose by it), and reiterated the terms previously accepted '[to avoid] the possibility of any future misconception', before announcing that the Treasury would nevertheless pay, if only to prevent any further delay in getting the buildings into use. The Governors wrote back to clear up one or two points, observing that most of the additional expense had been incurred in providing extra security 'at the desire of the Department over which your Lordship presides', and reminding his Lordship en passant that they had gratuitously undertaken the management of the establishment and had given their land without remuneration. This round would appear to have gone by common consent to the Governors, for when, after the buildings had been in use for less than a month, it was found necessary to apply for the salaries of two additional keepers with a third in prospect and an increase in the salary of the head keeper, the allowances were made promptly and without demur.

The buildings thus provided stood in two blocks, one each for men and women, at the back of the main hospital, separated from it except for staff access and designed so that there should be no communication between criminal and ordinary patients. Internally they were similar in design to other parts of the hospital: on each floor individual sleeping rooms opened off a single long gallery which served as a day room, but the accommodation was cramped and gloomy, and the need for security made these blocks more prison-like than anywhere else in Bethlem. Overcrowding soon became a problem, not solved by an extension for thirty more patients added to the male block in 1836 or by the commissioning in 1849 of a special wing at Fisherton House, Salisbury (a provincial licensed house, now The Old Manor Hospital), to receive criminal lunatics of the less dangerous kind.

One of the first admissions to the new buildings when they were opened in 1816 was appropriately James Hadfield, making the by now familiar journey between Newgate and Bethlem for the last time, though a further twenty-five years were to pass before his death in 1841. The remainder of his incarceration was not wholly without incident, as is revealed in a tantalizing glimpse through a chink in the Bethlem Sub-committee minutes for 1826: 'James Hatfield applying for liberty to hold communication with a Female through the Railings, the permission was refused on account of the great indecency of his conduct on former occasions.'

Margaret Nicholson and Bannister Truelock, however, were not moved from the Incurable wards to the new department, which seems to mark official recognition of their informal status in the hospital as against that of the official though not yet statutorily defined 'Criminal Lunatics' who had now come into being.[6] These fall into two groups, one of which had either been found 'not guilty' or had not even been brought to trial, and so could not possibly justify the title 'criminal'; the other, while undoubtedly criminal and generally lunatic, could more appropriately have been named 'lunatic criminals'. The first type were admitted under the 1800 (Hadfield) Act by royal warrant: the second were admitted by warrant of the Home Secretary under legislation of 1816 (*56 Geo. III c. 117*), which provided for the transfer to an asylum of convicted prisoners who became insane after being sentenced. In 1840 this provision was extended by *3 & 4 Vict. c. 54* to include prisoners certified as insane while awaiting trial, under sentence of death, and most other categories except civil prisoners, after which the second group also included people who could not fairly be termed 'criminal'. It also, once word had got about, generally included a few who could not be termed 'lunatic', but who were possessed of histrionic talent and a distaste for the convict hulks.

The discharge of patients on recovery (or because they had never been insane in the first place) was also at the discretion of the Home Secretary, on the recommendation of the medical officers, who had to furnish a quarterly report on the state of body and mind of every patient. Discharge might mean no more than a return to prison, but of the 650 men admitted between 1816 and 1864 fifty-nine were 'discharged to their friends', and twenty-eight of the 120 women

[6] Patients continued to be admitted occasionally 'at the recommendation of the Secretary of State', and even after the transfer of the Criminal patients to Broadmoor a number of these more informal cases remained, to be the subject of quarterly returns and maintenance accounts until the death of the last survivor in 1885.

were similarly sent home.[7] Of these, nine men and nine women had committed murder or manslaughter; but in cases where serious and/or violent crimes were involved there must have been exceptional circumstances before it was accepted that no danger to society remained. Edward Oxford, who fired at Queen Victoria in 1840, for example, was in Bethlem for twenty-four years (though finally freed from Broadmoor), although he was reported 'sane' in every quarterly return from his admission and was described as conducting himself with great propriety at all times.

It was to this Criminal Lunatic Asylum, run by Bethlem Hospital but ultimately under the authority of the Home Office, that Daniel McNaughton became the 219th admission on 13 March 1843 at the age of 29, directed thither under the provisions of the Act of 1800 and accompanied by a Royal Warrant which has been removed from its proper place in the hospital's records; and to say this is to cover just about everything of note relating to his uneventful stay in the hospital which cannot be learnt from the sources (quoted *in extenso* by Dr Rollin on p 91).

Thereafter Daniel McNaughton passed almost completely from the public eye, of which he had been, for so brief a period, the unwilling cynosure, and in which he had left something rather more than a note. By the time the *Quarterly Review* came to visit the Criminal Department in 1857 McNaughton was too boring to rate even a mention amongst the far more dynamic company of men such as the Rev. Hugh Willoughby, 'who fired a pistol two years since at the judge at the Central Criminal Court', or 'the unfortunate Captain Johnson, of the ship "Tory", who, in a fit of extraordinary excitement during a mutiny on board his vessel cut down some of his crew'. And on 26 March 1864 he passed from Bethlem itself, to the newly-built Broadmoor Asylum, where his death little more than a year later is described by Dr Rollin.

Even by the time of McNaughton's admission, the Criminal Department was overcrowded and outdated, and structurally incapable of improvement. It was almost impossible to provide employment or diversion for the inmates, and the only pastimes readily available were fives and running in the exercise yard, and knitting and reading in the crepuscular galleries. For men such as Edward Oxford who were prepared to teach themselves four modern and two ancient languages in between fives, draughts, interior decoration and learning the violin, this may have been enough; but for the vast majority the conditions were plainly inadequate, and became ever more plainly so as the rest of the hospital was rapidly reformed during the 1850s.

Sir Charles Hood, whose humanizing of Bethlem between 1852 and 1862 is one of the outstanding contributions to its history, was able to do little more than lament over the Criminal Department, and although on his arrival he had been in favour of its retention at Bethlem, he was soon as anxious as anyone for its removal elsewhere. In 1857 he was able to clear one of the ordinary wards, and turn it over to forty of the 'better class' of criminal patients, when a library

---

[7] I am grateful to Miss Barbara Bowron for these figures, taken from her statistical analyses of discharges from the Criminal Department compiled for an Open University study.

was also provided for them; but by this time plans were already afoot to build a completely new State Criminal Lunatic Asylum at Crowthorne in Berkshire, to accommodate 600 patients including all those currently at Bethlem.

While this asylum, Broadmoor, was still being built another Select Committee of the House of Commons was appointed, to look this time into the operation of the various pieces of legislation passed since the last one. The result of these deliberations was the 1860 *Act to make better Provisions for the Custody and Care of Criminal Lunatics (23 & 24 Vict. c. 75)*, often known as The Broadmoor Act, and for the first time statutorily defining the term 'Criminal Lunatic'. Since this definition included 'any person for whose safe custody during her pleasure Her Majesty is authorised to give order, or whom [the] Secretary of State might direct to be removed to a lunatic asylum under any of the Acts hereinbefore mentioned, or under any other Act of Parliament . . .', it might be wondered whether the former lack of precision was not preferable.

Broadmoor Asylum was opened for women patients in 1863, and in May of that year 19 of the 20 women from the Bethlem Criminal Department were transferred there. The twentieth, Mary Anne Beveridge, was totally blind, and in consequence 'the Government have allowed her to remain here, as she is much liked for her mild and gentle behaviour & is also accustomed to find her way about; she is much pleased at being allowed to remain'. She was transferred to the Incurable department where, except for a mysterious transformation into 'Elizabeth' in the quarterly returns, she remained unchanged and contented until her death in 1873.

Between February and July 1864 all but one of the male 'Government patients' were transferred to Broadmoor in groups of about six to eight at a time, and McNaughton, now listed in the returns as 'unhealthy, imbecile', travelled with the ninth group. At twenty-one years, his was the ninth longest residence in the male Criminal Department at the time of the move, a mediocre distinction wholly in keeping with his generally undistinguished career in the hospital. Clearly his physical condition at this time was not so serious as, for example, the one patient who was left behind on account of ill health, and who died in the Incurable Department the following year.

Dr Helps, now Resident Physician, noted with satisfaction in his Annual Report for 1864 that 'It is a subject of the greatest congratulation to every one connected with this Hospital, that the Government has seen fit to take special charge of this class of patients, and to remove them to an Asylum designed for their detention and safe custody, where all association with other classes of patient is avoided. The whole of the 112 criminals sent to Broadmoor, arrived at that Asylum without a single casualty, although several of them were most violent and dangerous to themselves and others. In three cases it was absolutely necessary to use handcuffs. We are much indebted to the Authorities of the South Western Railway, who successfully made every arrangement for their comfort and safe transit.'

With equal satisfaction the Governors promptly sent to the Home Office a bill for the 30 new suits and 83 partially-worn suits of clothing with ditto underclothing which the patients had taken with them to Broadmoor, and set about demolishing the Criminal buildings and reinstating the ground. The several accounts for expenditure on this purpose which they sent in during the following year and which included such items as 'Removing a quantity of rubbish' and 'Refreshment to Police from June 16th to August 7th', suggest that the Governors may have been feeling slightly nostalgic about the imminent loss of their old sparring partners, and were determined to make the last round a good one.

WHAT WE THOUGHT ABOUT IT ALL

Alexander Walk

Professor Nigel Walker, in the chapter reprinted here from his *Crime and Insanity in England*, says that 'it is difficult to find a clear statement of the medical objections to the McNaughton Rules at this date', i.e. in the 1850s. This is indeed true, but the following extracts provide some samples of medical and more particularly psychiatric opinions in the twenty years or so following the trial. In selecting these I have avoided material which has already been quoted by Professor Walker, e.g. Forbes Winslow's books, Bucknill and Tuke's Manual, or the evidence given to the Capital Punishment Commission of 1864–66.

The *Lancet*, Leading Article, 18 March 1843

(This article appeared after the trial, but before the publication of the Judges' replies.)

THE circumstances connected with the death of Mr. DRUMMOND, painful as the review of them must be to all right-thinking and right-feeling men, suggest several considerations of such importance that we regard it as a duty to comment upon them at some length.

Leaving the medical details of the case, we would advert to one of the most momentous, and what has been made one of the most difficult questions in jurisprudence or in morals. The intricacy of the subject resides, first, in the difficulty of determining the precise line of demarcation between the extremes of bad temper, fanaticism, or moral depravity, and the commencement of actual insanity; and, secondly, where the insanity of the party is indisputable,—in the difficulty of holding, with a just hand, the balance between the compassion that is due to a miserably afflicted being, and the value of an indefinite number of human lives, which may be sacrificed, immediately, to his hallucination, or, more remotely, to the contagious example of his misguided acts. The first of these difficulties, however, applies to the subject when regarded in a moral, or pathological, rather than in a legal light, because the law never has made, and never can make, subtle distinctions between sanity and insanity; while, at the same time, extenuating circumstances,—arising out of the various conditions of body and mind in which an individual may have been placed at the time of the commission of a given act,—have always been allowed some influence in modifying the rigid course of criminal law. It is with the second difficulty, then, that we have principally to deal, namely, that involved in the case of a lunatic who commits murder. In such a case the murder may have been committed during a paroxysm of furious insanity, or during a lucid interval, or, what is much more frequent than either, under the influence of a permanent monomania. If the crime have been perpetrated during a lucid interval, the law cannot deal

113

with the lunatic otherwise than as with a sane person, although, in the event of his execution, a moral view of the case must leave a painful impression on the mind arising from the doubt how far a lunatic is, at any time responsible for his actions.

But, if the fatal deed have been committed under circumstances which show that the perpetrator is unequivocally mad at the time of its commission, the law in its present state acquits him of all guilt. The question, then, becomes whether the law ought to remain as it is in such cases, or to be altered. It has been contended that a lunatic can incur no moral guilt under any circumstances, and that the argument must, therefore, be taken up on an entirely different ground. The execution of a lunatic for murder could answer no end of justice; but the points for consideration are, whether his execution would act as an example to deter other madmen from similar desperate deeds, and, admitting that it would do so, whether we should be justified in sacrificing the life of one madman in order to promote the safety of an indefinite number of other lives.

Now, on the one hand, it may be argued, first, that we have no right, on the ground of simple expediency, or to prevent a contingent evil, to sacrifice the life of any human being, for, on the same principle, we might be justified, at the first outbreak of an highly malignant and contagious disease, in putting to death the first persons who were seized with it, and burying their bodies with quick-lime. Secondly, that madness being the most dreadful calamity which can afflict a human being, it would be the height of cruelty for man to raise his arm against one already so awfully stricken by the hand of GOD. Thirdly, that lunatics, although readily influenced by the contagion of crime, are much less apt to be impressed by the example of punishment. On the other hand, to the first and second of these arguments it may be answered, that there is no true parallel between the case of a lunatic and that of a man seized with a malignant and contagious disease, because the life of the latter is of value to himself and others, while that of a mischievous lunatic is but a fitful and dismal dream, the termination of which, by natural causes, should be hailed as a blessing. In answer to the third argument it may be urged, that the effect of example in deterring lunatics from committing murder, has been found to be considerable, if we may judge from the few instances in which the lives of madmen have been sacrificed by the law; while the influence of example in promoting the propensity to murder and suicide has been most strikingly exemplified in this metropolis, within the last two or three years. In 1810, BELLINGHAM, unquestionably a lunatic, was hanged for the murder of Mr. PERCEVAL, and from that time until 1841, not a single political assassination was perpetrated in this country, throughout the most exciting and troubled times that have long been known in England. OXFORD was acquitted for his late attempt on the life of the QUEEN, on the ground of insanity, though, in our opinion, with very doubtful propriety; and other similar attempts almost immediately followed. Not a week had elapsed from the trial of M'NAUGHTEN for the murder of Mr. DRUMMOND, and his acquittal on the ground of insanity, ere another madman openly threatened the lives of her MAJESTY and Sir ROBERT PEEL, and that of Mr. GOULBURN was menaced by a person for whom, had he put his threats in execution, the plea of insanity would probably have been set up.

Such, we conceive, is a fair and simple statement of the question. It is one in which the most important interests of society, and that political justice which binds the state to protect the lives of its citizens, appear to be at variance with our feelings of humanity towards a dangerous and offending yet guiltless individual.

Since the foregoing remarks were written the subject of the plea of insanity in cases of imputed murder has been introduced in the House of Lords, in a very elaborate speech by the LORD CHANCELLOR, who suggested that the judges should be called, questioned, and required to explain what they deem to be the existing state of the law in relation to that great branch of criminal judicature. When we have heard the exposition of these learned and influential persons we shall return to the subject, in the meantime embracing this opportunity of stating it to be our firmly-established conviction that at the late trial of M'NAUGHTEN evidence was received which was not strictly admissible,

114

—that in the opening speech of the counsel for the prosecution no reference to the *insanity* of the accused ought to have been made,—that the opinions of medical men who had only heard *the trial* ought not to have been received,—that the counsel for *the prosecution* should have replied to the arguments and pernicious statements of the counsel for *the prisoner*,—that the judge should have summed up on the *whole case*, leaving it fairly to *the jury* to found their verdict upon the belief which they conscientiously entertained,—after hearing the evidence,—whether M'NAUGHTEN did or did not know that he was doing *wrong* when he levelled the pistol at the back of his unfortunate victim.

The *Lancet* did not return to the subject as promised. Instead it published two letters from Dr Robert Dick affirming his strong belief in McNaughton's responsibility.

Dr Davey's Pamphlet

One of the first asylum doctors to attack the views soon to be embodied in the McNaughton Rules was Dr J. G. Davey, at that time a medical officer at Hanwell and later one of the two Superintendents at Colney Hatch. In 1843 he published a pamphlet entitled *Medico-Legal Reflections on the Trial of Daniel McNaughton; with Remarks on the Different Forms of Insanity and the Irresponsibility of the Insane.* This was reviewed and summarized in the *Medico-Chirurgical Review* (July 1843) and in Elliotson's *The Zoist*. The following extracts are from the latter (*Zoist*, VI, 1843):

RECENT unfortunate events have prominently brought the question of insanity before the public, and this in a manner and on an occasion the most unfavourable for the calm and philosophic exercise of the judgment on the subject. Even those however the most disposed to make allowance for these disturbing causes on the national mind, have been startled and shocked at the burst of animalism, the explosion of wild, aimless, senseless, vindictive feeling which has taken place, and which embodied itself in one wide-spread and all but universal cry for blood.

Amidst this clamour of ignorance, it is at once a relief and gratification to us, to see a man of Dr. Davey's acquirements and opportunities for observation, stepping forward to endeavour to stem the tide of popular error and diffuse more correct ideas on the subject, a result we think he can scarcely fail to achieve, if his "Reflections" meet with the circulation which their object and tendency render desirable, and to which their merits entitle them. . . . Many men possess no knowledge, on the subject of Insanity, but none no opinions, and the misfortune is that too frequently the latter are clung to with a tenacity inversely proportionate to the stability on which they rest. Dr. Davey observes, and we cordially unite with him,

"It would be a perfect waste of time to enter into the various and contradictory statements, made both by physicians and lawyers, relative to the real *nature* of insanity; its characters and criteria; suffice it to say, and we do so without the slightest fear of a rational contradiction, that the general ignorance of the structure and uses of the brain, in a state of health, necessarily prevented all parties, whether medical or not, from making anything more than a very slight approach to the elucidation of those several phenomena which constitute disease."

Let those who have been accustomed to discourse very glibly of mania, monomania, dementia, &c. and who have themselves been under the illusion that each word represented an individual and specific disease, in the nature of which they were necessarily as learned as in the etymology of its appellatives, listen to Dr. Davey:

"The term *insanity* conveys the idea of unsound mind, and in order to express its varieties, the words mania, melancholia, monomania, dementia, &c., are in common use. Such import no more than a very general notion of the character of the disease. . . . Disease of the brain, may either be confined to a part, or it may affect the whole; and the disease, or impairment of function, may be at the same time either the consequence of excessive or diminished action, and in any case it may be either functional or organic, either idiopathic or symptomatic. The indications of which several pathological conditions are those recognized by the general term of insanity. Now, disease of any part of the body, including of course the brain, is indicated by an interruption to its particular and healthy action; hence it follows that, if as we have shewn the brain possesses parts or organs whose functions consist of respectively, Caution, Veneration, Self-esteem, Firmness, Acquisitiveness, Destructiveness, Combativeness, Ideality, Gaiety, Hope, &c., it follows, I say, that a derangement of the *mind*—considered in the abstract— might be caused by disease affecting one, or two, or more of such functions exclusively. Herein consists the only clue whereby to unravel the mysteries of mental derangement, of, in one word, insanity."

What a thorough disgrace it is to the civilization of the present day, that lawyers should be heard in our courts of justice raking up musty precedents, and quoting as *authorities* the opinions of men who lived two centuries ago, and knew no more of the nature of insanity, than they did of electricity, magnetism, or the polarization of light, who in fact, neither recognized, nor understood, the possibility of any insanity but that of the intellect, and made the test for amenability to the law, consist in the possession of "as much understanding as ordinarily a child of fourteen years hath." Those venerable judges are not however to be blamed; they were men learned in their day— men who never perpetrated the absurdity, of allowing their own judgment to be fettered by the opinions of predecessors, who possessed less means of coming to a sound conclusion than themselves. Such indications of wisdom were reserved for the Britons of the nineteenth century, a race prolific in discoveries in physical science, but trammelled and bowed to the earth by the chains of opinion, and lamentably wanting in that sterling independence, and strong common sense, which characterized so many of their ancestors. . . .

Dr Davey argues:

"that no *insane person* has every mental faculty diseased. I believe there is not *one* within the walls of Hanwell, even including the idiotic and fatuous, who does not retain some few powers of the mind, relating either to the intellectual, moral, or animal compartments. Every case of insanity, then, is more or less *partial*." . . .

"There are in the Hanwell Asylum, kings, queens, bishops, apostles, deities, &c., &c., almost innumerable. We have taken considerable pains to learn the real state of the minds of these patients; and our decided opinion is, that their several assumed personifications must be regarded only as a *morbid colouring* to their several deranged moral feelings; as a voluntary and tangible ideal of their innate, involuntary and morbid impressions. We have never seen but one case of the kind in which it has appeared to us that the patient had the slightest belief in her '*illusion*.' " . . . . —"the speech and actions of the lunatic must be regarded only in the light of *symptoms* of the abnormal condition of the affections and propensities; which, under circumstances of *health*, as well as *disease*, impart *the character* to man. An apt yet highly painful illustration of the nature of our position is afforded in the condition of one suffering from hydrophobia. Though impelled to the most extraordinary and rabid conduct, the sufferer still retains a perfect *consciousness* of all he may do or say. We have observed this till within even a very short period of dissolution."

Dr. Davey shows the irrationality, the absurdity, and the cruelty both to the individual and his relatives, of making '*consciousness*'—the extent of the impairment of the intellectual functions, &c., the test of insanity and measure of accountability. We trust Dr. Davey has given the death blow, to a doctrine so utterly based on delusion, and so pernicious and unjust in its effects. . . . The only difference between the finest specimens of humanity that ever lived and the worst, has been that of organization and circumstances, over which neither had any control. Merit and demerit are words without meaning when applied to the actions of a finite being;—many men deserve pity, but none punishment. What lessons of charity and forbearance does this benign doctrine inculcate! No sooner is it recognized, than what was before obscure becomes clear, and we cease to be shocked and bewildered by the painful alternative of being obliged to do violence either to justice or benevolence; and we see at once that we have only one simple object to pursue—*the safety of society, with the infliction of the least possible amount of suffering on the dangerous party consistent with effecting this object:* and an enlarged consideration of the question in all its bearings, will, we are convinced, announce to us the gratifying fact, that not only are these two results perfectly compatible, but that each is best attained by the same means.

No effect can take place without a cause; and it is a necessary eternal law of organized being, *that preponderating desire shall always be the antecedent to volition, and volition always the sequent to preponderating desire.* Folios may be written on the subject of "*free will*," but the question lies in a nut-shell; and all the interminable discussion which has arisen on it, has proceeded from the difficulty men have found in discriminating between the freedom which man has to follow his inclinations, and that absolute liberty to choose his own conduct, and consequently his own desires, which he has not. The query then—"Is man a free agent?" resolves itself into a question of definition. If free agency be defined to mean merely that a man is free to act according to his inclinations, the query must be answered in the affirmative; but if the term be used in its usual acceptation, that is, implying that man is a responsible being, possessing not only the power of doing what he likes, but of *choosing his likings*, then has this finite being no such prerogative. Endow a machine with consciousness, and let each movement arise from the accumulation of a certain quantum of desire, and you have a man, —a machine endowed with unlimited freedom as far as the moving power being seated within himself is concerned, but no more free to act in opposition to his mechanism— his nature—than the stars are to shoot from the paths which nature has laid down for them to traverse.

Thomas Mayo and his Reviewers

Dr Thomas Mayo, author of several works on insanity, published in 1847 his *Clinical Notes and Reflections: with Remarks on the Impunity of Murder in some Cases of Insanity.* This was the subject of a review essay in the *British and Foreign Medical Review,* and both the author and the reviewer were further criticized in a long article in the *Journal of Psychological Medicine,* then recently founded by Forbes Winslow.

From the *British and Foreign Medical Review,* July 1847 (p 225 ff):

We look to judiciously devised plans for the reformation of juvenile offenders, as amongst the most important means of social amelioration. We believe that the instances will be found to be comparatively few, in which the higher moral feelings are incapable of being called forth by appropriate means, and in which the reason may not be trained into the habitual regard of them as the dominant motives to action. In cases in which, from long repression, or from original peculiarity of mental constitution, these higher feelings are found incapable of being thus developed, and the lower passions and propensities exert themselves without control, we can scarcely regard the individual as a free agent; his condition is more akin to that of brutes; and society has certainly a

117

right to restrain him from the indulgence of his appetites and passions in a way which shall be prejudicial to others, whilst at the same time he has a right to such treatment from society as shall be curative as well as restrictive.

This is the state to which Dr. Mayo has drawn attention in his 'Elements of the Pathology of the Human Mind,' (1838); and it is not inappropriately termed by him *brutality*. He regards it as characterized by the original deficiency or the abolition of the moral sense; and distinguishes it thereby from insanity, in which he considers that there must be intellectual perversion. We cannot agree with him in his definitions; because we do not recognise the moral sense as a single faculty or element, but rather as the collective result of all the higher moral tendencies; and because, moreover, we by no means think that the term insanity ought to be restricted to cases of intellectual perversion. But as to the general features of the condition itself, and the light in which the actions of the individual should be viewed, we are quite in accordance with him. . . . We believe that the tendency of an enlightened system of criminal legislation, based upon a correct psychology, will be to break down the barrier which at present stands between those who are held excused from all responsibility on the ground of insanity, and those who are deemed fit subjects for the extreme penalty of the law. On the one hand, the treatment of those recognised as criminal lunatics, may be so conducted as to deter from the imitation of their example, instead of suggesting and even encouraging it, as it has frequently done. On the other hand, the treatment of criminals reputed to be sane, will approximate to that which is found most efficacious in the cure of madness. In this manner the courts will be relieved from some of the most trying questions which at present come before them; and the ends of justice will be far more completely satisfied. For example, why should not an insane ward be established in our chief prisons, instead of a criminal ward in our lunatic hospitals? At present, as Dr. Mayo well remarks, in regard to many of the criminal lunatics confined in Bethlem Hospital, "the enduring confinement is in itself a dreadful punishment. But in these cases there is a sad expenditure of unfruitful suffering; for the confinement being entirely and sedulously deprived of the character of a punishment operates unpreventively." And the preventive influence of the restraint is of course altogether lost, when the criminal, being regarded as cured of his insanity, is let loose again upon the world. . . .

Our readers will have seen that we have hitherto avoided all allusion to the question of death-punishment in such cases; but we may now briefly explain our views upon this subject. We do not hold with those who maintain that society has *no right* to take the life of any individual; for if it were demonstrated that capital punishment had more influence than any other infliction in deterring from crimes of certain classes, we should feel justified in upholding it, even though we must thus abandon all idea of reforming the offender. We could be content to leave the fate of the criminal in another world to that Being who searcheth the hearts of men. But from the best evidence we have been able to collect, the punishment of death *has not* this deterring influence; and since the feeling of the intelligent middle classes has been strongly excited against it, so many instances have occurred in which the slightest deficiencies of evidence have been regarded as sufficient grounds for the entire acquittal of the prisoners, or the slightest suspicions or even suggestions of insanity have been held to shield them from responsibility, that the punishment has lost much of its former certainty, and the fear of it necessarily becomes far less operative as a motive for the prevention of crime. We could enumerate many instances of this kind; but they would lead us too far away from our present inquiry. The abolition of death-punishments would be, in our minds, a great step towards that improvement in our criminal legislation to which we look forward;—the treatment of all criminals to a certain extent as lunatics, that is, the devising of a system of discipline in which the reformation of the offender (in other words, his restoration to a well-governed state of mind) shall be a no less prominent object that the prevention of crime in others;—and, on the other hand, the treatment of all such as are at present excused from responsibility on the ground of lunacy, as criminals, that is, carrying on the discipline necessary for their restoration to mental health in such a manner as to have the character of a punishment. We are well aware that there are vast difficulties in the way of such a scheme as we propose. Old systems and prejudices have too long interposed barriers to all improvement; and opportunity has scarcely yet been afforded for estimating what may be reasonably anticipated from a change of method,—still less, for determining what are the kinds of punishment which most completely unite the requisites we have indicated. But we are Utopian enough to have an almost unlimited confidence in the efficacy of education,—using that term in its most comprehensive sense,—as regard the prevention of the first crime; and in the efficacy of an improved method of prison discipline as regards the reformation of the offender, and the consequent prevention of future offences by the same individual.

From the *Journal of Psychological Medicine*, 1848, Volume 1, p 38 ff:

WHILE all agree that the plea of insanity may, and that it in many instances does, absolve from the consequences of criminal acts, the greatest diversity of opinion exists as to the responsibility or irresponsibility to be attached to individual acts, the result of the individual varieties of mental disease.

Hence the law, assuming it as an axiom that insanity may or may not render its victim irresponsible, has endeavoured to frame a test whereby the measure of responsibility may be so meted that the ends of justice in the prevention and punishment of crime, as the dictates of humanity in the acquittal of those by disease deprived of their responsibility, be alike attained.

This test, according to the law of England, is the presence or absence, at the time of committing the act, in one of diseased mind, of the consciousness of right and wrong. "Before a plea of insanity," say the fifteen judges, "should be allowed, undoubted evidence ought to be adduced that the accused was of diseased mind, and that at the time he committed the act he was not conscious of right and wrong." And again, "that nothing could justify a wrong act, except it was clearly proved that the party did not know right from wrong."

When in criminal cases the plea of insanity is set up, the usual practice is for the jury, empannelled to try the guilt of the accused, likewise to decide on the evidence adduced how far mental disease has rendered the party irresponsible.

To the solving of this difficulty, our juries are, as at present constituted, totally unfit. Respectable men, but ignorant alike of the constitution of the human mind in health and of its varied symptoms in disease, it is strange they have ventured, and been so long suffered, and that too when the life of a human being hangs in the scale, to decide this important question.

No wonder there is no unanimity of principle in their verdicts! And well may Dr. Mayo remark, that "the philosopher cannot fail to observe, that the views both of judges and advocates themselves are insensibly lowered down to the dimensions of the very incompetent body in whom the decision ultimately rests." (p. 179.)

And yet, on the majesty of England's law, and on the value of the test furnished by it, has all the slur been cast, when jurors, alike ignorant of philosophy and of medicine, have failed rightly to administer the same; when even the very test has ofttimes been falsely applied to the case in question by physicians ignorant of mental disease.

The accurate diagnosis of bodily disorder requires a knowledge alike of healthy and morbid structure, and he who without this knowledge would attempt to decide upon the presence of and to treat disease is but an empiric.

And so, but in a far higher degree, does the correct discrimination of mental disease demand a perfect knowledge of the healthy action of the mind—of mental philosophy and of mental pathology in its varied phases of moral and intellectual disorders,—and the physician who without these requisites would attempt to apply to individual cases

119

of insanity the legal test of responsibility and irresponsibility, is, whatever his other qualifications may be, acting in this instance the part of an empiric, and dishonestly undertaking a task he must feel himself unfit to grapple with.

Taking, then, these circumstances into consideration—the frequent incapacity of the medical witnesses to judge of the state of mind of the accused, the constant unfitness of the jury for the forming of a just verdict,—*we believe it would be better in all instances to try the guilt by the jury, and then, in any suggested case of insanity, to have a separate inquiry as to the state of the criminal's mind and capacity, conducted by physicians conversant with mental disease.*

The opinions advocated by the writer in the "British and Foreign Medical Review," we would briefly examine.

He questions, as we have seen, "the autocratic nature of the moral principle or conscience," and states, further on, "that the ethical judgments of men should be guided, not by any fixed and determined standard of right and wrong applied to actions, but by the balance of the motives which have led to the actions in question," (p. 230;) and that "it is in a great many cases difficult to decide upon the right course, simply because it is difficult to strike the balance between contending motives."

In opposition, we assert *that the moral principle does exist in the healthy mind, and that it decides with an "autocratic" power on what is morally right and wrong.*

We confidently appeal to the personal experience of every unprejudiced reader, if there be not an inward principle, the still small voice of conscience, declaring, irrespective of outward circumstances, and in opposition often to every wish of the offender, what is moral guilt and what is not; deciding too, though faintly, on the very principles which actuate an all-just God, "if our heart condemn us, God is greater than our heart, and knoweth all things; but if our heart condemn us not, then have we confidence toward God."

The reviewer—presumably Forbes Winslow himself—here enumerates the different varieties of insanity under the headings of 1. Idiocy or Amentia; 2. Imbecility, including Dr Mayo's 'Brutality'; 3. General Insanity or Mania; 4. Partial Insanity, including moral insanity and monomania; 5. Melancholia. His remarks on the last two are here quoted:

MONOMANIA. This disease is characterized by the presence of a delusion or series of delusions, having generally reference to the person so affected, and unattended by maniacal excitement. On subjects unconnected with his delusions, the monomaniac converses rationally, and often argues acutely regarding it.

This intellectual disorder, in very many instances, supervenes on the state of moral insanity we have just described. Such was the progress of this disease in the case of William Stalker, detailed by Dr. Lockhart Robertson, "in which morbid perversion of the moral feelings preceded the supervention of intellectual delusions, and led to the commission of murder." (p. 7.) Similar instances are related by Dr. Prichard, in his excellent Treatise on Insanity. Stalker was tried at the Cumberland Lent Assizes, 1847, by Mr. Baron Alderson, and most justly acquitted, "as unconscious of right and wrong, and unfit to appreciate his position as a moral agent responsible to the laws of God and man."

There are, however, other instances of monomania, in which the disease is, to a great extent, centred in the intellectual hallucinations, in which persons, as Dr. Thurman says, "are perfectly able to distinguish right from wrong, and in whom the moral sense is neither obliterated nor altogether perverted." Such Dr. Mayo regards Macnaughten to be:

"In his assumption of a conspiracy against him on the part of the members of the government, he was truly insane and irresponsible; but this delusion granted, he might still be deemed capable of appreciating the fact, that to defeat a conspiracy by an act of assassination is quite contrary to the laws of this country."—P. 177.

The law, which justly acquits the morally insane, as being of diseased mind, and unconscious of right and wrong, will in like manner absolve from criminal responsibility those in whom to this disease is superadded a delusion.

Cases of monomania, on the other hand, unattended by perversion of the moral principle, the law declares to be, under all circumstances, responsible for their conduct. "Notwithstanding," say the judges, "the party committed a wrong act while labouring under the idea that he was redressing a supposed grievance or injury, or under the impression of obtaining some public or private benefit, he was liable to punishment."

In the justice of this decision we entirely concur.

"If," says Dr. Mayo, alluding in another place to Macnaughten, "as I believe to have been the case, he was and is a monomaniac, he was not therefore *prima facie* incapable of learning, or of teaching others, by the example of his punishment, that a strong desire of vengeance, or, if you please, of prevention of mischief, must not be gratified in defiance to the laws of his country. . . . .

"Had his friends viewed him as liable to capital punishment, in case of an outbreak against society, of which, in kind, he seems to have given them ample notice, it is reasonable to presume that some means of cure or of prevention might have been resorted to by them. . . . .

"His punishment would have afforded an invaluable example to thousands of ill regulated minds, in which a seed of insanity springs to life in a hot-bed of evil passions, or wayward dispositions, or over-stimulated imaginations . . . . The great, the good, the high-placed, who, in this country, are likely also to belong to the two first classes, are placed (*by the ignorant application of the legal test by unqualified juries and physicians*) under the influence of circumstances over which they have no control, in direct exposure to the knife of privileged assassins; privileged indeed in two ways, for they enjoy the immunities of presumed sanity before they commit the crime, and of presumed insanity after its commission."—p. 198, *et seq.*

5. MELANCHOLIA. This disease we defined as being a depression amounting often to a suppresion of all the mental manifestations, alike of the intellectual and of the moral, which may or may not be attended with a delusion.

It is evident that in this disorder the action of the moral principle is weakened, if not suspended, so that the verdict of "temporary insanity" in cases of self-destruction, (as regards which act alone, the criminal responsibility of those suffering from melancholia is ever a matter for legal decision,) is founded alike on justice and on the legal test for insanity—the loss of consciousness of right and wrong.

We have now, as far as our limits will admit of, considered the interesting question of responsibility and irresponsibility, as connected with the question of insanity, and we have seen that the legal test of the same is based on sound philosophy, as also, that *were it competently administered*, it is well adapted, while granting immunity to those by disease rendered unconscious of right and wrong, to restrain by a check they are able to appreciate—viz., the dread of punishment—the ill-regulated passions of those of the partially insane, whom disease has not deprived of this consciousness.

A Post-McNaughton Case

In the same Volume 1 of the *Journal of Psychological Medicine* (pp 169 ff) there is a report of the trial at the Old Bailey of John Ovenston, charged with attempted murder. The plea of insanity was raised, and the witnesses included Dr Conolly and Dr Forbes Winslow.

One of the judges was Mr Justice (Baron) Maule, who had been one of those to whom the McNaughton questions had been put, and who had differed from his colleagues in objecting to the general nature of the questions.

This is the first criminal case to be reported in a specifically psychiatric journal in England.

Ovenston, aged 59, had failed to pay a debt owed to a Mr Crawley, and in consequence his goods had been sold under a judge's order. On the same day he had gone to Crawley's counting-house and shot him, and immediately afterwards shot himself. Both men survived.

Mr. M'Murdo, surgeon to the gaol of Newgate, and also of St. Thomas's Hospital, deposed that the prisoner was under his care, both at the hospital, and in the gaol after his committal. He had seen him continually, and noticed particularly his conduct and demeanour, but never observed anything to lead him to believe that he was of unsound mind.

Cross-examined: The prisoner was very much depressed, but he should consider that he was in general a reserved man. Any great losses or distress would have effect upon the mind of a man partially affected by insanity. If a person committed an act of violence from insanity produced by such a cause, he should expect that it would last some time, and that the party would not appear quite calm and collected immediately afterwards. . . .

Mr. CLARKSON addressed the jury for the defence. He said that a most painful duty was cast upon himself and his learned friend, in having to defend the unfortunate man at the bar; and the jury would have observed, by the course taken in cross-examination, that they never for a moment attempted to deny that it was his hand that committed the act; but they did hope to satisfy the jury that at the time it was committed the prisoner was in such a state of mind, as not to render him criminally responsible for the act, of which he was undoubtedly guilty. If he should succeed in establishing that fact to their satisfaction, he reminded them that it would not have the effect of relieving him from all punishment, but he would be placed in such safe custody as would render it impossible for him to do any violence either upon himself or any other person in future. The learned counsel then proceeded to comment upon the circumstances of the case, and he put it to the jury whether, if the desperate attempt made by the prisoner upon his own life had been successful, and instead of being in their present situation, they had been called upon to assist the coroner in an inquiry as to the means by which he met his death, they would have had any difficulty in coming to the conclusion that at the time he destroyed himself he was in a state of temporary derangement? The sole question they were called upon to decide was, the state of mind of the prisoner at the time he committed the act; and if he should show them by undoubted testimony that during the whole of his life the prisoner had been remarkable for his kind and humane character, and that his mind had been overwhelmed by the distress and misfortunes that had come upon him, the climax of which was the sale of all he possessed, under the execution, and which had completed his ruin, he did not think the jury would find any difficulty in coming to a conclusion that it was during a temporary paroxysm of madness, thereby occasioned, that he committed the act with which he was now charged. He was ready to admit that almost immediately afterwards the reason of the prisoner returned to him, and that at the present moment he was perfectly sane; but this did not in any way affect the proposition that he had submitted to the jury, that at the time when the act was accomplished he was not in such a state of mind as to be responsible, criminally, for what he did. The learned counsel then read extracts from several works

122

upon the subject of insanity, to show that in a great proportion of cases it was occasioned by pecuniary difficulties or domestic affliction, and that the number of cases of insanity arising from moral causes was infinitely greater than from physical ones; and he said he should satisfy the jury, by the evidence of Dr. Conolly, the principal physician of Hanwell Lunatic Asylum, and other eminent men, that this was the case, from their own experience; and they would also state to them that, in their opinion, the mind of the prisoner was temporarily destroyed by the prisoner's difficulties, and the sale of his property under the execution; and that they had no doubt that at the time the prisoner made the attack upon Mr. Crawley, he was not at all aware of the consequences of what he was about to do. . . .

Mr. Shear, clerk to an attorney, had known the prisoner several years, and considered him a man of unusually kind disposition. Witness had acted professionally for the prisoner, and knew that he had sustained heavy losses, several of them almost simultaneously, and he observed a great change in his conduct afterwards, and did not appear to understand the advice that was given to him, or if he did, he could not act upon it, and he also observed a great change with regard to his memory. He also said frequently, with great energy, there must be a conspiracy among some people to ruin him. Mr. Bond was an intimate friend of the prisoner, and he lost 600*l.* by the bankruptcy, a large sum by the sale of his furniture, and became responsible to the extent of 500*l.* as the assignee. During the nine months prior to the transaction, the prisoner had lost in debts from intimate friends more than 2,000*l.*, and this was independent of the transaction with Bond.

Mr. H. B. Hall had known the prisoner twenty-two years. Latterly he had observed a decided difference in his conduct, and he exhibited strong excitement, apparently brought on by his troubles, and his mind was so affected that he could not cast up three lines of figures correctly. In addition to his pecuniary troubles, a lady friend of his committed suicide last November, and he frequently alluded to the circumstance, and it seemed to prey upon his mind. Since the year 1844 the prisoner had sustained losses to the amount of 3,800*l.* A short time back the prisoner used frequently to write upon large placards the words, "Statute of Limitations Act here;" and this referred to the circumstance of an intimate friend who owed him a large sum of money having pleaded that statute to an action brought again him. He frequently appeared wild and raving, and on the 12th of August his conduct was not that of a reasonable being, and he kept running in and out of the house. Witness saw him on the morning of this unfortunate transaction, and he appeared haggard and worn out, and said that he had passed a sleepless night, and burst into tears.

Mr. J. H. Utting deposed that he had known the prisoner for twenty years. He had latterly observed a very material alteration in him. Saw him in June, 1847, upon business, and found him quite a different man to what he used to be, and his memory continually failed him, and he did not appear to know what he was about. Witness had been employed by the prisoner, and he would frequently order him to do things and immediately afterwards he would countermand the order, and acted in a most extraordinary manner. . . .

Dr. Conolly was then called as a witness. He deposed, that he was chief physician to Hanwell Lunatic Asylum, and had besides the care of a private establishment of his own, and had devoted his entire attention to diseases of the mind, and at the present time he had upwards of a thousand patients under his care. He had heard the whole of the evidence in this case, and had also had an interview with the prisoner in Newgate, and he had applied his attention and experience to all the circumstances, and the impression conveyed to his mind from all the facts was, that at the time the prisoner made the attack upon Mr. Crawley he was not in a sound state of mind. He had known many cases where pecuniary losses and domestic affliction had deprived the mind of reason. This happened, in fact, in innumerable cases, and they were more frequently the causes of insanity than any others of a physical nature. In his opinion the mind of

123

the prisoner had been gradually losing its power from the difficulties in which he felt himself surrounded, and that the crisis had arrived when he committed this act; and he did not consider that his being at the present time, or very soon after the transaction, in a state of perfect sanity, in any way affected the opinion he had formed, or was at all inconsistent with that view of the question. Dr. Conolly added, that at the present time he was acquainted with several perfectly analogous cases.

Cross-examined: He did not go the length of saying that he was unconscious of what he did, but he believed he was acting under an impulse which he could not control, and that he could not distinguish the wickedness of the act, although he was conscious that he was committing it.

Baron Maule: Then you are of opinion that at the time he was not capable of knowing that he was committing a guilty act.

Dr. Conolly: I think so.

Dr. Forbes Winslow and Mr. Streeter, surgeon, were also examined, and they concurred entirely in the view of the case taken by Dr. Conolly.

Baron Maule then briefly summed up, and the jury, after deliberating a short time in the box, expressed a wish to retire. They were absent for half an hour, when they returned into court and gave a verdict of not guilty, on the ground of insanity.

The prisoner was ordered to be detained during Her Majesty's pleasure.

REMARKS ON OVENSTON'S CASE BY THE EDITOR

THIS case has been made the subject of much comment in the public journals of the day, and the medical men who were called upon to give evidence in favour of the plea of insanity, have been held up to censure for the view they took of Ovenston's state of mind at the moment he committed the offence which brought him before the judicial tribunal of his country. Dr. Conolly has particularly been referred to, and his examination has been canvassed with great freedom. It is not our intention to question the right of journals not strictly professional in their character, to discuss, with almost unrestricted liberty, the opinions which any scientific man may give in elucidation of matters which are made the subject of investigation in our criminal or other courts. These criticisms ought, however, to be penned with much caution, particularly when they have reference to points so extremely difficult of satisfactory solution as those connected with the morbid phenomena of the human mind, in relation to the degree of responsibility and knowledge of right and wrong existing at a given moment. Again, it is not exactly fair to the medical witnesses to judge of the amount or description of evidence submitted to them for consideration, and upon which they have based their opinion, from the necessarily abridged accounts reported in the papers of the day. The evidence in Ovenston's case, in all its minute details, was submitted to the medical witnesses, and many very interesting and important particulars came under their notice, which did not appear in the report of the trial, and which, in fact, were not brought at all under the cognizance of the court. The particular facts referred to certainly threw a great light on the case.

It should be recollected, that in the cases in which the plea of insanity is urged in extenuation of crime, the medical witnesses often stand in a peculiar and painful position. Upon the value of such evidence there cannot be, among liberally minded and intelligent persons, two opinions.

Dr Hood's Views

In 1860 Dr W. C. Hood (afterwards Sir William Hood), Resident Physician to Bethlem Hospital, published as a pamphlet a 'Letter on Criminal Lunatics',

124

addressed to the Chairman of the Commissioners in Lunacy (Lord Shaftesbury). A review of this pamphlet, by Dr Bucknill, appeared in the *Journal of Mental Sciences* for July 1860 (Vol VI, p 513).

The following extract is from the review:

Criminal Lunatics. A Letter to the Chairman of the Commissioners in Lunacy. By W. C. HOOD, M.D., Physician to the Royal Bethlem Hospital. London: Churchill, (Pamphlet, pp. 28.)

No one can speak with the authority of so much experience and knowledge on the subject of criminal lunatics as the able physician of Bethlem, and his well timed and well written pamphlet is very acceptable now that the new State Asylum is approaching completion.

Dr. Hood points out the indiscriminate and not very accurate use of the term, "criminal lunatics," and the wide distinction between those whose offence has been the result of insanity, perhaps neglected, and those whose insanity has been the sequel of crime. . . .

Dr. Hood points to the distinction that must be drawn between those lunatics who have been convicted of slight offences, and those who have been guilty of graver crimes, and he proposes to extend the jurisdiction of the Commissioners of Lunacy, over the former class, and to empower them to discharge on the guarantee of friends or relations, that they shall be prevented from again disturbing the public peace. But a mere guarantee without penalty in case of infraction of its conditions, would be of little service; besides, it would confer no power over the conduct of the person discharged, however dangerous it might be. A more efficient plan would be to place a doubtful case under the surveillance of some relative or medical man who should enter into recognizances to superintend the mode of life of the discharged prisoner, and to whom statutory power should be granted somewhat equivalent to that possessed by a Committee of the Person over a Chancery lunatic.

As for extending the jurisdiction of the Commissioners in Lunacy, we are convinced that it will be found needful to do so over all criminal lunatics whatever their degree of crime or their condition of mind. . . .

Dr. Hood commenting upon the several cases who, acquitted on charges of murder on the plea of insanity, had displayed no symptom thereof during their residence in Bethlem, points to one of the main causes of this mischievous fiction in the manner in which "specialist" physicians lend themselves to be the instruments of the lawyers to whom the defence is entrusted. . . .

The remedy which Dr. Hood proposes is, that there shall be two trials, one to determine the state of mind, and the other to ascertain the commission of the offence.

The following is the legislative formula into which Dr. Hood proposes to cast this opinion for practical use, in the sketch of a statute with which he concludes his pamphlet.

"If any prisoner shall appear on arraignment or during trial to be insane, or if on the trial of any prisoner evidence be given that such prisoner was insane at the time the offence with which he or she is charged was committed, it shall be lawful for the court before which such prisoner is arraigned, or being tried, to postpone such trial if it see fit, and to direct that at the same or some following assize or session, the state of the prisoner's mind be made the subject of separate inquiry before a petty jury; independent medical testimony in every such case being directed by the court to be provided by summons of one or more medical men. And in the event of the prisoner being found by the jury on such separate inquiry, to be insane when arraigned, or during trial, or when the offence with which he or she is charged was committed, as the case may be, then in every such case the prisoner shall be sent to the county asylum or other proper receptacle for insane persons, and be dealt with as is herein above provided for persons duly

125

certified to be insane while imprisoned in any prison or other place of confinement."

When a prisoner so found insane shall be recovered, the author proposes that he shall be removed back from the asylum to the prison, and at the following or some subsequent assize shall be tried for the offence.

There are grave objects to this plan of a double trial. First, there is the double trouble and expense; then there is the delay before the second trial would take place, during which evidence would decay—nothing is more evanescent; then there is the impossibility of separating the inquiry into the state of mind from the inquiry into the offence. The one almost invariably illustrates the other. Very often the character and circumstances of the offence constitute the main evidence of sanity or insanity. . . .

Although we differ from Dr. Hood on one or two points to which, as critics are apt to do, we have given a prominent place in the above notice; on other subjects mooted in his excellent pamphlet we entirely concur, and we have no doubt that our associates will be as much pleased as we have ourselves been, with the general tenor of his wise and humane opinions.

Davey Returns to the Attack

In 1858, at the Annual Meeting of the Association of Medical Officers of Hospitals and Asylums for the Insane (afterwards the Medico-Psychological Association), when Dr John Conolly was President, Dr Davey read a paper on 'The Relations between Crime and Insanity' in which he expanded the arguments he had put forward 15 years earlier.

Recalling the questions put to the judges after the McNaughton trial he quoted their reply:

that before a plea of insanity should be allowed, undoubted evidence ought to be adduced that the accused was of diseased mind, and that at the time he committed the act he was not conscious of right or wrong. This opinion related to every case in which a party was charged with an illegal act, and a plea of insanity was set up. Every person was supposed to know what the law was, and therefore nothing could justify a wrong act, except it was clearly proved the party did not know right from wrong. If that was not satisfactorily proved, the accused was liable to punishment, and it was the duty of the judges so to tell the jury when summing up the evidence, accompanied with those remarks and observations as the nature and peculiarities of each case might suggest and require.

With regard to the third question, viz.: 'In what terms ought the question to be left to the jury, as to the prisoner's state of mind at the time when the act was committed?' the judges did not give an opinion.

The fourth question was—'If a person under an insane delusion as to existing facts, commits an offence in consequence thereof, is he thereby excused?'

The answer to this question was, that 'the judges were unanimous in opinion, that if the delusion were only partial, that the party accused was equally liable with a person of sane mind. If the accused killed another in self-defence, he would be entitled to an acquittal; but if committed for any supposed injury, he would then be liable to the punishment awarded by the laws to his crime.' . . .

Now if one will be at the pains to analyse the peculiar expressions herein employed by the peers and judges, we must then conclude that their nature and tendency are to limit the enquiry, in every particular, to the state of the mere knowing faculties of the human mind, as existing in the individual charged with the commission of crime; and, at the same time to ignore the ever active qualities of our psychical nature, *i.e.* our moral feelings or affections; upon which the character of each one of us depends; and which, in themselves, constitute, both under circumstances of health and disease, of sanity or

126

insanity, our individual motives to thought and action, their various degrees of intensity, and duration, &c.

Thus the sentences "insane delusion;" "the accused knew he was acting contrary to law;—"supposed grievance, or injury;" "supposed public benefit;" . . . "idea of redressing a supposed grievance;" "under the impression of," &c. occurring in the first question and its reply; and those "afflicted with insane delusion;" "was not conscious of right or wrong;" "did not know right from wrong," in the second [question and its reply], including the following, viz, "an insane delusion, as to existing facts;" "if the delusion were only partial;" "any supposed injury," as found in the fourth question and answer; also, "whether the prisoner was conscious at the time of doing the act; and "whether he was labouring under any, and what, delusion at the time," forming part of the last question,—relate only to the condition of the intellect, *i.e.* the perceptive and reflective faculties, in him whose infringement of the moral law is, or is not the consequence of cerebro-mental disease. It follows then, that the several tests which the ingenuity of the peers and judges has created, tests held to discriminate the sane from the insane, the responsible from the irresponsible, constitute a mere sham, a metaphysical chimera, in short an idle fiction, a *delusion*.

It is now too late in the day to doubt that the springs of all human action, whether or not these belong to the sane or insane mind, are to be sought for, not in the understanding of this man or that, not in the brilliancy or otherwise, of the knowing faculties, but in the tone and quality of his moral feelings, *i.e.* his affections and his propensities. . . .

Let me ask—Is not this a matter with which our Association may well interest itself? Can we do a better thing than urge on the attention of the Legislature the repeal of a law which not only does not accomplish the original end in view, but which has the effect of adding, to some extent, to the number of capital punishments—of, in fact, *hanging the madman:* than whom there can be no greater claimant on either our individual sympathies, or on the protective laws of this great country!!

The preceding statements, which apply to the condition of the intellect among the insane, may not seem altogether conclusive to some minds. However, those who doubt that cerebro-mental disorder is, as a very general rule, confined to the emotional faculties and propensities, will do well to lose no time and visit the modern asylum, whether public or private. The evidences of order, and of quiet and good management, the scene of industry which will meet the eye, and the general propriety which will be found to characterise the whole establishment, will readily enough assure the visitor that such could hardly be brought about if the patients were not in some way within the reach of a wholesome and controlling supervision. Now this same supervision is successful only because it appeals in its detail, in an eminent degree, to the knowing faculties of the mass of the patients. If the insane were so *unconscious*, or so ignorant, as they are very commonly supposed, they would then be found unaffected by the many influences now made available for their amelioration and recovery.

It is concluded, then, that *consciousness*, or the ability to distinguish *right* from *wrong*, is no criterion of either a sound mind or of responsibility; that, in fact, nine-tenths of those insane persons who possess the physical power necessary to the commission of violence, *know* full well what is going on about them; and that, moreover, they will commonly manifest, during even the greatest excitement, an acute intelligence, and not unfrequently really surprise one by the force and brilliancy of their reasoning powers. . . .

The manner in which the peer and the judges have considered the subject of "insane delusion," its nature and operation on the morbid mind, and the consequence thereof in so far as criminal acts are concerned, is singularly infelicitous. A "*delusion*," so called, holds much the same relation to the insane mind as a simple prejudice does to the mind of him in the enjoyment of "*mens sana in corpore sano.*" Neither the *delusion* nor the *prejudice* are really believed; they indicate without doubt some innate feeling or emotion, some dominant affection or passion, wherewith the physical nature of the

127

party, be he insane or sane, is imbued. Both the delusion and the prejudice may be, I feel confident, regarded as the external and ostensible sign or criterion of the internal, and otherwise invisible mental bias or psychical tendency; both the delusion and the prejudice are but the exponents of the ever-active affections and propensities. . . .

In conclusion, let this fact sink deeply into the memories of all present. Within a comparatively few years many lunatics have been hanged, more have been transported, and I make no doubt that there is hardly a borough or a county jail, in which one or more insane persons may not be found; and all this, because mental disease is not understood; and because too, the present efforts of the bench and the bar are to ignore all sound views of the disease, and to perpetuate the crude notions of lunacy which have ever existed; and, lastly, because no responsible body of men, like this one, has taken up this all-important question, or ventured to urge its consideration on the legislature.

In the following year, when the Association had Sir Charles Hastings as its President, Dr Davey read a similar but shorter paper and this time proposed formally that a committee be formed 'to put itself in communication with the Legislature with a view of exposing the present defects in the law as it affects the insane charged with crime'. This was carried, and a committee of four members was appointed.

There is no further record of the committee's actions, let alone of its recommendations having had any success. But at the Annual Meeting in July 1864, Dr Harrington Tuke proposed the following resolution and this was unanimously agreed to:

'That so much of the legal test of the mental condition of an alleged criminal lunatic which renders him a responsible agent because he knows the difference between right and wrong is inconsistent with the fact, well known to every member of this meeting, that the power of distinguishing between right and wrong exists frequently among those who are undoubtedly insane, and is often associated with dangerous and uncontrollable delusions.'

Harrington Tuke subsequently gave evidence on these lines to the Capital Punishment Commission, as described in the next chapter (p 130).

128

THE RULES IN ACTION*

N. D. WALKER

It was some little time before the importance of the judges' answers, and their defects, began to be appreciated. English doctors were neither swift nor strong in following the lead of the American, Isaac Ray, who had argued that knowledge of the nature of the act, ability to tell right from wrong, or delusion, were much too narrow a test of criminal responsibility. In the year before McNaughton's case a short book entitled *The Different Forms of Insanity in relation to Jurisprudence* had been published by J. C. Prichard, of Bristol. But Prichard was more concerned to instruct than challenge the judges. His book was much less original and provocative than Ray's, and he did little more than confuse the issue with his talk of moral insanity.

In any case, Prichard died a few years after McNaughton's case, so that it was left to the more superficial F. B. Winslow to carry the torch lit by Ray. By 1854 Winslow was a fully accepted authority on the subject, and he devoted one of his Lettsomian Lectures[1] to the difficulties posed for medical witnesses both by the legal tests of insanity and by counsel's sophistical methods of cross-examination. Although he illustrated and criticized tests such as the right-wrong test, he did not, for some unaccountable reason, mention either McNaughton's case or the judges' answers to the Lords' questions. He objected strongly to the way in which medical witnesses were questioned by counsel when insanity was an issue and had some good tactical advice for alienists who found themselves in the witness box. But it is not easy to make out from his verbose and anecdotal lectures exactly what he supposed the law to be or how he would have liked to reform it.

Almost inevitably therefore both Winslow's and Ray's points of view came to be confused with the contemporary tendency to widen the definition of insanity by recognizing and including new subdivisions of it, such as 'moral insanity' and 'instinctive insanity', examples which were given some prominence in Prichard's books. Ray's main point was that, *whatever was included in insanity,* the exemption of the insane from punishment should not turn on intellectual tests of the kind applied by English judges but simply on the question whether 'the mental unsoundness . . . embraced the act within the sphere of its influence';

---

* Reprinted (with minor amendments) from *Crime and Insanity in England*, Vol 1. Edinburgh University Press, 1968.

[1] F. B. Winslow, *Lettsomian Lectures on Insanity* (London, 1854): see the third lecture.

in other words, whether he did it because of his insanity or whether his act was unconnected with his insanity. For the understanding of his point it was unfortunate that he and his contemporaries were also trying to popularize a wider conception of insanity.

The concept of moral insanity and its connection with 'psychopathy' have been discussed elsewhere.[2] Equally important, however, was the notion of 'instinctive' or 'impulsive insanity', which, like moral insanity, had been described by Pinel and imported by Prichard. The latter described it thus:

> In this disorder the will is occasionally under the influence of an impulse, which suddenly drives the person affected to the perpetration of acts of the most revolting kind, to the commission of which he has no motive. The impulse is accompanied by consciousness; but it is in some instances irresistible; some individuals who have felt the approach of this disorder have been known to take precautions against themselves; they have warned, for example, their neighbours and relatives to escape from their reach till the paroxysm should have subsided.[3]

He goes on to explain that while it can take serious forms such as homicidal mania and pyromania, it can also be responsible for behaviour such as kleptomania.

Prichard himself did not think that someone who had struggled with an insane impulse and lost should be excused punishment, and it was hardly surprising that lawyers should have been even more firmly of this view. The young Fitzjames Stephen (1829–94)—at that time a briefless barrister living more by journalism than by legal practice—was highly critical of the notion of 'irresistible impulse' in a paper to the Juridical Society in 1855:

> There may have been many instances of irresistible impulse of this kind, although I fear there is a disposition to confound them with unresisted impulses. . . .[4]

He was prepared to recognize that there might be cases in which the impulse had been irresistible, but pointed out that it should not be assumed either that all insane impulses were of this kind or that irresistible impulses were confined to the insane. 'If a prisoner is to be acquitted it must be because the impulse is irresistible, because the act is not wilful—if he is to be called insane it must be because the impulse is unaccountable. . . . The guilt turns upon the wilfulness of the act and not upon the insanity of the prisoner.'

While it is difficult to find a clear statement of the medical objections to the McNaughton Rules at this date, the main criticism was probably that they made no allowance for this phenomenon of irresistible impulse. A resolution which Dr Harrington Tuke persuaded the Association of Medical Officers of Asylums for the Insane (soon to be renamed 'The Medico-Psychological Association) to

[2] In *Crime and Insanity in England* (1968, 1973: Edinburgh University Press), Vol II, ch 9.
[3] In *On the Different Forms of Insanity in Relation to Jurisprudence* (London, 1842).
[4] J. F. Stephen, *On the policy of maintaining the limits at present imposed by law on the criminal responsibility of madmen* in Papers read before the Juridical Society, 1855–8 (London, 1855).

adopt at the time of the appointment of the Capital Punishment Commission in 1864[5] condemned the right-wrong test on the grounds that 'the power of distinguishing between right and wrong exists frequently among those who are undoubtedly insane, and is often associated with dangerous and *uncontrollable* delusions' (my italics). What they seem to have meant was that some insane persons should be excused because their delusions led to uncontrollable impulses.

In his own evidence to the Capital Punishment Commission Dr Tuke argued that no insane man should be held responsible to the extent of being punished capitally, although he saw no harm—and indeed considerable corrective value—in applying less irrevocable punishments, such as penal servitude, to them. He also favoured the idea of separating the trial of the prisoner's responsibility from the trial of the facts—an expedient with which California and one or two other American States were later to experiment. In the end the Commission refused to make any recommendation on the law regarding insanity, on the ground that this was not confined to capital cases: the same argument was again found convenient in the nineteen-fifties.

It is interesting to watch Fitzjames Stephen, who in his younger days had so stoutly defended the McNaughton Rules, later undergoing a change of heart, and especially on the subject of irresistible impulse. His *General View of the Criminal Law*, written in 1861 and 1862, was respectful towards the Rules. Nevertheless, without any apparent sense of disloyalty to them, he was prepared to grant, as a somewhat academic point, that if an impulse were irresistible the accused was entitled to be acquitted because 'the act was not voluntary and was not properly his act'. But 'If the impulse was resistible, the fact that it proceeded from disease is no excuse at all'. Infanticide was the sort of case in which he was readiest to admit the probability that the impulse really was irresistible. His reading on the subject included Ray, Prichard and Winslow.

By the time he embarked on the codification of the English criminal law in the early eighteen-seventies he was firmly convinced that it should exempt an offender who had been 'prevented by disease affecting the mind . . . from controlling his own conduct'.[6] His proposals were criticized by such influential judges as Bramwell and Cockburn, who was by then Lord Chief Justice, and in any case the Select Committee was opposed to codification. But Stephen did not let the argument rest there. In his *History of the Criminal Law of England*,[7] written with the authority of someone who was now a Queen's Bench Judge, he argued that the Rules were not a complete statement of the law on the subject, at least at the time when they were formulated, although he was prepared to grant that because they had come to be regarded as a complete statement his point had become rather academic. With this reservation he held that the judges had dealt only with examples of the way in which insanity can lead to ignorance or mistake, and had not dealt (for they had not been asked to deal)

---

[5] Report and Minutes of Evidence before the Royal Commission on Capital Punishment, 1864–6: in British Sessional Papers, 1866, xxi.
[6] J. F. Stephen, *Digest of the Criminal Law* (London, 1877).
[7] J. F. Stephen, *History of the Criminal Law of England* (London, 1883).

with cases in which the emotions and the will are affected. He summed up his view as follows:

> If it is not, it ought to be the Law of England that no act is a crime if the person who does it is at the time . . . prevented either by defective mental power or by any disease affecting his mind from controlling his own conduct, unless the absence of the power of control has been produced by his own default.

He proposed a solution rather like the verdict of diminished responsibility which his Scottish contemporary, Lord Deas, had introduced.

But since this solution was not yet open to English juries, Stephen was prepared to make sure that they interpreted the law in his way. In 1881 he presided at the trial in Newcastle-on-Tyne of William Davis, a thirty-eight-year-old labourer who had attempted to murder his sister-in-law because, as he told the police, 'the man in the moon told me to do it. I will have to commit murder, as I must be hanged'—a line of reasoning reminiscent of Hadfield's. Medical witnesses testified that he suffered from *delirium tremens* (although sober at the time), and that he would know what he was doing but would be unable to control his actions and unable to distinguish right from wrong. Stephen's summing-up had all the appearance of orthodoxy, for he told the jury that they must follow 'the great test laid down in McNaughton's case', and must ask themselves whether Davis knew at the time that the act he was committing was wrong. But he then did his best to disguise the distinction between self-control and knowledge of right and wrong:

> As I understand the law, any disease which so disturbs the mind that you cannot think calmly and rationally of all the different reasons to which we refer in considering the rightness and wrongness of an action . . . may fairly be said to prevent a man from knowing that what he did was wrong. . . . Both the doctors agree that the prisoner was unable to control his conduct, and that nothing short of actual physical restraint would have deterred him. . . . If you think there was distinct disease caused by drinking, but differing from drunkenness, and that by reason thereof he did not know that the act was wrong, you will find a verdict of not guilty on the ground of insanity. . . .[8]

The jury did think so.

Since Stephen's formula was more favourable to the accused than the orthodox interpretation of the law, even the creation of the Court of Criminal Appeal in 1907 did not discourage the occasional judge from following his lead. Thus, for example, at the trial of Fryer, a soldier who had strangled his fiancée, Mr Justice Bray explained the McNaughton Rules to the Gloucester jury, but continued:

> That is the recognized law on the subject; but I am bound to say it does not seem to me to completely state the law as it now is, and for the purpose of

[8] R. v. Davis (1881), 14 Cox 563.

today I am going to direct you in the way indicated by a very learned judge, Fitzjames Stephen, . . . If it is shown that he is in such a state of mental disease or infirmity as to deprive him of the capacity to control his actions, I think you ought to find him what the law calls him—'insane'.[9]

They did.

In 1922, however, True's case[10] at last gave the Court of Criminal Appeal its opportunity to state an authoritative view. Ronald True had murdered and robbed a prostitute after boasting beforehand that he was going to commit murder. He used a spectacular and unnecessary amount of violence, and this undoubtedly helped to prejudice both public and jury against him. The defence brought witnesses who testified to his bizarre and violent behaviour at other times and to his addiction to morphia. Evidence as to his insanity was given by two psychiatrists and two prison medical officers, including Norwood East, who later became the established authority on forensic psychiatry, and a member of the Prison Commission. They all agreed that he was insane and abnormally deficient in moral sense. The two psychiatrists agreed that he had acted under an uncontrollable impulse; but Norwood East's view was not so clear. He was subjected to a most confusing examination, in which counsel's questions were constantly interrupted by Mr Justice McCardie, who seemed anxious to air his own knowledge both of psychiatry in general and of particulars of the case which had not been brought out in evidence. In his summing-up McCardie made it quite plain to the jury that in his view True had known the nature and wrongness of his act, but told them that they could bring in a special verdict if they thought that he had been 'deprived of the power of controlling his actions'. As to whether this had been so, however, he seemed sceptical, and after an absence of an hour and a half the jury rejected the defence.

The Court of Criminal Appeal, who upheld the verdict, said more or less openly that the judge had been too generous to True when he told the jury that irresistible impulse would have constituted criminal insanity. The McNaughton Rule, which mentioned only knowledge of the nature and quality of the act or of its wrongness, was 'sufficient and salutary'.

So far as the courts were concerned, that was that. But True himself was reprieved by the Home Secretary on the grounds of his mental condition, and the result was an outcry of protest, culminating in a short debate in the Commons. (It is a measure of the change in popular feeling about capital punishment in England that this was the last case in which a decision *not* to hang a man was so strongly criticized: later protests were all against hanging.) But the Home Secretary's explanation did not completely satisfy his critics, and the Government resorted to the manoeuvre of appointing a Committee 'to consider what changes, if any, are desirable in the existing law practice and procedure relating to criminal trials in which the plea of insanity as a defence is raised, and whether any, and if so what, changes should be made in the existing law

[9] R. v. Fryer (1915), 24 Cox 405.
[10] R. v. True (1922), 16 Cr. App. R. 164; and see D. Carswell (ed.), *The Trial of Ronald True* (London, 1923) for a full account of the trial and appeal.

and practice in respect of cases falling within the provisions of section 2(4) of the Criminal Lunatics Act, 1884' (the section dealing with psychiatric inquiries instituted after sentence by the Home Secretary).[11] In composition the Committee was not only overwhelmingly legal (the only non-legal members were the permanent head of the Home Office and one of his senior subordinates); it was also official to an extent that would nowadays be considered quite improper. It contained the two civil servants mentioned, the Attorney-General, the Solicitor General, Senior Treasury Counsel (who had prosecuted True), and the Director of Public Prosecutions. The nearest thing to an unofficial member was Sir Herbert Stephen, son of Fitzjames Stephen, and he was a Clerk of Assize. The chairman was a Lord Justice of Appeal, Lord Atkin (1867–1944).

Clearly Lord Birkenhead, who as Lord Chancellor was responsible for the appointment of the members, was doing his best to ensure that their report would contain no embarrassing surprises. But it did. Although it contained no medical members, the Committee received memoranda from both the British Medical Association and the Medico-Psychological Association (later the Royal Medico-Psychological Association and now the Royal College of Psychiatrists). The latter made a radical proposal which would have abrogated the McNaughton Rules and in effect substituted Isaac Ray's formula ('Was the accused insane at the time? If so, has it nevertheless been proved . . . that his crime was unrelated to his mental disorder?') Less radical was the British Medical Association's recommendation, which in effect simply added irresistible impulse to the other tests in the McNaughton Rules. The Atkin Committee preferred this solution, and recommended that 'it should be recognized that a person charged criminally with an offence is irresponsible for his act when the act is committed under an impulse which the prisoner was by mental disease in substance deprived of any power to resist'. The drafting was clumsy but the meaning was plain.

But legislation on these—or any other—lines in this field did not appeal to the Government, who took no steps to implement the report. Eventually Lord Darling introduced a private member's bill which would have enlarged the Rules by excusing those offenders who, through some mental disease, were 'wholly incapable of resisting the impulse to do the act'. But the Lord Chancellor, now Lord Haldane, opposed the bill. Although in theory the idea was right, he argued, in practice it would mean that juries would be asked to decide an impossible question. Moreover, it would allow the defence of insanity to be offered by large numbers of shoplifters, many of whom were kleptomaniacs. This was an odd argument: did he really think that a shoplifter would offer a defence which might lead to indefinite detention in Broadmoor? But if a shoplifter *were* to choose this defence, and really *were* a kleptomaniac, why should he or she have less right to be excused conviction than a murderer? He contended that it was better to rely on the Home Office to ensure, as they did, that no case of 'uncontrollable impulse' was ever executed, but he did not answer the awkward question whether any cases of uncontrollable impulse were ever

[11] Report of the Committee on Insanity and Crime (1924), Cmd. 2005, HMSO.

allowed to go to prison for non-capital crimes such as attempted murder. In the face of official discouragement, Lord Darling found little support, and his bill was rejected by the Lords.

The Select Committee which was set up by the Commons to discuss capital punishment in 1930 recommended a re-examination of the law on insanity, but made no proposals of its own.[12] It was left to the post-war Royal Commission on Capital Punishment to re-open the subject.[13] Although concerned with many other aspects of the death penalty, it discussed the criminal responsibility of the mentally disordered with more comprehensiveness, precision, and understanding that any other officially appointed body has so far done in this country.

It was, however, insanity as a defence, with which they, and the witnesses who gave evidence to them, were chiefly concerned. By this time many people —judges as well as psychiatrists—were prepared to say openly that the Rules were being widely stretched by some (though by no means all) judges, and on occasion were not even mentioned at all. There seemed to be a tendency on the part of judges—and there certainly was on the part of juries—simply to ask themselves whether the accused had been shown to have been insane, and if so to decide in his favour without really giving thought to the tests in the Rules. Nevertheless the Commission felt it necessary that the letter of the law should be brought up to date. Like the Atkin Committee they were faced with two schools of witnesses. The Royal Medico-Psychological Association (probably under the influence of Norwood East) was no longer in favour of abrogating the Rules, but was content to rely on the 'increasing elasticity' with which they were interpreted. But the abrogation of the Rules was favoured by other witnesses, including the former Home Secretary, Lord Templewood, and all but four members of the Commission (Mr Fox-Andrews, Miss Florence Hancock, Mr Macdonald and Mr Radzinowicz) adopted this solution. They recognized that so long as mere insanity was not acceptable as coextensive with irresponsibility, juries must decide whether this or that insane person should be held responsible in law. What they doubted was whether any up-to-date formula could be devised to help the jury. True, the Rules were being honoured only by lip-service; but it was impossible to define an irresponsible state of mind with any precision, and any attempt to do so would inevitably exclude cases which ought to be included. The jury should be left to decide whether the insanity was such that the accused should not be held responsible, a question no more difficult than many others which they had shown themselves capable of deciding, for example in civil actions involving technical or professional negligence. The last of these sentiments echoes Hale's stout confidence in the English jury:

> Yet the law of England hath afforded the best method of trial that is possible of this and all other matters of fact, namely by a jury of twelve men all concurring in the same judgement. . . .

The Commission's solution was surgery of the heroic kind; but would it have

[12] Report on the Select Committee on Capital Punishment (1930), HMSO.
[13] Report of the Royal Commission on Capital Punishment, 1949–53, Cmnd. 8932.

saved that frail patient, criminal responsibility? Lord Cooper, Lord Justice General for Scotland, had already told them roundly that whatever judges said to juries, the latter simply retired and asked themselves 'Is this man mad or is he not?' If there were any juries which did more, the new formula would soon have put a stop to that. The Commission's argument began with the assumption that insanity and irresponsibility were not to be treated as coextensive; but whatever their solution meant in theory that is the result which it would have had in practice. Certainly the Infanticide Acts allowed juries to think in this way in the special cases in which mothers murdered their last-born infants; but that is not what the Commission intended. Moreover, their argument glossed over an awkward gap when it said that any attempt at a formula would exclude cases which ought to be included. By what criterion could one tell whether this or that case 'ought' to have been included? Could the criterion be expressed in words, or was it ineffable? If in words, were they quite unsuitable for use in a judge's summing-up? No doubt the Commission could have answered these questions; what is surprising is that they did not.

Conscious, however, that their solution did not command universal assent, they offered as a second choice the proposal which the British Medical Association had persuaded the Atkin Committee to adopt, and were still urging: the addition of a new question to the tests of the Rules, namely 'Was the accused incapable of preventing himself from committing his act?'[14] This time there was only one dissenter, Mr Fox-Andrews, the only English counsel on the Commission, who preferred that the Rules should remain unaltered, but if not, be abrogated. His argument in support of this somewhat difficult position was that the Rules could not be improved, so that those who were dissatisfied with them should be in favour of their abolition!

There can hardly have been another Commission whose report was composed so well but to so little purpose. Every one of their major recommendations was rejected by the Conservative Government of 1953, which—in so far as it could be said to have had a united view on so controversial a subject as capital punishment—seems to have been trying to preserve the *status quo ante*. One of the reasons which was given for rejecting the Commission's proposals on the law of insanity was that they extended beyond the law on murder. This time-worn argument, which had been used by the Commissioners of 1864 to justify their refusal to deal with the same subject, could hardly have been more superficial. The Gowers Commission had been asked in 1949 to consider 'whether liability under the criminal law in Great Britain to suffer capital punishment for murder should be modified, and if so to what extent and by what means. . . .' The most frequent defence to a charge of murder was insanity; it was seldom offered to a non-capital charge; and it had never been suggested to them that they should exclude it from their report. The Government's arguments were clearly opportunistic rather than genuine.

[14] This recommendation has found more favour in other parts of the Commonwealth than in Britain: see, for example, the Nigerian Criminal Code and the Criminal Justice (Northern Ireland) Act, 1966.

McNaughton's ghost faded away not as the result of any official decision to exorcise it, but simply from neglect, as the result of the new defence of diminished responsibility. That, however, does not belong to this story, and there are other developments to be described. So far I have concentrated on the main theme: the controversy over the exhaustiveness or otherwise of the Rules, and their silence on the subject of irresistible impulses. But there were other issues. The most important was probably the meaning of 'wrong'.

Although the McNaughton Rules were supposed to be a statement of the law as it then was, this is one point on which Tindal and his colleagues seemed to be embroidering their statement with a recommendation. In previous trials the question put to the jury had been, in effect, 'Was the accused able to distinguish right from wrong in general?'—that is, 'could he have given sensible answers to questions about the rightness and wrongness of different sorts of action?' No doubt some of Tindal's colleagues had in fact put the question in this way. But collectively they agreed that it should now be phrased in a more practical and more readily answerable form: 'Did he know that what he *was* doing was wrong?' But they hastened to say that the old form of the question 'rarely if ever' led to any mistake with the jury: it was merely not quite so 'accurate' as the form in which they put it.

Did 'knowing that the act was wrong' mean 'recognizing that it was generally accepted as morally wrong', or 'believing oneself in its moral wrongness' or 'being aware that it was an infringement of the criminal law'? For a man might recognize that his act would be morally condemned by his fellow men, and yet believe it to be morally right; or he might recognize it to be criminal, and yet either believe that it would not be morally condemned by his fellow men, or believe that they would be mistaken in condemning it.

Before McNaughton's case, as we have seen, neither judge nor jury distinguished clearly between sinfulness and illegality. But the judges' replies to the Lords' questions show that they certainly did:

> If the accused was conscious that the act was one which he ought not to
> do, and if that act was at the same time contrary to the law of the land, he
> is punishable.

In other words, it was his *knowledge* of its objective moral wrongness, together with the *fact* of its illegality, which made him punishable. Stephen, too, when he defended the Rules in his paper for the Juridical Society in 1855 (loc. cit., p. 75) clearly interpreted them in this way. It was probably Townley's case which made the lawyers think a little more deeply.

Townley was a man from a respectable Manchester family whose fiancée in Derbyshire had broken off the engagement because she preferred someone else. He wrote asking her to see him, and when he arrived from Manchester they went for a long walk, at the end of which he cut her throat. Making no attempt to escape, he said to the people who found them: 'I told her I would kill her. She knew my temper', and behaved with 'apparent indifference'. His defence was insanity, and Forbes Winslow was the chief medical witness. (It is interesting

137

to note that both his interviews with the prisoner had been conducted in the presence of the prison governor and without any disclosure of his name or purpose to the prisoner.) Townley had showed several clear symptoms of insanity, saying that six conspirators were plotting his destruction, and that he had as much right to deal with his unfaithful fiancée as with any other property of his; he had no remorse, and recognized no man's right to judge him. On the other hand, Winslow seemed to admit under cross-examination that Townley knew he was breaking the law. Baron Martin, who referred to several earlier cases but made no mention of the McNaughton Rules, told the jury in effect that the question for them was whether Townley knew that his act was contrary to the law of God and punishable by the law of the land. Townley was convicted and sentenced to death.[15]

It is very difficult to reconcile this with the McNaughton Rules: indeed, it is not certain that Baron Martin would have been greatly concerned to do so. But Townley's case emphasized the problem posed by the Rules. Was a man to be acquitted if he admitted to knowing that his act was both illegal and morally condemned by his fellow men, yet said that to him it had seemed right? How was one to judge his sincerity? The test would cease to be whether he had 'knowledge' of any objective fact, and would become something quite different. Even 'knowledge' of the moral views of one's fellow men was dangerously close to subjectivity. If objectivity was the aim, the most objective fact was the illegality of the act; and some judges took the view that knowledge of its illegality should be the test.

By the time, therefore, that he came to write his *Digest of the Criminal Law* in 1877 Stephen had to recognize two points of view; and he simply said that 'wrong' meant either morally wrong or illegal. (He did not discuss the rather academic possibility that a man might know his act to be morally wrong yet deludedly believe it to be legal, so that it is not clear whether he would have stuck to his formula through thick and thin.)

The pendulum had begun to swing, and in 1916 it swung further still, when Codère's case came before the Court of Criminal Appeal during the First World War.[16] Georges Codère was a Canadian infantry lieutenant who was known in his regiment as 'Fou Codère', and had been regarded as so abnormal as to be unfit for active command in France. While stationed in England he conceived

[15] Immediately after the trial Baron Martin wrote to the Home Secretary that the conviction was in his opinion just, but that two doctors had declared Townley 'absolutely insane'. Grey asked Martin what his view was, but Martin hedged. The Lunacy Commissioners were then asked to examine the prisoner, but reported that, though not of sound mind, he had been responsible for his act within the meaning of the McNaughton Rules. Townley's family, however, were well-to-do and his lawyers were resourceful. A scrutiny of Lord Normanby's Act of 1840 showed them what could be done. At the same time as the Lunacy Commissioners' report there arrived at the Home Office a certificate by three local justices and two doctors that they had examined Townley and that he was insane. It was now only forty-eight hours before tne time fixed for the execution, and although there were legal flaws in the certificate Grey decided to respite the prisoner, and shortly afterwards transferred him to Bethlem. There, at Grey's request, he was examined yet again by Meyer of Broadmoor, Hood of Bethlem, and two other doctors, who said unequivocally that he was of sound mind. Townley was transferred again, this time to the penitentiary at Pentonville, where he put an end to the tragi-comedy by committing suicide.

[16] R. v. Codère (1916), 12 Cr. App. R. 21.

138

the idea of murdering a Canadian sergeant, possibly for the latter's money. After trying unsuccessfully to enlist the help of friends (who humoured him but do not seem to have warned the sergeant), he lured his victim to the officers' quarters and battered him to death with great violence, afterwards cutting his throat nearly to the spine. He then asked two of the officers' servants to help him clear up the mess and put the body in a stable. At least one of them, who was both dull-witted and terrified of Codère, obeyed him, and later waited on him at table as he calmly dined with his colonel and major. Codère tried to put the blame for the killing on this servant, but was soon under arrest himself. His defence was insanity, but was rejected by the jury, Mr Justice Darling having told them that 'wrong' meant 'contrary to law'.

His counsel argued before the appellate court that it was not enough that he knew the act to be contrary to law: the jury should have been told that they must acquit him unless they also thought that he knew it to be morally wrong. For some not very clear reason—perhaps as a safety precaution—counsel complicated the issue by resting this argument not merely on the McNaughton Rules' clear interpretation of 'wrong' which has just been quoted, but also on the phrase 'nature and quality of the act'. He maintained that 'nature' referred to the physical characteristics of the act, but 'quality' referred to its morality. The Court of Criminal Appeal were understandably sceptical about this part of his argument, but less pardonably rejected his interpretation of 'wrong' in the McNaughton Rules. The Rules said quite plainly that 'if the accused was conscious that the act was one which he ought not to do (i.e. conscious of its moral wrongness) and if that act was at the same time contrary to the law of the land (i.e. as a matter of fact, not of his knowledge) he is punishable'. The clear implication is that if the act was illegal, but he was *not* conscious of its moral wrongness, he was not punishable. Yet although they quoted this very passage the court interpreted it in a perverse sense.

They said that the wrongness of the act could not be judged by the standard of the accused, but only by 'the ordinary standard adopted by reasonable men', and went on to argue that 'once it is clear that the appellant knew that the act was wrong in law, then he was doing an act which he was conscious he ought not to do'. In effect they were maintaining that while the McNaughton Rules clearly said that the test was knowledge of moral wrongness and not of illegality, in practice knowledge of the former could safely be inferred from proved knowledge of the latter! Yet, as Stephen had emphasized, Hadfield's case had demonstrated that a man could know his act to be illegal yet think it right (as Hadfield must have done, for he was trying to be hanged without breaking God's commandments). They rejected the appeal, but hinted that the Home Secretary ought to reprieve Codère, which he did.

With Windle's case in 1952 the pendulum finally reached its furthest point, and stuck there.[17] Francis Wilfred Windle was 'a man of little resolution and weak character', married to a woman who was eighteen years older and suffering from a mental illness. She talked persistently of suicide, and Windle himself

[17] R. v. Windle (1952), 2 Q.B. 883 (C.C.A.).

139

became preoccupied with her state until his workmates were tired of hearing about it. Eventually one of them said 'Give her a dozen aspirins'. Windle gave her a much larger dose than this and killed her, telling the police later that he supposed he would be hanged for what he had done. One doctor at his trial said that he had been suffering from the form of communicated insanity called *folie à deux*, which his wife had no doubt succeeded in imposing on his weak personality. But the judge (Mr Justice, now Lord Devlin) ruled that there was no issue of insanity to be left to the jury. On appeal, counsel put forward more or less the argument that had been attempted in Codère's case (although without the confusing point about the meaning of 'quality'): he argued that the McNaughton Rules did not apply to a case in which there were no delusions, but that in any case by 'wrong' they meant morally wrong, and that cases such as Hadfield's were precedents for acquitting men who knew they were breaking the law but thought they were acting rightly.

The Lord Chief Justice, Lord Goddard, rejected this view with an argument which was, if anything, even less closely reasoned than his predecessor's in Codère's case:

> Courts of law . . . can only distinguish between that which is in accordance with law and that which is contrary to law. There are many acts which we all know, to use an expression to be found in some of the old cases, are contrary to the law of God and man. In the Decalogue are the commandments 'Thou shalt not kill' and 'Thou shalt not steal'. Such acts are contrary to the law of man and they are contrary to the law of God. In regard to the Seventh Commandment, 'Thou shalt not commit adultery', it will be found that so far as the criminal law is concerned, though that act is contrary to the law of God, it is not contrary to the law of man. That does not mean that the law encourages adultery: I only say it is not a criminal offence. The test must be whether an act is contrary to law . . . In the opinion of the court, there is no doubt that the word 'wrong' in the McNaughton Rules means contrary to law, and does not have some vague meaning which may vary according to the opinion of different persons whether a particular act might not be justified. . . .

Goddard had gone a step further than Lord Reading in Codère's case, and was flatly maintaining that 'wrong' in the McNaughton Rules meant 'illegal', although it is difficult to see how the crucial passage could be construed thus. Even more curious was the logic with which he tried to show that in any case this is the sensible view. 'Courts of law can only distinguish between that which is in accordance with law and that which is contrary to law.' Granted: but were they being asked to do more? Nobody had suggested that they should decide what was or was not morally wrong. At most they were being asked to accept two propositions. First, that the reasonable man regarded wife-killing as morally wrong. Second, that because of his insanity Windle did not (the fact that they may have doubted both that he was insane and that he believed his action right is irrelevant here). As for the differences between the law of God and

140

the law of man, all that this point did was to dispose of Lord Reading's argument that a person who knew the law of man could be assumed to know what was wrong in the eyes of God.

It is only towards the end of his argument that Goddard hints at what really worried the court. This was the vagueness of the test if 'wrong' meant 'morally wrong'. Certainly there would be occasions—although this was hardly one of them—in which it would not be easy for the court to say whether the reasonable man would have regarded the accused's action are morally wrong or not—for example in the case of a genuine mercy-killing. And although Goddard did not raise it, a curious question *might* be raised in such a case. If 'morally wrong' meant 'regarded by the reasonable man as morally wrong', and if it were likely that the reasonable man would not regard mercy-killing as morally wrong, would this weaken or support the defence of the mercy-killer whose insanity had strengthened his conviction that he was doing right?

However that may be, Windle's case, which is regarded as the last word on the subject, was the final step in the courts' retreat from the test which Spigurnel applied to the young felon in the fourteenth century: whether he knew good from evil. Like most retreats, it was dictated by expediency and carried out in confusion.

Finding cases where a decision has been determined by the precise interpretation of 'the nature and quality of the act' is not easy. In Codère's case, as we have just seen, counsel argued unsuccessfully that 'quality' meant 'morality'; but he did so probably as a safety precaution in case he failed with the argument that 'wrong' meant subjectively wrong. It is significant that discussions of the meaning of 'nature and quality' refer either to cases from other jurisdictions—chiefly Australia and the USA—or to imaginary situations. Stephen instances a man who wounded someone when he thought he was breaking a jar, and another man who strangled someone when he thought he was squeezing an orange; but he does not name the men or give references for their cases.[18] Almost certainly he was using his imagination; and later writers have simply used his illustrations.

According to the McNaughton Rules the accused's ignorance of the nature, quality, or wrongness of his act should be due to 'a defect of reason, through disease of the mind'. The use of the word 'reason' and the omission of words such as 'will' or 'self-control' is of course consistent with the cognitive nature of the tests themselves, but does not seem to have given rise to any special difficulty.

For the same reason there have been very few actual cases in which the verdict has turned on the precise meaning of 'disease of the mind'. It has been pointed out by J. A. Hobson that although 'insanity' in McNaughton's day was commonly used, even by doctors, in such a way as to include 'imbecility', the two have since then come to be distinguished, so that a psychiatrist might have to say that an accused was *not* insane *but* an imbecile.[19] Yet even Hobson cites only one case—Straffen's—to support his contention that this has in practice excluded some offenders who would otherwise have satisfied the McNaughton

[18] See J. F. Stephen, *A General View of the Criminal Law* (London, 1863).
[19] In (1955), 9, *Howard Journal*, 2.

Rules. Norwood East, who probably gave psychiatric evidence in more criminal trials than any other single doctor in the period between the wars, told the Gowers Commission in 1950 that he had never come across a case in which it had been held that the accused did not come within the Rules because mental deficiency was not a disease of the mind.[20]

The explanation is undoubtedly that if psychiatric witnesses were prepared to testify that the accused's disorder deprived him of the knowledge of what he was doing or of its wrongness, then neither judge nor jury would normally be concerned to draw distinctions between insanity and mental deficiency. Had the tests been less stringent the distinction would have been less academic; but as it was, a person who satisfied one of the tests satisfied the court.

Straffen's case did not occur until two years after Norwood East had given evidence to the Royal Commission. John Straffen was a youth of low intelligence who at the age of 21 had, by his own later admission, strangled at least two very young girls on the outskirts of Bath. When he came to trial he had been found unfit to plead and had been committed to Broadmoor. Six months later he escaped and within a few hours strangled another small girl within a short distance of the hospital. At his second trial[21] his counsel made no attempt to have him found unfit to plead: his defence was that it was not he who killed her but that in any case he was insane within the meaning of the McNaughton Rules. In support of this second contention counsel pointed out that he had not only been certified as a mental defective at the age of ten but had been found unfit to plead at his first trial the year before. Medical witnesses for the defence also stressed his lack of moral sense and his inadequate appreciation of the wrongness of killing the girls (he claimed to have done it merely to annoy the police). The prosecution's medical witnesses, while agreeing that he was of low intelligence, said that he was neither insane nor completely unaware of the wrongness of killing. Considerable play was made with the fact that he knew 'Thou shalt not kill' to be one of the Commandments and that he knew the penalty for murder.

Mr Justice Cassels' summing-up was clearly unfavourable to Straffen:

> ... ask yourselves whether you are satisfied by the defence that at the time when he did that murder he was insane within the meaning of the criminal law; not that he was feeble-minded; not that he had a lack of moral sense; not that he had no feeling for the victim or her relatives; not that he had no remorse; not that he may be weak in his judgement; not that he fails to appreciate the consequence of his act; but was he insane through a defect of reason caused by disease of the mind, so that either he did not know the nature and quality of his act, or, if he did know it, he did not know it was wrong?

Although he offered the jury a choice between 'not guilty', 'guilty but insane', and 'guilty', it is not surprising that they chose the last of these verdicts. Straffen's

[20] loc. cit., p. 119.
[21] Fully described by L. Fairfield and E. P. Fullbrook in *The Trial of John Thomas Straffen* (London, 1954).

appeal, which was not in any case based on this part of his defence, was dismissed, and he would have been hanged if the Home Secretary had not advised a reprieve. He was not sent to a mental hospital but has been kept in various prisons ever since.

It is conceivable that in the few years which remained before the introduction of the defence of diminished responsibility in 1957 there were subsequent cases in which Cassels' policy of distinguishing insanity from mental deficiency was followed. If so, I have not found them. It is even more unlikely that there have been any since 1957.

The distinction between a disease of the mind and a disease of the brain troubled courts for a short period in the middle of the nineteen-fifties. Charlson had seriously injured his son while in a state of automatism which was attributed by a medical witness to a tumour in his brain. The defence was not insanity but automatism, and he was acquitted. A year later a similar defence was attempted by Kemp, who had caused grievous bodily harm to his wife while in an abnormal state which was the result of hardening of the cerebral arteries. His counsel submitted that his state was not yet a disease of the mind (although at least one of their medical witnesses thought that it might develop into one) and that the proper verdict was therefore a complete acquittal, as in Charlson's case. The prosecution's medical witness thought that the arteriosclerosis had caused 'melancholia', and that this, which was undoubtedly a disease of the mind, had been the cause of Kemp's attack on his wife. Mr Justice Devlin took the view that 'disease of the mind' had not been intended to distinguish between brain and mind, but to make it clear that the 'defect of reason' must not merely be attributable to causes such as a bad upbringing. For safety he added the not altogether consistent argument that arteriosclerosis did seem to affect the mind in a way that could be called a disease. Kemp was therefore less fortunate than Charlson and was found guilty but insane.[22]

Although Devlin had tried to distinguish Kemp's case from Charlson's, the general opinion among judges seems to have been that Charlson had been too fortunate, and that the proper course in his case also would have been to regard his disorder as a disease of the mind and find him guilty but insane. Certainly this is what Lord Denning said when Bratty's case reached the House of Lords.[23] Indeed, he went so far as to say that 'any mental disorder which has manifested itself in violence and is prone to recur is a disease of the mind'. This in its turn is open to criticism. The phrase 'mental disorder' makes the dictum sound like a tautology: did he mean to say 'cerebral disorder'? And what about a mental or cerebral disorder which was prone to recur but manifested itself not in violence but in theft? Presumably he would have included this had Bratty's crime been theft.

The rule that drunkenness is not insanity, but that prolonged drinking may produce what is a 'disease of the mind', which was firmly established by Hale's time, has remained more or less unaltered since.

Tindal and his fellow judges had dealt in a particularly logical way with the

[22] R. v. Kemp (1956), 40 Cr. App. R. 121.
[23] See Bratty v. A.G. for Northern Ireland (1962) 46 Cr. App. R, 1, H.L.

143

difficult problem raised by delusion. In order to support a defence of insanity the nature of the delusion must be such that if it had been true the accused would be exempt from punishment. If he thought he was killing him in self-defence he would be excused; if he was revenging himself for an imaginary injury he would not. In practice, however, deluded offenders have been defended on the ground that they did not know the nature and quality of their act, so that this rule is nowadays regarded by authorities such as Professor Glanville Williams as being in desuetude.[24] Glanville Williams has found one case, in 1930, in which a man called Kenneally was charged with wounding a fellow workman with intent to murder him. He had been under the insane delusion that he had received news of his father's death and that the other man had killed him. Even if true this would not have justified his attack, and it was probably for this reason that he was advised by counsel to plead 'guilty'. However that may be, he was sentenced to ten years' penal servitude, and appealed. By that time he had been certified and transferred to an asylum, and the Court of Criminal Appeal reduced his sentence to three years, which probably meant that he would not have to go back to prison when he was discharged. Had he pleaded 'guilty but insane' he would probably have succeeded.[25]

I myself was present at an unusual trial in 1964. A West Indian called Male had been committed for trial at Oxford Assizes for the theft of a piece of cheese and a packet of biscuits from a supermarket. He suffered from the delusion that he was one of the Prophets who had returned to redeem the world, and that he had a right to any food that he needed. His delusion was therefore such that had it been true his taking of the food would not have been larceny, since it would have been done under a *bona fide* claim of right. (In the event, his counsel did not offer a defence of insanity, which could at best have resulted in indefinite detention in a mental hospital. Instead, he took the bolder line that his client was not guilty, since he genuinely believed that he had a right to the food. This defence might well have forced the judge to direct an acquittal; but the latter raised the question of Male's fitness to plead. Another jury was empanelled to try this issue, but decided that Male was fit to plead; at a third trial he pleaded guilty and was made the subject of a hospital order.)

It has always been an essential part of procedure for the accused to bring forward some evidence of insanity if he wished to offer this as a defence. As Tindal and his colleagues put it, 'every man is presumed to be sane until the contrary be proved to [the jury's] satisfaction' and later they used the words 'clearly proved'. Since this in effect seems to saddle the accused with the burden of disproving *mens rea*, it is not easy to reconcile it with the general principle that this is for the prosecution to prove. The difficulty was not recognized in 1843 because the general principle had not been clearly stated; indeed, it was not until 1935 that it was plainly laid down by the House of Lords in Woolmington's case.[26] It was said then, in passing, that insanity was an exception; but

[24] Glanville Williams, *Criminal Law: the General Part*, 2nd ed. (London, 1961).
[25] R. v. Kenneally (1930), 22 Cr. App. R. 52.
[26] R. v. Woolmington (1935), A.C. 475.

144

lawyers have had great difficulty in justifying the exception. Glanville Williams does so by arguing that what rests on the accused is merely an *evidential* burden —that is, the necessity of producing some evidence pointing to insanity—and that once this has been done the *persuasive* burden—or arguing that the accused was not insane within the meaning of the Rules—then lies on the prosecution. But this does not seem to be honoured in practice.

Instead, it was conceded[27] soon after Woolmington's case that while the burden of proof of insanity rested on the accused, it was not quite so heavy as the burden which normally rests on the prosecution. Whereas the latter had to produce evidence which proved *mens rea* (and other matters) beyond reasonable doubt, the accused's evidence need only point *on a balance of probabilities* to insanity within the meaning of the Rules.

No evidence need be given by witnesses with psychiatric or indeed medical qualifications, although nowadays an attempt to set up the defence without such evidence would have little chance of success. In the eighteenth century, as we have seen, it was exceptional for the accused to be able to produce a doctor to confirm his insanity: only the well-to-do were in a position to do this. In the eighteen-thirties, although the Newgate surgeon appeared quite frequently at the Old Bailey to testify to the state of mind of the accused, his place was some-times taken by the governor. Even after the medical profession had been recog-nized by statute, and asylum doctors had become acknowledged as specialists, it was not impossible for the accused to rely on his or her state of mind as a defence without calling a medical witness. In 1878 Eliza Dart threw her child and then herself into the Serpentine. Both were rescued and she was indicted for attempted murder. Although the case is not adequately reported,[28] her defence seems to have been that her state of mind deprived her of the intention to kill: on being rescued she had exclaimed 'Save the child, let me die'. The prosecution submitted that if this was her defence she should produce scientific evidence as to her state of mind, but Mr Justice Brett ruled that it was a mistake to suppose that this *must* be done: if the facts indicated unsoundness of mind, that was enough. As late as 1910 an Old Bailey jury found William Backwell (who had shot a woman friend) guilty but insane on what appears to have been nothing more than the evidence of himself and his friends (although it is true that he claimed to be under medical treatment).[29] Although I do not know of any later example, the Privy Council made it clear in the South Australian case of Brown[30] that this was still theoretically possible in 1960: 'their Lordships are not of course suggesting that legal insanity cannot be sufficiently proved without medical evidence. The previous and contemporaneous acts of the accused may often be preferred to medical theory.' Nowadays, however, legal aid and the National Health Service make it unnecessary as well as unwise for the defence to dispense with psychiatric testimony.

A much-criticized feature of McNaughton's trial had been the way in which

[27] By the Privy Council in Sodemann's case (1936), 2 A.E.R., 1138.
[28] R. v. Dart (1878), 14 Cox 143.
[29] R. v. Backwell (1910), CCCSP, p. 492.
[30] A.G. for S. Australia v. Brown (1960), 44 Cr. App. R. 100 (P.C.).

the judges had allowed Drs Winslow and Philips, whose only knowledge of McNaughton had been gained from hearing the evidence of others and watching his demeanour in court, to testify as to his mental state at the time of his act. Tindal and his colleagues had defended themselves rather half-heartedly on this point in the Rules; they admitted that it was not quite proper, but thought that where the facts were not in dispute the question became 'one of science only', and while it could not be demanded as a right it could be allowed. Six years later, in Frances' case, Baron Alderson and Mr Justice Cresswell (who had been among the judges who composed the Rules) took the line that a physician who had merely been in court throughout the trial could not be asked whether the prisoner was insane: only what were the symptoms of insanity or, assuming particular facts to be true, whether they indicated that the prisoner was insane. To allow more would be to substitute the witness for the jury.[31]

The principle that it is for the jury and not for medical witnesses to decide whether the defence is satisfied has been maintained to the present day, although in Matheson's case[32] the Court of Criminal Appeal conceded that if the medical evidence was 'all one way' a jury's verdict which disregarded it should be set aside. Although Matheson's defence was not insanity but diminished responsibility, no doubt the concession applies to the defence of insanity.

But even if the medical evidence is all one way, it is the duty of the prosecution to probe its soundness, as was made clear in the case of Ahmed Din. He was a Pakistani, aged 46, who lived in Birmingham with his wife and some of his ten children. They had a somewhat younger friend of 29, Ansari, who used to visit them, sharing Din's bed while the wife slept with the children. Din conceived the idea that his wife was unfaithful to him with Ansari and told her to ask Ansari to leave; but she said she could not do so, and denied that the relationship was more than that of 'brother and sister'. Din stabbed Ansari one night in their bed with great ferocity. His defence was diminished responsibility, and two medical witnesses (including a prison medical officer) supported it with a diagnosis of paranoia. They were cross-examined by the prosecution, but only in order to see whether the accused should not be found 'guilty but insane'. Mr Justice Stable intervened, and elicited from both witnesses the admission that the only evidence of Din's paranoia was his belief that his wife was unfaithful to him with Ansari, and that there had in fact been suspicious occurrences. Neither side had asked the wife to testify. The judge criticized the prosecution for not probing the medical evidence more thoroughly, and told the jury that it was for them to decide whether Din's belief was a delusion or reasonable. The jury then rejected the defence, and on appeal Stable's direction to them was upheld.[33]

A feature of the English system of trial which is the subject of recurrent criticisms is the way in which it treats psychiatric witnesses like any other kind of witness. They must be called either by the defence or by the prosecution; their

[31] R. v. Frances (1849), 4 Cox 57.
[32] R. v. Matheson (1958), 42 Cr. App. R. 145.
[33] R. v. Din (1962), 42 Cr. App. R. 116.

opinions are elicited by question and answer; they are cross-examined and re-examined; and if they appear to be contradicting each other it is the jury who at the end of the day decides who is telling the truth. Like the witness who identifies an assailant, the psychiatrist is treated as if he is testifying to an ordinary matter of fact. As on so many points, it was Isaac Ray who had the temerity (on the other side of the Atlantic) to question the merits of the system which Hale had extolled so proudly. Ray thought it ridiculous that the jury should be allowed to decide between conflicting medical witnesses, of whom one might be an authority, the other an ignorant nobody. The procedure seemed to him much inferior to its French counterpart, under which the court could appoint *experts* to inquire into the mental state of the accused and report on oath to the court. Bucknill and Forbes Winslow, who greatly resented the way in which he had been cross-examined by counsel, proposed a similar procedure in the eighteen-fifties. Harrington Tuke, another experienced psychiatric witness, suggested it to the Capital Punishment Commission of 1864–66, who ignored him.

The British Medical Association proposed to the Atkin Committee in 1923 that there should be an impartial panel of psychiatric experts to which the accused should be referred if suspected of being mentally disordered, and which would furnish copies of its report both to prosecution and defence. At the trial, they suggested, 'evidence should be tendered in person by the expert or experts who examined the accused, and should be considered by the court in deciding the responsibility or otherwise of the accused'. The Medico-Psychological Association, who submitted a similar proposal, made it clear that the experts should be open to cross-examination by either side, who would also have the right to call their own expert witnesses. Presumably they hoped, not unreasonably, that the authority of the impartial expert would simply make it unprofitable to exercise this right. The Atkin Committee (who included only lawyers and civil servants) gave these ideas short shrift. 'The panel would have to range over the whole of England and Wales, and we think that in some parts of the country there would be a difficulty in finding suitable members. In no case would it be possible to leave medical testimony to members of the panel and thus prevent an accused person calling evidence of his own doctor or doctors not on the panel. The conflict of medical opinion could not by such means be prevented.' One is left with the feeling that they had not really studied the proposals with care.

By the time of the Royal Commission on Capital Punishment of 1949–53 the two medical associations were no longer in favour of the idea; but other medical witnesses were, and the Commission, though they apologized for dealing with it rather briefly, gave it a more thorough consideration than any of their predecessors had done. They admitted that it need not preclude the cross-examination of the impartial experts, nor the calling of other medical witnesses by either side; but the possibility that the jury might give more weight to the impartial experts seems to have struck them as an objection rather than as an advantage. On the whole they seem to have been conscious of difficulty in producing strong arguments against the innovation, and had to fall back on the argument that it 'would mean a fundamental change in the procedure of our courts . . . and would have repercussions so far beyond the limited field of our inquiry that we should not feel justified in recommending it'. This was an appeal to conservatism and their terms of reference rather than to logic.

So much for developments in procedure and interpretation. What was happening in practice? For example, what changes had there been in the success rate of the insanity defence since the eighteen-thirties? So far as trials at the Old Bailey are concerned it is possible to answer this question up to 1912, but not after, since the Sessions Papers ceased to be published in the spring of the following year. Since they had by this time become extremely bulky, containing reports of more than 1,500 cases a year, it was out of the question to examine more than a few short periods. I chose the last four years of the series, and two intermediate periods of three years each. One was in the early eighteen-fifties, nearly a decade after McNaughton's case, which could by then be presumed to have made some of its impact on the courts. The other was the early eighteen-eighties, and was chosen partly because it was more or less intermediate between the other two, partly in the hope—which was not to be realized—of finding some mention of Queen Victoria's new form of special verdict.

The result can be seen in Table I. In the eighteen-fifties and eighteen-eighties the frequency of 'insanity cases' seems to have been $6\frac{1}{2}$ and 8 per thousand, higher than in any previous period since the seventeen-sixties; and by the Edwardian years it had risen higher still. Part of the increase may have been due to the tendency to deal with petty offences at summary courts, thus leaving the Old Bailey with a greater concentration of crimes carrying serious penalties; but this was not the case as early as the eighteen-fifties, when many of the charges were trivial ones of uttering counterfeit coins. At least part of the trend must reflect a genuinely greater likelihood that a mentally disordered prisoner would be recognized as such: a trend which must have been at least partly attributable to the increasing efficiency of medical attention. In many of the insanity cases the witnesses included the medical officer of Newgate or other gaols.

On the other hand, the success-rate did not rise with the frequency. If anything it was slightly lower than previously—about four in ten as compared with five in ten. It was not until the end of the century that it began to climb again, until just before the First World War it was about seven in ten. For if we turn to the national statistics in Table II, the picture they present is consistent with this. Although they do not unfortunately give us any information about frequencies or success-rates, they show that from the last decades of the nineteenth century there was a steady rise in the murderer's chances of benefiting from a plea of insanity.

The nineteenth century was not, as is so often supposed, a period during which the eighteenth-century's unwillingness to accept pleas of insanity was gradually relaxed. On the contrary, for most of the century lawyers were becoming increasingly concerned, articulate, and restrictive about such pleas, so that an increase in their frequency, which in the seventeen-fifties had been accompanied by a greater willingness to accept them, now merely meant that more of them were unsuccessful. It was not until the last decades of the nineteenth century that the second major relaxation of attitude commenced. This was not

TABLE I

Old Bailey trials during selected periods between 1740 and 1913 in which the sanity of the accused was questioned

Period	Trials at which the prisoner's fitness for trial was questioned Ad	—successfully B	mental state was considered as an excuse C	—and accepted De	'Success-rate', i.e. cols. B+D as % of A+Cf E	Frequency of A+Ce per 1,000 accused persons F
1740–4	—	—	9	3		
1745–9	—	—	15	5	28·5%	4·6
1750–4	—	—	11	2		
1755–9	1	1	16	7		
1760–4	1	—	17	9	50·0%	7·2
1765–9	—	—	15	8		
1780–4	—	—	12	7		
1790–4	3	3	11	4	41·3%	4·4
1795–9	1	—	19	5		
1800a	1	—	2	1		
1801–5	—	—	23	12		
1806–10	2	2	22	7	50·0%	4·7
1811–5	1	1	14	9		
1834–6b	2	2	23	12	56·0%	2·9
1851–3	6	4	23	7	37·9%	6·4
1881–4	2	2	38	15	42·5%	7·9
1909–13c	5	5	51	34	69·6%	13·0

The laboriousness of the task ruled out the examination of the entire series. A few quinquennia were therefore selected around dates which were of interest, and the gaps between them were filled in when it became clear that the period was of special interest. In the nineteenth century the annual numbers of trials increased greatly, and periods of three or four years, which yielded as many cases as eighteenth-century quinquennia, were examined: since other statistical information was available, greater intervals were allowed. The total number of trials scanned was about 55,000.

a The year of Hadfield's trial has been deliberately excluded in calculating the rates in columns E and F.
b The period was chosen because the published national judicial statistics begin in 1834.
c The series ended in April 1913, not with a whimper but a bang—the trial of Mrs Pankhurst for trying to blow up a building.
d The figures excludes cases of deaf-mutism.
e These figures are included in the previous column.
f Columns A and B must be included because of the likelihood that if the prisoner's fitness for trial had not been questioned his mental state would have been considered as an excuse, and because in some early cases it is not clear whether the case should be classified as an instance of A or C.

Period	A Persons for trial (as annual averages)	B Unfit to plead	C Acquitted as insane	D Found of diminished responsibility
			(as percentages of A)	
1834–43	65·3	2·0%	7·5%	—
1844–53	72·6	4·7%	7·5%	—
1854–63	68·0	5·7%	10·1%	—
1864–73	63·7	5·8%	9·6%	—
1874–83	63·6	8·8%	10·4%	—
1884–93	68·4	11·4%	11·0%	—
1894–1907	62·6	8·2%	22·6%	—
1908–13	70·7	7·8%	26·4%	—
1914–18	52·2	15·1%	26·0%	—
1919–22	74·0	10·5%	20·6%	—
1923–30	54·8	14·2%	28·1%	—
1931–38	56·5	16·2%	31·2%	—
1939–45	No figures published for the period of the War			
1946–56	72·4	21·2%	22·5%	—
1957–64	103·9	11·1%	6·3%	28·5%

a Strictly speaking, persons brought to trial on indictment for murder.

the consequence of any *cause célèbre,* or indeed of any single identifiable event, but a gradual process.

For this was the period during which British psychiatry, which had hitherto been the preserve of a handful of somewhat controversial pundits, began to establish itself as a respectable discipline. The multiplying of asylums recruited more and more doctors. The discoveries, real or apparent, of neurologists opened up the prospects of a scientific basis for alienists' theories. More particularly, the increasing numbers of convicts, many of them serving very long

B+C+D	'Landmarks' used as dividing points
(as percentages of A)	
9·5%	
	McNaughton's case
12·2%	
16·8%	
	Capital Punishment Commission
15·4%	
19·2%	
	New form of special verdict
22·4%	
30·8%	
	Court of Criminal Appeal created
34·2%	
41·1%	First World War
31·1%	
	Infanticide Act: True's Case: Atkin Committee appointed
42·3%	
	Commons Committee on Capital Punishment
47·4%	
	Second World War
43·7%	
	Homicide Act
45·9%	
	Capital punishment suspended for murder in 1965

sentences, presented the medical officers of the prisons with psychiatric problems which could not be ignored. Moreover, although psychiatry had not yet achieved the popularity with the educated layman which was to have such an impact on the outlook of the twentieth century, its importance was beginning to be appreciated by legislators and lawyers, including—as we have seen—Fitzjames Stephen himself, whose own declining years were to be clouded by mental disorder.

From the First World War onward we must rely on Table II. The percentage of successful pleas of insanity in murder trials continued to rise steadily until 1938. It was exceptionally high during the 1914–18 war, no doubt because the percentage of mentally normal murderers was reduced by the absence of so many able-bodied men from normal life. In contrast, special verdicts were less frequent than usual in the years immediately following the war, when many murders were committed by those mentally normal men when they returned home to find their women unfaithful, jobs hard to get, and civilian life an anticlimax. Although unfortunately no such figures can be obtained for the Second World War, there was a similar drop in the percentage of special verdicts in the years of demobilization.

It is surprising, however, that the percentage continued to rise in the nineteen-twenties. For in 1922 not only did the Court of Criminal Appeal finally rule out irresistible impulse as a defence, but also the Infanticide Act provided mothers who killed their babies with a safer defence than insanity. The interference must be that the effects of these events were more than counterbalanced by a greater readiness on the part of medical witnesses, judges, and juries to consider defences of insanity from male murderers. By the nineteen-thirties nearly one-third of murder trials ended in a special verdict, and nearly one-half ended either in a special verdict or a finding of 'unfit to plead'. But at this point some sort of high-water mark seems to have been reached. Even in the early nineteen-fifties, after the 'demobilization murders' were over, the combined percentages of murderers found 'unfit to plead' or 'guilty but insane' did not rise above 44 per cent; and not even the addition of a new defence, diminished responsibility, could raise the percentage much higher.[34]

---

[34] See my *Crime and Insanity in England*, Vol. 1, Chapter 9.

THE McNAUGHTON RULES IN THE UNITED STATES

ABRAHAM S. GOLDSTEIN and MARTIN MARCUS

For more than a century, the *McNaughton* rules have played a central role in discussions of the insanity defence in the United States.[1] A voluminous literature, often polemical in tone, has held them responsible for much that is problematic not only about the defence but also about the criminal law, expert testimony, the adversary process and the jury system. The result has been a remarkable degree of consensus that a new rule was urgently needed, and that such a rule would serve in some fundamental way to reshape the criminal law.

Unfortunately, these discussions of *McNaughton* did not, until recently, do very much to place the words of the rules in the full context of trial and related processes. Without a realistic sense of this context, it has been extraordinarily difficult to appraise claims and counterclaims and to determine which of the many issues raised in the literature genuinely deserved consideration.

In this article, we shall supply some of the missing context. We shall examine not only what the words of *McNaughton* have meant in the United States, but also the effect they have had upon the evidence presented and the arguments made in cases raising the insanity defence. Though space does not permit us to present the full context here, a realistic appraisal must take into account that the defence is only a part of the law dealing with the mentally ill offender. Competing processes and defences succeed in drawing off a large proportion of those who might win acquittal by reason of insanity. Such offenders may be diverted from the criminal process through the exercise of police and prosecutorial discretion, and through referral to 'helping' agencies which are not directly involved in law enforcement. Civil commitment proceedings may be initiated in lieu of prosecution, and even if criminal charges are brought, the offender may be found incompetent to stand trial. In either case, he may face indeterminate detention in a mental hospital. If he is competent to stand trial, he may choose not to raise the insanity defence but instead to plead guilty and hope the

[1] The matters discussed herein are treated at greater length and with more detailed references in A. Goldstein, *The Insanity Defense* (Yale University Press, 1967), from which portions of this article have been taken. Additions and changes have been made in text and notes to reflect developments since 1967. Copyright retained by Abraham S. Goldstein. The authors are grateful to Bruce Mann, J.D., 1975, for his assistance in the research for this article.

153

judge will consider his mental condition at sentencing.[2] Or he may proceed to trial and offer another defence to which his mental disorder is relevant in order to reduce the gravity of the charge against him. In some jurisdictions, for example, he may enter a plea of 'partial responsibility', which resembles the English law of diminished responsibility; in others he may claim that his mental condition negated a specific intent, or that it disorted the innocent behaviour of another person into a provocation for his own act. If he asserts, as some States allow him to do, that his disorder rendered his act involuntary (e.g. automatism) or prevented the formation of the *mens rea* required for offences charging only general intent or recklessness, he may even win outright acquittal, rather than conviction for a lesser offence.

These competing processes and defences prove attractive to most mentally disordered offenders, who fear the indeterminate detention which usually follows a 'successful' insanity defence. The result is that the defence of insanity is not asserted very often. Nevertheless, it retains a significance out of all proportion to the frequency with which it is raised. The reasons are deeply rooted; they can be traced to the difficulty of setting limits on personal responsibility and of determining whether blame and 'guilt' should attach to persons who commit 'crime' while mentally ill.

The *McNaughton* rules occupy only a portion of the American law of insanity. That law has developed considerable texture and variation in the past 142 years, principally because there are 51 legal systems in the United States, each of which has been free to choose its own definition of the defence. Several tests now compete with *McNaughton*. Nevertheless, the rules remain the sole definition in 21 States; in another 11 States, they are part of a formula which adds some form of 'irresistible impulse' or 'control' rule. And where they have been replaced by a rule recommended by the American Law Institute, they survive in a modernized form in the first part of the new rule.[3]

I

The words of *McNaughton* do not need repeating here. They emphasize knowledge of the sanctions threatened by the criminal code while saying nothing about self-control. The tacit assumption is that powers of self-control are strengthened by knowledge of sanctions; and that any injustices which might result—to those who have nevertheless been unable to control their conduct—are less important than exerting the maximum possible pressure toward conformity with law. The rules also seem to assume that the community at large, acting through the jury, would be willing to 'exempt' offenders from the criminal

---

[2] There has been a good deal of controversy on the question whether the court or prosecutor may assert the defence over the objection of the accused. The cases point increasingly towards permitting them to do so, see e.g. Whalem v. United States, 346 F. 2d 812, 818 (D.C. Cir. 1965); United States v. Robertson, 507 F. 2d 1148 (D.C. Cir. 1974); cf. Lynch v. Overholser, 369 U.S. 705 (1962). But the general *practice* is to leave it to defendant and his counsel to raise the defence or not.

[3] See the Appendix for a detailed list of American jurisdictions and the rules they curren:ly follow. Two States use a different test, the 'product' rule.

law only if they obviously did not know what they were about. Nevertheless, important questions of interpretation arise. What illness may qualify as a 'disease' of the mind? Is 'know' to include emotional appreciation of the impact of an act upon both offender and victim or is it to be limited to abstract awareness? Does 'wrong' refer to legal or moral wrong?

Given the age of *McNaughton*, it would be reasonable to assume that every one of these questions, and countless others, had been construed again and again in judicial opinions or settled by statute. The fact is, however, that even in the United States—with its multiplicity of state and federal jurisdictions and its litigious bar—there has been surprisingly little judicial construction of the *McNaughton* wording.

The absence of authoritative interpretation does not mean that *McNaughton* has been ignored. On the contrary, it was for a very long time the focal point of intense controversy. The rule has been condemned as retributive in nature, making scapegoats of offenders who could not possibly have acted otherwise; and lauded as uniquely suited to serve the deterrent function of the criminal law. In the United States, however, it is the critics' *McNaughton* which has dominated the debate. The picture they present is that of a restrictive rule which reflects an outmoded faculty psychology; it sees thought processes as separated into cognitive, emotional, and control components and classes a man as insane only if he suffers from serious cognitive or intellectual impairment. This, the critics argue, is at odds with the 'new psychology' which sees man's personality as dynamically integrated and his mental condition as necessarily unsound if any part of its functioning is disordered.

The principal consequence of *McNaughton* is said to be that it denies to the jury the 'insights of modern psychology' because it restricts the flow of expert testimony and makes the defence unavailable to the great majority of those who suffer from serious mental illness—because so few psychotics suffer from major cognitive impairment and most who do are so deteriorated that they will not be competent to stand trial.[4]

This interpretation of *McNaughton* has been dinned into the professional literature for so long that it is generally assumed there can be no other. As a result, the elimination of *McNaughton* and willingness to adopt a newer, more flexible rule has been treated as a test of liberal faith. It is not at all certain, however, that the critics' *McNaughton* is an accurate portrait. If an adequate assessment of the rules is to be made, *McNaughton* must be seen as it is presented to the jury and as the jury is likely to understand it. An examination must be made of its effect upon counsel considering whether to assert the defence, upon the evidence admitted to prove and disprove it, and upon the expert testimony offered by the parties. But first, we must see how the words themselves have fared in the American courts, and determine the limits they set to our inquiry.

---

[4] See the references collected in *Durham* v. *United States*, 214 F. 2d 862, 870–71 (D.C. Cir. 1954).

'Disease of the mind'

There has been almost no judicial definition of mental disease in cases concerned with the *McNaughton* rules. The words are usually presented, without explanation, as part of the charge to the jury. What little law on the subject does exist is found in cases which reject effort to assert insanity by persons whose mental conditions are clearly marginal. In this group are cases involving alcohol intoxication, narcotics withdrawal, temporary insanity, and borderline mental defects.

The intoxication cases say it is ordinarily not enough for the defendant to show that, at the time of the crime, his thought processes were seriously distorted by alcohol or narcotics. And the 'temporary insanity' cases conclude that it is not enough that the defendant acted during an 'emotional frenzy'. More generally, the defence is said to be unavailable to 'a person of weak intellect or one whose moral perceptions were blunted or ill developed'. The focus in these cases is not so much on whether the defendant entertained the requisite mental state at the time of the crime as it is upon whether he had, in addition, a disease —preferably one of 'a fixed or prolonged nature'. But the cases are silent as to what diseases would qualify. The question is not treated as one of law at all, but rather as if the necessary link could be provided by the testimony of expert witnesses. If they are willing to affirm that the frenzy, or the distortion, was attributable to a mental disease and are willing to name and describe the disease, then the issue will ordinarily be passed to the jury. The disease named most often is some form of psychosis; the assumption has been that psychopathy and other non-psychotic illnesses would not qualify.

The only other cases touching directly on the definition of 'mental disease' are those discussing a mental 'defect', such as a low IQ or some other form of mental retardation. The rule seems to be that such defects qualify as mental diseases and will exculpate the defendant if they are severe enough to deprive him of the 'knowledge' specified in *McNaughton*.

'Know'

The word 'know' has been at the centre of the controversy surrounding McNaughton. Most critics read it as referring to formal cognition or intellectual awareness alone. They distinguish this, the 'law's' meaning, from what they describe as the 'psychiatric' meaning—which they take to connote a fuller, deeper knowledge, involving emotional as well as intellectual awareness. This fuller knowledge can exist only when the accused is able to evaluate his conduct in terms of its actual impact upon himself and others and when he is able to appreciate the total setting in which he is acting. According to the critics, the law's type of knowledge is to be found even in the most serious psychoses. Indeed, to borrow from a well-known comment, it is absent only in the 'totally deteriorated, drooling, hopeless psychotics of long-standing and congenital idiots'.[5] The consequence, the argument continues, is that *McNaughton* directs jurors to hold responsible a great many persons who are seriously disturbed

[5] Zilboorg, *Mind, Medicine and Man*, 273 (1943).

and makes it virtually impossible to assert the defence successfully. Moreover, since only a handful of psychotics do not 'know' in this restricted sense, efforts to expand the concept of 'disease' to include those who are not psychotic are doomed to fail.

The assertion that 'know' is narrowly defined has been made so often and so insistently that it comes as a surprise to find that very few appellate courts have imposed the restrictive interpretation. Most of the courts which have addressed the question have favoured a rather broad construction. In six of the twenty-one States that use *McNaughton* as the sole test of insanity, the jury is told that an accused 'knows' only if he 'understands' enough to enable him to judge of 'the nature, character and consequence of the act charged against him', or if he has the 'capacity to appreciate the character and to comprehend the probable or possible consequences of his act'.[6]

Commenting on the Canadian practice which uses the broader wording, the Canadian Royal Commission on Insanity concluded that 'the act must necessarily involve more than mere knowledge that the act is being committed; there must be an appreciation of the factors involved in the act and a mental capacity to measure and foresee the consequences of the violent conduct'. In this view, the word 'appreciate' draws most psychoses under the *McNaughton* rules, because it addresses itself to the defendant's awareness of 'the true significance of his conduct'.[7] And the California court, in *People* v. *Wolff*, noted that 'our trial courts place a commendably broad interpretation upon the *McNaughton* "knowledge" test'.[8] It is 'knowledge "fused with affect" and assimilated by the whole personality—so that, for example, the killer was capable of identifying with his prospective victim'—which the California court had in mind. It went so far as to incorporate elements of an 'irresistible impulse' rule into its *McNaughton* formula, saying:

'If through disorder of the faculties a prisoner is incapable of controlling his relevant acts, this may afford the strongest reason for supposing that he is incapable of forming a judgment that they are wrong, and in some cases even of understanding their nature ... If the disease or mental derangement so governs the faculties that it is impossible for the party accused to reason with some moderate degree of calmness, in relation to the moral quality of what he is doing, he is prevented from knowing that what he does is wrong.'

In the remaining fifteen *McNaughton* jurisdictions, the jury is simply given the words of the rule, without explanation, and left to find the 'common sense' meaning from their own backgrounds or from the materials presented to them at trial. Nowhere, however, are they told they must adopt a restrictive interpretation.

---

[6] Several other *McNaughton* States followed this practice but have since adopted the ALI rule.
[7] Report of *Royal Commission on Law of Insanity as a Defense in Criminal Cases* (Canada), pp. 12–13 (1955).
[8] People v. Wolff, 394 P. 2d 959, 961–2 (Calif. 1964).

'Nature and Quality of the Act'

The phrase 'nature and quality of the act' is sometimes omitted completely from the charge to the jury. More often, it is either stated to the jury without explanation or treated as adding nothing to the requirement that the accused know his act was wrong. The underlying theory is that if the accused did not know the nature and quality of his act, he would have been incapable of knowing it was wrong. There have been a few efforts to treat the phrase as if it added something to the rules. In England, for example, it was once suggested that 'nature' meant the act's physical nature, while 'quality' referred to its moral aspect. The court rejected the suggestion, holding that 'nature and quality' refers solely to the physical character of the act.[9] In the United States, the rule seems to be similar, though the Wisconsin Supreme Court has held that 'nature and quality' gives 'important emphasis' to the realization of the wrongfulness of an act. It marks the distinction between 'vaguely . . . [realizing] that particular conduct is forbidden' and 'real insight into the conduct'.[10] This construction illustrates the close connection between the definition of 'know' and that of 'nature and quality'. The broader reading of 'nature and quality' carries with it the broader construction of 'know' and *vice versa*. To know the quality of an act, with all its social and emotional implications, requires more than an abstract, purely intellectual knowledge. Likewise, to talk of appreciating the full significance of an act means that 'nature and quality' must be understood as including more than the physical nature of the act.

'Wrong'

In those situations where the accused does not know the nature and quality of his act, in the broad sense, he will not know that it was wrong, no matter what construction 'wrong' is given. But assuming both 'know' and 'nature and quality' are read narrowly and the defendant knows the physical nature of his act, does 'wrong' mean moral or legal wrong? The *McNaughton* judges said that a person is punishable 'if he knew at the time of committing such crime that he was acting contrary to law; by which expression we . . . mean the law of the land'. The matter was somewhat confused by a second passage in the opinion which addressed the question of actual and constructive notice:

If the question were to be put as to the knowledge of the accused solely and exclusively with reference to the law of the land, it might tend to confound the jury by inducing them to believe that an actual knowledge of the law of the land was essential in order to lead to a conviction; whereas the law is administered on the principle that every one must be taken conclusively to know it, without proof that he does know it. If the accused was conscious that the act was one which he ought not to do, and if that act was at the same time contrary to the law of the land, he is punishable.[11]

The English courts have sought to remove the ambiguity by holding that the accused must have been aware that the act was legally wrong, though this clarifi-

[9] R. v. Codère, 12 C.A.R. 21, 26–27 (Cr. Ct. App. 1916).
[10] State v. Esser, 115 N.W. 2d 505, 521 (Wis. 1962).
[11] McNaughton's Case, 10 Clark & Fin. 200, 210–11 (1843).

158

cation has been criticized recently on the ground that 'knowledge of the law is hardly an appropriate test on which to base ascription of criminal responsibility to the mentally disordered'.[12]

In the United States, the issue has seldom been raised. The word is generally given to the jury without explanation. Where it has been considered, the courts have split. One group holds that an offender is classed as sane if he knew the act was prohibited by law. A second group takes the position that 'wrong' means moral wrong 'according to generally accepted standards' and offers, as an illustration of insanity, the defendant who thought it morally right that he should kill (e.g. because he was ordered to do so by God) but knew it was legally wrong.

The opponents of *McNaughton* have urged the adoption of this second view because of its seemingly liberalizing tendency. They are often unclear, however, whether 'moral wrong' is to be judged by the personal standards of the accused or by his awareness that society views the act as wrong. The latter, which is probably the one meant by the courts, adds very little. This is because most cases involving the insanity defence will involve crimes sufficiently serious to make society's moral judgement identical with the legal standard. It might even be argued that in such cases society's moral condemnation will be more apparent to the accused than the fact that he violated the law, so that the use of a standard or 'moral' wrong would narrow the defence—e.g. a man may think he has the defence of self-defence or superior order and yet feel it is immoral for him to kill. If the attempt to draw the distinction between moral and legal wrong adds little or nothing to the defence, the only reason for urging it must be that some writers see it as a way to broaden an otherwise narrow definition of 'know'. The apparent hope is to bring to the jury's attention the moral, and emotional, perspective of the defendant.

The most pressing questions about *McNaughton* have been left unanswered; the key words remain undefined or only partially defined. Portraying the rules as rigid and narrow and condemning them wholesale would seem, therefore, to be unjustified. It may be, however, that the rules' impact is felt not when the jury is instructed on the law, which is all we have considered thus far, but at other stages of the process—as when evidence of mental illness is offered, or when experts seek to explain the facts of mental disease. Certainly, the criticism most frequently made of *McNaughton* is that it 'keeps out evidence of the defendant's mental life', denying the jury 'the true picture of the defendant's mental condition' and the 'insights of modern psychology'. This is presumably done by the trial judge who interprets the rules narrowly and admits only such evidence as satisfies their terms. But the critics seldom cite cases and leave unclear not only the kinds of evidence that will be barred but also the precise objections that would be levelled. For example, will the court exclude lay evidence of aberrational behaviour by the accused at various times in his life? Will it exclude

---

[12] R. v. Windle, [1952] All Eng. Rep. 1, 2. The criticism is in Great Britain, Home Office, *Report of the Committee on Mentally Abnormal Offenders*, sec. 18.8 (1975) (the Butler Committee Report).

evidence of his teachers, or of psychiatrists, psychologists, or social workers who had contact with him in the past? Will it prevent a psychiatrist who examined him for purposes of trial from testifying in full regarding his examination?

There is virtually no support in American law for the view that *McNaughton* is responsible for inhibiting the flow of testimony on the insanity issue. The almost unvarying policy of the courts has been to admit *any* evidence of aberrational behaviour so long as it is probative of the defendant's mental condition, without regard to the supposed restrictions of the test used to define insanity for the jury.[13] Virtually never does one see exclusions of the sort of lay evidence which is a staple of the insanity defence—that the defendant wept, or that he was given to violent rages, or that he threatened to throw his child out the window.

Even when the evidence offered seems to fly in the very face of *McNaughton*, it has been admitted. *State* v. *Carlson* is an excellent illustration because it involved evidence of lack of self-control, the principal area allegedly removed from consideration by *McNaughton*. A medical witness was called to testify that an electroencephalograph test showed the defendant could not control his behaviour. This testimony had been rejected by the trial judge because

it appeared that . . . [the doctor] would attribute any misconduct to irresistible impulse, rather than lack of ability to distinguish between right and wrong, and only the latter is the test of insanity under Wisconsin law.

The Supreme Court of Wisconsin held that the trial court had erred:

We are of the opinion . . . that if the offered testimony, together with other expert testimony, had sufficiently tended to prove that at the time of the offence, defendant was subject to a compulsion or irresistible impulse by reason of the abnormality of his brain, the testimony should have been admitted. *Even under the right-wrong test, no evidence should be excluded which reasonably tends to show the mental condition of the defendant at the time of the offence* [emphasis supplied].[14]

The reason, said the court in a later opinion, is that a defendant who can show lack of the power to control his actions may generate a reasonable doubt in the minds even of jurors applying the *McNaughton* standard.[15] Another example of the breadth of inquiry possible under *McNaughton* is *State* v. *Wolak*.[16] There the defendant had offered his criminal record into evidence as part of an effort to prove he was a 'constitutional psychopath'. The trial judge admitted the evidence, but then charged the jury that such evidence could be considered 'for the sole purpose of determining his credibility as a witness'. This was reversed on appeal because a history of crime was an 'essential link in the proof' of psychopathy which was, in turn, probative of the insanity defence. These cases are not exceptions. The American Law Institute found

[13] Wigmore states the rule to be that when insanity is in issue, 'any and all conduct of the person is admissible in evidence'. I. Wigmore, *Evidence*, Sec. 228 (1940).
[14] The quotations are at 93 N.W. 2d 354, 360–61 (Wis. 1958).
[15] The more recent case is State v. Shoffner, 143 N.W. 2d 458, 463 (Wis. 1966).
[16] 140 A. 2d 385, 393–4 (N.J. 1958); see also State v. Foster, 354 P. 2d 960, 973 (Hawaii, 1960).

no American case . . . where a trial court excluded evidence or refused to charge on a defence of insanity merely because the evidence in support of the defence related to neurosis or psychopathic personality or other mental disturbance rather than a psychosis.[17]

The claim that *McNaughton* limits the admission of evidence often takes the form that the rules place the psychiatrist in a 'straitjacket'; he is allegedly required to testify in terms of a definition of 'know' which is limited to formal cognition and excludes any emotional appreciation of the act and its consequences. Here again there is no such general rule. An analysis of numerous trial transcripts shows that the psychiatrist is regularly permitted to explain his interpretation of the words of the rule.

In *People* v. *Roche*, for example, Dr Brody, a psychiatrist for the defence, testified that the dictionary defines 'to know' as meaning 'to perceive with full clarity'. To a psychiatrist, he continued,

mere memory of details, or recitation of what has gone on, does not necessarily imply the knowledge, the full knowledge, the ethical consequences, or the moral consequences, or full understanding of what the man is doing . . . A child, a reasonably bright child, or a schizophrenic, may say he hit someone with a club and [he] bled from the scalp, or even that they die, and might go so far as to say that it is wrong to do so, but unless there is a certain amount of integration of the personality, and an ability to realize with full emotional clarity the consequences of his act, psychiatrists do not feel that such rote recitation of memory implies knowing, in the full sense.

He did not 'see how a schizophrenic [like Roche] can perceive with full clarity'. His conclusion, therefore, was that Roche did not know right from wrong at the time of the crime. For the prosecution, Dr Herman defined 'know' as referring to 'an intellectual level', 'a collection of information which is reasonably pertinent to . . . average individuals'. In his view, Roche did know right from wrong at the time of the crime. The trial judge adopted neither construction of the critical word. Instead, he told the jury to use the 'commonly accepted' meaning of 'know', thereby passing to it the choice between the broad and the narrow views.[18]

Cases like *Roche* are common. They present to the jury both testimony that the accused 'verbalizes' that it is wrong to kidnap and also that he does not know right from wrong in the 'broad sense'; that he was 'intellectually aware of the nature and social consequences of his deed' and yet lacking in 'a normal emotional awareness of the impact this act might have on his own life or [that of his victim]'; that, in one sense, he knew what he was doing but, in another, he did not because of the 'shallowness of [his] understanding . . . [and] insight'; or because 'his judgement was blunted by the emotions and he would not bother about thinking about the effects of his acts on right or wrong'.[19] The

---

[17] ALI, *Model Penal Code*, Tent. Dr. No. 4, App. A. to Commentary, Sec. 4.01, p. 162 (1955); see also State v. Odell, 227 P. 2d 710, 719 (Wash. 1951); R. v. Codère, [1916] 12 Crim. App. Rep. 21, 24, Att'y Gen'l for N. Ireland v. Gallagher, [1963] A.C. 349, 372 et seq.; but cf. R. v. Wilkinson, 1 Crim. L. Rev. 22, 144 (1954).
[18] The quotations are at People v. Roche, Trial Tr. 382–83, 399, 422, 476, aff'd without opin., 128 N.E. 2d 323 (N.Y. 1955).
[19] The quotations are from McKenzie v. United States, Trial Tr. 200, rev'd 266 F. 2d 524, 535 (10 Cir. 1959); Comm. v. Chester, 150 N.E. 2d 914, 917 (Mass. 1958); State v. Lucas, Trial Tr. 532–33, 541, aff'd 152 A. 2d 50 (N.J. 1959); Warner v. State, 84 So. 2d 314, 315 (Fla., 1955).

choice among the conflicting interpretations is then made by the jury, which is aided in the matter by its common sense, by counsel in their closing arguments, and by its appraisal of the experts and of the entire case.

It is apparent that existing rules of law do not force a narrow view of *McNaughton* upon the participants at trial. Generally, trial judges do not vary the *McNaughton* formula and the trial judge imposes no restrictive interpretation when he charges the jury. But if all this is true, the question remains: what is it about *McNaughton* which impedes the trial of the insanity defence?

A first clue comes from the fact that there are forces in addition to the case law which define the scope of the defence. The question of responsibility is, after all, presented through an adversary process which leaves the principal initiative to the parties. Judges will not ordinarily ask for evidence which is not presented to them. They will not rule on objections which are not made. They will not tell counsel and expert how to present their positions. Even if the legal rules make the defence available to persons suffering from serious mental illness, it hardly follows that it will be asserted by all of them. The attitudes of the participants may be as important as rules of law in determining the effective range of the defence.

The most important of these attitudes has been the operative assumption of American psychiatrists and lawyers that the law regards insanity and psychosis as identical. In their testimony, psychiatrists often define insanity as a 'psychotic reaction' and psychosis as 'the medical term for insanity'. A man who does not have the symptoms of psychosis (e.g. 'delusional beliefs' or 'hallucinations') is 'for that reason . . . considered to be sane'. If he is 'in contact with reality', then he is 'sane in our sense'.[20] As the trial takes shape, the defence tries to bring its evidence within the framework of a psychosis, the prosecution outside it. Equating insanity with psychosis has two contradictory consequences. It confirms the earlier assertion that *McNaughton* does not limit the defence to a small group of 'totally deteriorated' psychotics. At the same time, it perpetuates the view that the 'lesser' mental illnesses cannot qualify.

The roots of the equation are to be found in the widespread assumption among lawyers that insanity describes medical entities, and among psychiatrists that psychosis is the only such entity which satisfies the law's requirements. The misunderstanding was facilitated by the tenets of pre-Freudian psychology which tended to see mental life as divided into discrete parts. And it reflected what is still the practice in civil commitment, which is the area of law most familiar to psychiatrists.

It would be misleading, however, to leave the impression that the continuing emphasis on psychosis is entirely a matter of drift. Underlying it is a more purposive element—the quite widespread feeling among American psychiatrists that all psychotics *should* be regarded as insane and that *McNaughton* restricts

[20] The quotations are from Howard v. United States, Trial Tr. 98, aff'd 229 F. 2d 602 (5 Cir. 1962); State v. Goza, 317 S.W. 2d 609, 612 (Mo., 1958); People v. Roche, supra n. 18, at Trial Tr. 497, 506, 508; State v. Lucas, Trial Tr. 1349, aff'd 152 A. 2d 50 (N.J. 1959); Johnson v. State, 76 So. 2d 841, 843 (Miss. 1955); Thomas v. State, Trial Tr. 307, aff'd 112 A. 2d 913 (Md. 1955).

the defence to a small number of psychoses. Psychiatrists holding these views tend to regard the equation of insanity and psychosis as accomplishing ends which may be contrary to law but which are justified by a higher moral obligation. Adopting the equation as a private definition, they communicate the definition to no one and answer 'no' to the *McNaughton* questions even when they believe a 'yes' is required. The dilemma, and the method of resolving it, is described by the Group for the Advancement of Psychiatry (GAP): The psychiatrist called upon to answer the *McNaughton* questions finds himself compelled to sacrifice his 'honesty' if 'psychiatric truth' is to carry the day. He must, therefore, answer in accordance with a 'tacitly understood convention' and aver that the mentally ill defendant did not know right from wrong, even when he did.[21] The most curious feature of the GAP position is its assumption that the psychiatrist must testify falsely in order to provide 'the psychiatric truth'. The fact is, as we have seen, that there is nothing in the form of the *McNaughton* questions, or in the directions of court or counsel, that prevents the psychiatrist from answering in accordinance with *his* understanding of what the questions mean. If he is asked whether a psychotic 'knows' right from wrong, he may properly construe 'know' as he understands the word—as including emotional as well as intellectual components, deep as well as formal comprehension. Cross-examination would then not involve him in 'contradicting himself' at all but only in explaining the assumptions underlying his testimony and in matching those assumptions with others presented by the cross-examiner in his questions.

The process described by GAP tends to perpetuate the *McNaughton* stereotype in several ways: first, it gives seemingly authoritative support to the narrow view, while at the same time calling for its rejection; second, by adopting private definitions, psychiatrists deny the courts the opportunity to provide authoritative interpretations; third, those who feel they must manipulate the process in order to participate in it tend to come away with a feeling of distaste for the insanity issue and a reluctance to become involved with it, thus reducing the pool of psychiatrists likely to testify in ways which might produce broadening interpretations.

Another source of the misunderstanding about *McNaughton*, perhaps the most important of all, is the tendency of psychiatrists to treat *jury* rejection of the insanity defence as if it represented 'the law's' affirmation of the narrow interpretation. If, for example, the jury finds a defendant guilty when there was ample evidence that he was psychotic, even that his cognition was seriously impaired, the criticis have held *McNaughton* responsible. This overlooks, of course, the fact that the jury has the *power* to decide cases for reasons which have nothing to do with the instruction on the law. Indeed, the phenomenon of jury disregard of law, sometimes amounting to nullification, is well known. The risk of such disregard is particularly great when the crime charged is a serious one, exciting a full measure of retributive and deterrent feeling. Moreover, the criticism ignores the extent to which the jury decision may be based on appraisals

[21] Group for the Advancement of Psychiatry, *Criminal Responsibility and Psychiatric Expert Testimony*, 5 (1954).

of the credibility of witnesses, lay and expert, who testify on opposite sides of the same issue.

Even if such considerations could be held constant, the defence would probably be rejected quite often. Jurors find it difficult to accept the idea of serious mental disorder unless it is accompanied by visible and gross psychotic symptoms—either a breakdown in intellect or the loss of self-control. In this respect, they share the reluctance of most people to concede that persons who seem very much like themselves may be seriously ill. Public attitudes regarding crime and mental illness, therefore, limit the practical utility of the insanity defence, in whatever form it may be cast and however freely evidence may be admitted.

History, psychiatric convention, public attitudes, and procedure combine to sustain a narrow view of *McNaughton* and in a sense to deny the legal process the opportunity to take a broader view. The stereotyped view is so firmly established in the popular culture of the defence that it has been acted upon regularly by lawyers and psychiatrists. It has been said so often that 'the law' refuses to accept the 'insights of modern psychology' and that the only psychotic who can qualify is one so deteriorated that he could not muster the resources to commit a serious crime, that counsel rarely see any purpose in pursuing the issue. The result has been either premature abandonment of the defence or a token presentation, supported by little or no testimony describing in detail the life history of the accused, or the parts of this history which demonstrate how his responses differ from the 'normal'.

The criticis of *McNaughton* may be correct when they allege that many defendants who are seriously ill are arbitrarily excluded from the insanity defence. But the fault lies less with the formulation of the defence than with its presentation. The responsible parties are counsel and psychiatrist who have contributed to a failure of the adversary process, allowing unwarranted assumptions about the meaning of the rules to govern their conception of the defence.

II

Soon after *McNaughton* was decided, its criticis began to suggest ways to 'solve' the problems it presented. The first was its failure to excuse from criminal responsibility a person whose mental disease prevented him from controlling his conduct, even though he knew what he was doing and that it was wrong. Though rejected in England,[22] 'control' rules have been adopted in some form in a majority of American jurisdictions; in some States they date back almost as far as *McNaughton*. These rules—misleadingly known as 'irresistible impulse' tests—are often criticized for limiting the defence to offenders whose behaviour was 'impulsive', despite the fact that most formulations are cast in terms of the defendant's capacity for self-control or free choice, and do not exclude

[22] The clasic English argument for excusing an offender on 'control' grounds is presented by Stephen, 2 *History of the Criminal Law of England*, 171 (1883). 'Control' rules were decisively rejected in R. v. Holt, 15 Crim. App. Rev. 10, 12 (1920); R. v. Kopsch, 19 Cr. App. Rep. 50 (1925).

persons whose loss of control was not 'impulsive'. In a process reminiscent of developments under *McNaughton*, this incorrect characterization of the 'control' rules contributed significantly to the belief that the *McNaughton* problem had not been 'solved' and the movement for a newer and better test of insanity continued.

Durham v. *United States* was the first of the relatively contemporary cases to establish a new rule. *Durham* took to heart the critics' complaints that *McNaughton* and the 'control' rules prevented psychiatrists from testifying to 'psychiatric truth'. The rule stated simply that 'an accused is not criminally responsible if his unlawful act was the product of mental disease or defect'. Freed by this formula from testimony tied to specific types of functional impairment or groups of symptoms, psychiatrists would, it was hoped, be able to 'inform the jury of the character of [the defendant's] mental disease' and juries would be 'guided by wider horizons of knowledge concerning mental life'.[23]

Durham's solution to the problems of *McNaughton* and the 'control' rules was to shift the courtroom controversy from the words of the insanity defence to the questions whether the defendant's disorder was a 'mental disease' and, if so, whether the disease 'produced' the act with which he stood charged. But this solution caused new problems which in turn were solved only by focusing insanity trials in the District of Columbia on the same functional impairments that are central to the older tests. Psychiatrists for the prosecution and defence often disagreed about whether disorders like psychopathy, sociopathy and narcotics addiction were 'mental diseases', and disputes over causation were equally common. But *Durham* had given the jury no standard by which to resolve the conflicting testimony. In *McDonald* v. *United States*, the Court concluded that it was necessary for trial judges to inform juries that 'mental disease or defect'

'includes any abnormal condition of the mind which substantially affects mental or emotional processes and substantially impairs behaviour controls.'[24]

While no comparable instruction was developed to define 'product', attempts to bring that concept within the common experience of jurors led inevitably to reliance on disabilities of knowledge and will as critical elements in determining whether the defendant's illness had caused his unlawful act. Despite these refinements, trials under *Durham* were plagued by conclusory psychiatric testimony that a particular act was or was not the product of a mental disease. The District of Columbia court continued its efforts to keep *Durham* alive by experimenting with a ban on such testimony,[25] but the ban proved ineffective. Finally, in *United States* v. *Brawner*,[26] the Court announced that it was abandoning *Durham* for a rule which, in its view, would require expert evidence to be framed in a way more meaningful to a lay jury. That rule was the formula

---

[23] Durham v. United States, 214 F. 2d 862 (D.C. Cir. 1954). The 'product' rule is stated at 874–875; the quotations are at 876.
[24] McDonald v. United States, 312 F. 2d 847, 851 (D.C. Cir. 1967).
[25] Washington v. United States, 390 F. 2d 244 (D.C. Cir. 1967).
[26] United States v. Brawner, 471 F. 2d 969 (D.C. Cir. 1972).

proposed by the American Law Institute. It returned the language of the District of Columbia's insanity test to the familiar themes of cognition and control.

The ALI rule is a modernized and improved rendition of the *McNaughton* and 'control' rules. It provides that

a person is not responsible for criminal conduct if at the time of such conduct as a result of mental disease or defect he lacks substantial capacity either to appreciate the criminality of his conduct or to conform his conduct to the requirements of law.[27]

By substituting 'appreciate' for 'know', it expresses a preference for the broader construction of *McNaughton* which holds that a sane offender must be emotionally as well as intellectually aware of the significance of his conduct. By using the word 'conform' it tries to divest itself from historic baggage and avoids any implication of 'irresistible impulse'. And by requiring only 'substantial' incapacity, it eliminates the risk implicit in the older cases which sometimes spoke as if 'complete' or 'total' destruction of the defendant's mental capacity was required.

The ALI rule has not won universal praise. Some have attacked it because it continues to rely on functional impairments, thereby ignoring (they claim) the teaching of modern science that the mind cannot be separated into compartments. These critics would resume the search for a standard which puts medically correct questions to the jury. Others make the opposite complaint, that the rule relies too heavily on a 'medical model' of insanity. They would abandon the search for 'correct' questions and simply tell the jury to acquit an offender who, because of a mental or emotional or behavioural impairment, 'cannot be justly held responsible for his act'.[28] Those who hold the first point of view forget that insanity is a legal concept, not a medical one, and ignore *Durham's* history, which teaches that functional definitions are needed to provide courts and juries with standards by which to evaluate evidence of mental illness. Advocates of the second position recognize that the defence is closely tied to the social objectives served by the criminal law, but would offer the jury a charge that only explains why the law wants to relieve people of responsibility; they would not provide a standard for judging who should be relieved.[29] These viewpoints swing from the extreme of giving the matter almost entirely to the psychiatrists to the opposite extreme of giving it entirely to the jury. The ALI rule is fast displacing *McNaughton* because it strikes a sensible balance between the two extremes— following in the *McNaughton* tradition but achieving a better blend of medical science and social purpose.

It is unlikely that the ALI rule has changed matters very much, for given the

[27] American Law Institute, *Model Penal Code*, Sec. 4.01 (1962). The proposal was presented to the Institute for consideration at the May 1955, meeting. The ALI rule also includes a second paragraph which follows: '(2) As used in this Article, the terms "mental disease or defect" do not include an abnormality manifested only by repeated criminal or otherwise antisocial conduct.' That paragraph has been more controversial. For details as to how each of the paragraphs has fared, see Appendix. Compare the alternative proposal made by the British Royal Commission on Capital Punishment 116 and 111 (1953).
[28] United States v. Brawner, 471 F. 2d 969, 1032 (separate opinion of Bazelon. J.).
[29] For Judge Leventhal's comments on the Bazelon proposal, see United States v. Brawner, *id.* at 986–9.

actual practice under *McNaughton*, it authorizes the admission of no more evidence than could have been offered in the past. It will, however, undo the effects of the unnecessary stereotyping of the older rules, and it provides a better instruction for the jury, especially in jurisdictions that had previously lacked a 'control' rule.

Even as *McNaughton* is fading, new proposals are being made to recast the words of the insanity defence or to incorporate it somehow into the general concept of *mens rea*, making it a defence if mental illness 'negatives' the mental element required for criminal liability.[30] But such proposals no longer command the attention they would have attracted a generation ago. It has become evident that the insanity defence, asserted in a contested criminal trial, cannot be equated with the larger problem of the mentally ill offender. It is raised too sporadically to serve as a general diagnostic device separating the sick from the bad. Its residual function today is to reinforce the idea of personal responsibility as an important cultural force—by asking a jury of laymen in a dramatic court-room setting to draw the line between those who can be expected to respond to the warnings of a criminal code, and those who cannot.

While the ALI rule may encourage lawyers and psychiatrists to make a more meaningful presentation of the insanity defence in cases in which it is raised, the current emphasis is not on the defence itself but on the larger problems surrounding it. Chief among these is the fear of indeterminate detention, which deters so many offenders from raising the defence. Increasing attention is being devoted to defining 'dangerousness' and to developing procedures for deciding who should be detained, for how long, and in what kind of setting. A corollary is the renewed effort to clarify the relation between the insanity defence and other defences and processes—civil and correctional—competing with it for the mentally ill offender.[31] It is to these problems, beyond the words of the insanity defence, that American courts and commentators are turning as the ALI rule gradually replaces *McNaughton* as the 'American' test of insanity.

APPENDIX

A. THE MCNAUGHTON RULES

Twenty-one states use some form of the *McNaughton* rules as the sole test of criminal responsibility: State v. Shaw, 471 P. 2d 715 (Ariz. 1970); People v. Darling, 372 P.

---

[30] See, e.g. Section 522 of Senate 1 (S.1) which provides:
 'It is a defence . . . that the defendant, as a result of mental disease or defect, lacked the state of mind required as an element of the offense charged. Mental disease or defect does not otherwise constitute a defense.'
This proposal was first put forward by the Nixon administration and is part of a Bill pending in Congress to revise the entire federal criminal code. See also Great Britain, Home Office, *Report of the Committee on Mentally Abnormal Offenders*, 222–230, particularly Sec. 18.20 and 18.30 (1975), which outlines a two-part definition of insanity. The first part, like S.1, would tie insanity to the concept of *mens rea*; the second would extend the defence to one who 'at the time of the act or omission charged . . . was suffering from severe mental illness or severe subnormality'. See generally, J. Goldstein and Katz, 'Abolish the Insanity Defense—Why Not?' 72 Yale L.J. 873 (1963) and A. Goldstein, *The Insanity Defense*, 220 et seq. (1967).
[31] See A. Goldstein, *The Insanity Defense*, ch. 10 to 12 (1967); Jackson v. Indiana, 406 U.S. 715 (1972); O'Connor v. Donaldson, 406 U.S. 715 (1975).

167

2d 316 (Calif. 1962); Picott v. State, 116 So. 2d 626 (Fla. 1960); Rev. Laws Hawaii Sec. 249–1 (1955); State v. Harkness, 160 N.W. 2d 324 (Iowa 1968); State v. Andrews, 357 P. 2d 739 (Kan. 1961); Lousiana Stat. Ann.-Rev. Stat. 14:14 (1942); Minn. Stat. Ann. Sec. 611–026 (1971); Johnson v. State, 76 So. 2d 841 (Miss. 1955); State v. Long, 139 N.W. 2d 813 (Neb. 1966); Sollars v. State, 316 P. 2d 917 (Nev. 1957); State v. Lucas, 152 A. 2d 50 (New Jersey 1959); State v. Potter, 204 S.E. 2d 649 (N. Car. 1974); State v. Throndson, 191 N.W. 628 (N. Dak. 1922); Dare v. State, 378 P. 2d 339 (Okla. Cr. 1963); Commonwealth v. Rightnour, 253 A. 2d 644 (Penn. 1969); State v. Nault, 314 A. 2d 627 (Rhode Is. 1974); State v. Allen, 98 S.E. 2d 826 (S. Car. 1957); State v. Waugh, 127 N.W. 2d 429 (S. Dak. 1964); Spurlock v. State, 368 S.W. 2d 299 (Tenn. 1963); State v. Jones, 529 P. 2d 1040 (Wash. 1974). Of the federal jurisdictions, only the Court of Appeals for the First Circuit still uses the *McNaughton* rules, U.S. v. Holmes, Fed. Cas. No. 15382 (1st Cir. 1858), but see Amador Beltron v. United States, 302 F. 2d 48, 52 (1st Cir. 1962).

B. A 'CONTROL' RULE IN ADDITION TO MCNAUGHTON

Eleven states use a 'control' rule in conjunction with some form of *McNaughton*: Breen v. State, 302 So. 2d 562 (Ala. 1974); Bell v. State, 180 S.W. 186 (Ark. 1915); Colo. Rev. Stat. '53, 39–8–1(2); Longoria v. State, 168 A. 2d 695 (Del. 1961); Mullins v. State, 115 S.E. 2d 547 (Ga. 1960); People v. Martin, 192 N.W. 2d 215 (Mich. 1971); State v. White, 270 P. 2d 727 (N. Mex. 1954); State v. Staten, 247 N.E. 2d 293 (Ohio 1969); State v. Kirkham, 319 P. 2d 859 (Utah 1968); Davis v. Commonwealth, 204 S.E. 2d 272 (Va. 1974); State v. Riggle, 298 P. 2d 349 (Wyo. 1956).

C. THE ALI RULE

Sixteen states and ten federal jurisdictions use the rule recommended by the American Law Institute. Paragraph one of the ALI rule allows each jurisdiction to choose whether it will cast the cognitive portion of the test in terms of the defendant's capacity to appreciate either the 'criminality' or 'wrongfulness' of his conduct. The second or caveat paragraph of the rule (see note 27) has also been treated as a separate option. For each of the jurisdictions listed below, the choice between 'criminality' and 'wrongfulness', the decision (if any) to accept or reject the caveat paragraph, and any significant variation from the official ALI language are indicated in parentheses. The state citations are Alas. Stat. 12.45.083 (a, b.) (1972) (wrongfulness; both paragraphs); Conn. Gen. Stat. Sec. 53a–13 (1969) (wrongfulness; both paragraphs); Idaho Code Sec. 18–207 (1970) (wrongfulness; both paragraphs); Ill. Rev. Stat. (Smith-Hurd Ann.) ch. 38 Sec. 6–2 (1961) (criminality; both paragraphs); Hill v. State, 251 N.E. 2d 429 (Ind. 1969) (wrongfulness; both paragraphs); Terry v. Commonwealth, 371 S.W. 2d 862 (Kentucky 1963) (criminality; both paragraphs); Maryland Ann. Code Art. 59 Sec. 25(a) (1970) (criminality; both paragraphs); Commonwealth v. McHoul, 226 N.E. 2d 556 (Mass. 1967) (either wrongfulness or criminality acceptable; no mention of second paragraph); Missouri Ann. Stat. Sec. 552.030 (1963) (wrongfulness; no mention of second paragraph); Mont. Rev. Code Ann. Sec. 95–501 (1967) (criminality, both paragraphs); New York Penal Law Sec. 30.05 (1965) ('conform' clause rejected; second paragraph rejected); Oregon Rev. Stat. Sec. 161.295 (1971) (criminality; both paragraphs); Texas Penal Code Sec. 8.01 (1973) ('did not know his conduct was wrong or was incapable of conforming . . .'; both paragraphs); Vermont Stat. Ann. Title 13 Sec. 4801 (1957) (criminality, both paragraphs); State v. Grimm, 195 S.E. 2d 637 (W. Va. 1973) (wrongfulness; no mention of second paragraph); State v. Shoffner, 143 N.W. 2d 458 (Wis. 1966) (wrongfulness; no mention of second paragraph; defendant may choose between *McNaughton*, for which state bears burden of proving insanity and ALI, for which the defendant has burden of proving insanity). The

168

federal citations are United States v. Freeman, 357 F. 2d 606 (2d Cir. 1966) (wrongfulness; both paragraphs); United States v. Currens, 290 F. 2d 751 (3d Cir. 1961) ('appreciate' clause rejected; both paragraphs); United States v. Chandler, 393 F. 2d 920 (4th Cir. 1968) (criminality; both paragraphs); Blake v. United States, 407 F. 2d 908 (5th Cir. 1969) (wrongfulness; both paragraphs); United States v. Smith; 404 F. 2d 720 (6th Cir. 1968) (either wrongfulness or criminality acceptable; second paragraph rejected); United States v. Shapiro, 383 F. 2d 680 (7th Cir. 1967) (wrongfulness; second paragraph neither accepted nor rejected); United States v. Frazier, 458 F. 2d 911 (8th Cir. 1972) (wrongfulness; both paragraphs); Wade v. United States, 426 F. 2d 64 (9th Cir. 1970) (wrongfulness; second paragraph rejected); Wion v. United States, 325 F. 2d 420 (10th Cir. 1963) (wrongfulness; no mention of second paragraph); United States v. Brawner, 471 F. 2d 969 (D.C. Cir. 1972) (wrongfulness; second paragraph adopted only 'as a rule for application by the judge . . .').

D. The Durham Rule

Three jurisdictions use some form of the *Durham* or 'product' rule: Maine Rev. Stat. Ann. Title 15 Sec. 102 (1963); State v. Pike, 49 N.H. 399 (1869), but see N. Hamp. Rev. Stat. Ann. Sec. 628:2 (1971) ('A person who is insane at the time he acts is not criminally responsible for his conduct.'); 14 Virgin Is. Code Sec. 14(4).

McNAUGHTON IN THE ANTIPODES

Louis Waller

Introduction

McNaughton travelled well. The case occupies as curious a position in Australian jurisprudence as it does in English. The answers of the judges to the less than elegantly drafted questions propounded to them by the House of Lords constitute the law on the defence of insanity in the three states where the criminal law has not been codified, namely, New South Wales, South Australia and Victoria. In the other three states the Rules clearly influenced the provisions of their Criminal Codes. In New Zealand their impact was even more substantial.

McNaughton travelled quickly. In 1871 Henry Field Furner, Victorian Crown Solicitor, compiled *The Practice of the Criminal Law of the Colony of Victoria*, which he described as 'a useful work', being 'a concise and practical exposition of the ordinary course of procedure in a criminal case in the colony . . .'.[1] Chapter XXVI is entitled 'Insanity'; it begins with this sentence:

> Under the plea of 'not guilty' evidence is *frequently given*, on behalf of the accused, that he was insane at the time he committed the offence charged.[2]

Then following extracts from Coke, Hale, Tracy J. in *Arnold's* case, Lord Lyndhurst, C.B., in *R. v. Offord*, Lord Denman, C.J., in *R. v. Oxford*, and, as the core of the eight-page chapter, the questions and answers in *R. v. McNaughton*.[3] No local case rates a mention, despite Mr Gurner's initial observation.

McNaughton in the statute book

In 1885, Dr W. E. Hearn, the first Dean of the Faculty of Law in the University of Melbourne and a member of the Victorian Legislative Council, produced a General Code of Law for the colony which was embodied in a Bill presented in the Upper House. This ambitious but unsuccessful project is briefly described by Barry, Paton and Sawer:[4]

---

[1] Preface, p iii.
[2] P 116. My italics.
[3] Pp 118–20.
[4] *An Introduction to the Criminal Law in Australia* (1948) (*English Studies in Criminal Science*, Vol VI), pp 20–1.

This draft dealt with the civil as well as the criminal law . . . and was based on Hearn's theories of analytical jurisprudence as set out in his *Legal Duties and Rights*.[5] There are many marginal references to the *Draft Code of Indictable Offences* as settled by the Commission of English judges over which Lord Blackburn presided in 1878–79. . . . The criminal part is woven into the general structure of the law.

Division 3. Matters of Excuse begins with subdivision (a)—Defective Intelligence. This has three sections. The first deals with the criminal liability of 'persons whose age does not exceed seven years'; the second with that of those over seven and less than fourteen; and the third, as its marginal note proclaims, with 'insanity'. It is largely the *McNaughton Rules* as they emerged in the Bill introduced unsuccessfully into the House of Commons in 1880. In Hearn's words, it provides:

No person shall be convicted of an offence by reason of an act done or omitted by him when labouring under natural imbecility or disease of the mind to such an extent as to render such person incapable of knowing the nature and the consequences of his conduct and of appreciating that it was wrong.

A person labouring under specific delusions but in other respects sane shall not be acquitted on the ground of insanity unless the delusions caused him to believe in the existence of some state of things which if it existed would justify or excuse his act or omission.

The Bill lapsed.

In New Zealand, however, the Draft Code of 1880 was adopted as the Criminal Code Act of 1893. Sec 23 provided for the defence of insanity in terms borrowed almost wholly from the McNaughton Rules.

In *Murdoch* v. *British Israel World Federation (N.Z.) Inc*, Myers, C.J. said the section was equivalent simply to a restatement of the Rules.[6]

The section is very similar to Hearn's draft, but has two significant additions.

(1) Everyone shall be presumed to be sane at the time of doing or omitting any act until the contrary is proved.

(2) No person shall be convicted of an offence by reason of an act done or omitted by him when labouring under natural imbecility or disease of the mind to such an extent as to render such person incapable of understanding the nature and quality of the act or omission, and of knowing that such act or omission was wrong.

(3) A person labouring under specific delusions, but in other respects sane, shall not be acquitted on the ground of insanity under the provisions hereinafter contained unless the delusions caused him to believe in the existence of some state of things which, if it existed, would justify or excuse his act or omission.

(4) Insanity before or after the time when he committed or omitted the act, and insane delusions, though only partial, may be evidence that the offender was, at the time when he committed or omitted the act, in such a condition of mind as to render him irresponsible for such act or omission.

This legislation was replaced by the Crimes Act 1961. But sec. 23, which provides for the defence of insanity is almost the same as the original provision

[5] (1883).
[6] [1942] N.Z.L.R. 600, at 625.

of 1893. The main difference is that *wrong* is now bracketed, as if by ranging shots: *morally* precedes it, and the phrase *having regard to the commonly accepted standards of right and wrong* follows it. *And*, which caused the usual difficulties, has given way to *or*.

In *R.* v. *McMillan*,[7] the most recent decision on the defence of insanity, Turner, J., speaking for the Court of Appeal, stated that there was no legislative intention to change the existing law by the addition of the new language. Its insertion was to make it quite plain that *wrong* (to be considered more substantially later) was to be interpreted in the manner of the High Court of Australia in *Stapleton* v. *The Queen*[8] and Dixon, J. (later the Court's Chief Justice) in *R.* v. *Porter*,[9] not after the fashion of the English Courts. It is in New Zealand, then, that the McNaughton Rules remain firmly embedded in the statute book, honestly given that form and authority which from the first they seemed to attract.

* * *

When Sir Samuel Griffith, Chief Justice of Queensland and later first Chief Justice of Australia, drafted the Queensland Criminal Code about fifteen years after Hearn's ambitious project, he too was influenced by the McNaughton Rules as they found themselves in the Draft Code of 1880. But the criticisms of the Rules already propounded by the end of the century made their mark on him. The Code provides, in what is now sec 27:

A person is not criminally responsible for an act or omission if at the time of doing the act or making the omission he is in such a state of mental disease or natural mental infirmity as to deprive him of capacity to understand what he is doing, or of capacity to control his actions, or of capacity to know that he ought not to do the act or make the omission.

A person whose mind, at the time of his doing or omitting to do an act, is affected by delusions on some specific matter or matters, but who is not otherwise entitled to the benefit of the foregoing provisions of this section, is criminally responsible for the act or omission to the same extent as if the real state of things had been such as he was induced by the delusions to believe to exist.[10]

Griffith provided a lengthy explanation and justification for this Section, which is worth extended reproduction, in that he refers succinctly to the criticisms which have been levelled at the Rules almost since the moment of their enunciation, and reveals a degree of scholarship in comparative law which may shame modern scholars.

There is, perhaps, no branch of the criminal law which has given rise to more discussion and difference of opinion than the relation of mental infirmity to criminal responsibility. . . .

[7] [1966] N.Z.L.R. 616, at 621.
[8] (1952) 86 C.L.R. 358.
[9] (1933) 55 C.L.R. 182.
[10] Exactly the same provision appears in the Western Australian Code of 1902.

The language of the learned Judges [in McNaughton's case] has been much criticized. Lord Chief Justice Cockburn said, 'What is meant by the nature and quality of the act I really do not know. Does it simply mean that the person committing the act knew what he was doing, or that he knew that the act was legally wrong or was morally wrong? What is meant by the alternative "or that the act was wrong"? Is this phrase meant to be synonymous with the "quality" of the act as just before mentioned? If not, what is the difference between the two forms of expression?' (Letter to Attorney-General 12 June 1879, p 15). In practice every judge amplifies the rule by telling the jury what in his opinion is meant by the 'nature and quality' of the act.

The subject has been much considered by the Continental nations of Europe. Before referring to the particular provisions of their Codes it may be desirable to offer a few observations on the general principles applicable to the matter. An act to involve criminal responsibility must be voluntary, as distinguished from involuntary (s. 25)—that is to say, it must be accompanied by volition. In order that an action may be accompanied by volition there must in the first place perception, more or less accurate, of the facts, then a determination or choice of the action to be taken upon those facts, and finally the action. If the person in question is incapable from mental disorder of rightly perceiving the facts, he should be treated on the same footing as a man who in good faith misapprehends the facts (s. 20). If he is for the same cause incapable of exercising the power of determination or choice, he should be treated on the same footing as a man who does an act independently of the exercise of his will (s. 25). So far there is little reason for controversy. But it is conceived that our law assumes the notion of duty. No one supposes that everyone or anyone knows all the provisions of the criminal law. Yet no one above the age of discretion (s. 31) is excused by ignorance of law (s. 24). Why is the distinction drawn at a particular age? Not, surely, because at that age knowledge of the law comes to a child, but because he is then supposed to be capable of knowing that some things ought not to be done, i.e. of apprehending the idea of duty. If this is so, there is a third element of criminal responsibility corresponding to the capacity of a child who has reached the age of discretion; and a person who by reason of mental disorder is in the condition of a child as to capacity of apprehending the notion of duty ought to be equally free from criminal responsibility. This last element seems to be wanting in the definition of insanity given in the Continental Codes, but it is, I believe, part of the law of England.

The following statement of the definition of insanity given in various Continental Codes and Draft Codes are taken from the Ministerial explanation made by Signor Zanardelli in introducing the *Italian Penal Code* to the Legislature in 1888. (The definition in the Draft Code as introduced was as follows: 'A person is not punishable who, at the moment when he committed the act, was in such a state of defect or morbid affection (alterazione) of the mind as to deprive him of consciousness of his acts or of the possibility of acting otherwise.')

Dutch Code: 'Incomplete development or morbid disturbance of the intelligence.'
German Code: 'Deprivation of understanding or condition of morbid affection of the mental faculties.'
Hungarian Code: 'State of unconsciousness or disturbance of the intellectual faculties.'
Code of Zurich: If the faculties of the mind of the accused 'were overturned in such a manner as not to possess the attitude of free determination or the discernment necessary to understand the criminal nature of the act'.
Austrian Draft of 1881: 'State of want of understanding or of deficient development or disturbance of the intellectual faculties.'
Russian Draft of 1881: 'Insufficiency of the intellectual faculties, or morbid disturbance of the activity of the mind, or state of unconsciousness.'

The definition actually adopted in the Italian Code may be thus translated: 'such a

173

state of infirmity of the mind (mentre) as to deprive him of consciousness of his acts or of freedom of action.' (s. 46)

The definition given in the text is substantially the same as this, with the addition of the element of moral capacity.

The *New York Code*, as amended in 1882, adopts the words of the Judges in McNaughton's case.

The Code Napoléon, which was enacted before the subject had been so fully considered as it has been of late years, puts insanity and compulsion together. 'It is neither crime nor misdemeanour (délit) when the accused person was in a state of insanity (démence) at the time of the act or if he was constrained by a force which he could not resist.'

(Code Pénal, At. 64.)

I believe that any direction to a jury which omitted a reference to any one of the three elements—capacity of perception, capacity of choice, and moral capacity—in a case in which such an element was material would be contrary to the Common Law. As to the reasonableness of the rule, as stated in the text, there is little room for doubt. A moment's consideration will suggest cases in which any two of the three elements may be present, while the third is absent, and in which it would be absurd to hold the actor criminally responsible. It is important to remember, however, that the absence of either capacity is immaterial, unless it arises from mental disorder or infirmity.

It will be observed that the rule stated in section 29 (sec 27), considered from the points of view to which attention is invited in this Note, is merely a particular instance of the application of the general rules determining the question of criminal responsibility stated in ss. 2, 26 and 31 (mistake and immaturity).[11]

But since that pioneering effort, faithfully copied by Western Australia, there has been little Australian legislative activity affecting the Rules. In 1924 Tasmania introduced its Criminal Code; sec 16 deals with the defence of insanity in terms Barry, Paton and Sawer describe as 'rather more precise' than Griffith's version.[12]

In the common law states the McNaughton Rules were left quite untouched by Parliament until 1974, when New South Wales copied the diminished responsibility provisions made part of English law by sec 2 of the *Homicide Act* 1957;[13] Queensland introduced a similar provision into its Code in 1961.[14] The stringent limitations of this novel provision make it clear that it is not intended to do more than supplement the Rules in prosecutions for murder.

*   *   *

MCNAUGHTON IN THE COURTS

A judgment of the Supreme Court of New South Wales sitting *in Banco* in 1908 will serve to set the stage. Frederick Green was charged with the murder of Lily Bridge, pleaded not guilty and relied on the defence of insanity.[15] Sly, J.

---

[11] *Votes and Proceedings of the Queensland Leg. Ass.*, 1897; Vol I, p 657.

[12] See Barry, Paton and Sawer, note (4) *supra*, pp 53–6.

[13] Inserting sec 23A into the *Crimes Act* 1900. See R. P. Roulston, *Introduction to Criminal Law in New South Wales* (1975), pp 41–6.

[14] See *R.* v. *Rolph*, [1962] Qd. R. 262; Roulston, Note (9) *supra*, at pp 45–6; P. Brett and P. L. Waller, *Criminal Law-Cases and Text* (3rd ed., 1971), pp. 695–7; Barry, J. in *R.* v. *Jeffrey*, [1967] V.R. 467 at 479–80.

[15] *R.* v. *Green*, (1908) 25 W.N. 93.

174

charged the jury by adopting 'the law contained in answers to the questions put to the Judges in the well-known case of *R. v. Macnaghten*'. Reid, K.C., counsel for Green, complained that the jury had been misdirected. He asked that they be given these instructions:

'(1) When insanity is set up, as in this case, and the evidence leaves the jury in doubt as to the responsibility of the accused, they should find a verdict of not guilty on the grounds of insanity.

(2) That the accused was not guilty if, at the time of the act alleged, he was prevented by reason of defective mental power from knowing the nature and quality of his act, or that it was wrong.

(3) That, in a case where an accused does not know the act is wrong, he is not guilty if he was prevented by disease of the mind from controlling his own conduct at the time of the occurrence.'

Sly, J. refused to re-direct the jury, but stated a case.

Sir Frederick Darley, C.J., said bluntly: 'Do you expect this court to upset Macnaghten's case?' Mr Reid answered, 'Candidly I do not . . .'. The Chief Justice: 'Then Mr Reid, we will say at once that we have no intention of upsetting Macnaghten's case.'

It was 1936 before the first substantial critical examination of the McNaughton Rules was made in the Australian Courts. In February of that year Arnold Sodeman was tried for the murder of a six-year-old girl.[16] After forty years the case still provokes controversy.[17] A very brief account of the facts—simple and, unhappily, not unique—is appropriate before the various requirements of the Rules and their administration are considered separately.

The girl's body was found lying beside a country road. Her hands were tied behind her back with a strip torn from her dress, which had been pulled up so that the lower part of her body was exposed. She had been gagged with underpants. The cause of death was suffocation. Sodeman who lived not far from the little girl, was questioned by police and confessed that he had killed her. He also admitted that he had killed three other girls, whose deaths had remained unsolved homicides for more than five years. The bodies of the other girls had been discovered in strikingly similar attitudes to that of the latest victim.[18] Sodeman was tried before Gavan Duffy, J. and a jury. His defence was that he was insane at the time. There was evidence that Sodeman's grandfather and father had died in mental hospitals. There was inconclusive evidence that his mother suffered from amnesia. There was evidence that Sodeman had fallen from a horse while drunk two years before the fourth killing and had been unconscious for some time. Three medical witnesses were called on his behalf,

[16] *R. v. Sodeman* [1936] V.L.R. (F.C., Vic.); (1936), 55 C.L.R. 192 (H.Ct. of Aust. and P.C.).
[17] A full account of this case is given in J. V. Barry, 'The Sodeman Case and the Defence of Insanity' (1936), 10 A.L.J. 3 and 95. See also Anon., 'Irresistible Impulse' (1936), 10 A.L.J. 130, and J. V. Barry, 'Irresistible Impulse—a Reply' (1936), 10 A.L.J. 176. The late Judge J. P. Bourke, who was one of Sodeman's counsel, was much affected by the case; more than 30 years afterwards he collaborated with Mr D. S. Sonenberg in a book *Insanity and Injustice* (1969) which discusses its whole background and circumstances.
[18] Cf. *R. v. Straffen*, [1952] 2 Q.B. 911; *R. v. Morris*, (1969) 54 Cr. App. R. 69.

175

of whom two were Government medical officers at Pentridge Gaol, where Sodeman was held pending his trial. Each of these witnesses deposed that, in his opinion, at the time of the commission of each killing the prisoner did not know the nature and quality of his act, and did not know it was wrong. The Crown called no medical evidence. The prisoner was convicted of murder and sentenced to death.[19] Sodeman sought to appeal to the Full Court of the Supreme Court of Victoria on the ground that the judge had misdirected the jury on the law on insanity, and on the burden of proof. That court dismissed his application.

A date for his execution was fixed by the Executive Council; Sodeman then sought special leave to appeal against his conviction from the High Court of Australia. Latham, C.J. arranged a special sitting of the High Court in Melbourne less than a week before the date of execution. But four judges only were available to consider the application, and the court divided equally. Accordingly, under the provisions of sec 23(2) of the *Judiciary Act* 1903–27, Sodeman's application failed. After the High Court gave its decision on 2 April 1936, Sodeman's solicitor asked the Victorian government for funds to permit an application for leave to appeal to the Privy Council. After a short period in which it seemed that Sodeman's execution would not be postponed, financial assistance was provided and the execution postponed. Sodeman's application was rejected by the Council, and he was executed on 1 June 1936.

After his execution a post-mortem examination was performed, 'which revealed definite evidence of inflammation of the membranes covering the brain. The pathologist's report read: "Enlarged cirrhotic liver, spleen atrophic, kidneys congested, brain congested and show an early lepto-meningitis with excess cerebrospinal fluid. There was some adherence to the mininges, slight atheroma of the aorta." '[20]

It is not difficult to understand, then, why the case is still regarded today as an unhappy episode in the history of the administration of criminal justice in Australia.[21] In the judgments nearly every aspect of the McNaughton Rules was canvassed, revealing attitudes and viewpoints which reappear in the later cases. Let me discuss each aspect briefly.

'*Every man is to be presumed to be sane*': *the Burden of Proof*. In *Sodeman's* case Gavan Duffy, J. began his charge by reminding the jury that the Crown had to prove every constituent part of the murder beyond reasonable doubt, and then said:

'But when you come to insanity, the position is entirely different . . . he himself has the burden of proving clearly to you that that insanity did exist.'[22]

[19] Barry, note (12) *supra*, at p 3. See Bourke and Sonenberg, note (12) *supra*, Chaps 8 and 9. This latter chapter contains most of Gavan Duffy J.'s summing up to the jury.
[20] Bourke and Sonenberg, *op cit*, p 121 (from Chap 15, by Dr L. Howard Whittaker, M.B., Dip.Psych.Med.).
[21] Cf *Tait* v. *R.*, [1963] V.R. 547 (1962). Tait unsuccessfully raised the defence of insanity, and then claimed he was insane just before the date of execution. The death sentence was ultimately commuted to imprisonment for life with the papers marked 'never to be released'. This extra-ordinary legal episode is recounted in C. Burns, *The Tait Case* (1962). See Brett and Waller, *op cit*, p 700.
[22] Bourke and Sonenberg, *op cit*, p 70.

In the Full Court, Sodeman's counsel argued that the jury had been misled into thinking that the accused bore the same burden on the issue of insanity as the Crown did on all the other issues. The jury should have been directed that it was only necessary for Sodeman to make out insanity upon a balance of probabilities.

There was the influential charge of Dixon, J. to a Canberra jury three years earlier in *R. v. Porter* to underscore that approach. But the Full Court, which concentrated wholly on this aspect of the charge, said there was nothing in the appeal.

In the High Court a few days later, Dixon and Evatt, JJ. both held that the standard which the accused must reach was on a balance of probabilities. Dixon and Evatt, JJ. decided that the jury would not have understood from the charge that the accused carried a lighter burden than the Crown. Latham, C.J. and Starke, J. took the same view of the standard, but thought that the charge was adequate. In the Privy Council it was made clear that the accused does not have to persuade the jury beyond reasonable doubt, but merely on a balance of probabilities.

Controversy about this aspect of the McNaughton Rules was not stilled by the last episode in *Sodeman's* case. Since the prosecution clearly carries a different burden as to those aspects of the case which it had to prove, confusion easily flows, and there is easy opportunity for argument on the correctness of the trial judge's instructions. 'Beyond reasonable doubt' and 'satisfy you upon a balance of probabilities' nudge each other in unhappily reciprocating chaos.

Apart from this practical problem, there remains the intellectual difficulty of requiring the prosecution to prove beyond reasonable doubt that the accused did have a guilty mind, and at the same time asking the accused to prove, on the balance of probabilities, that he did not have one. In a paper which combines legal history and the philosophy of law with a clear understanding of the forensic process, 'A Legacy of Hadfield, M'Naghten and Maclean', Sir Owen Dixon refers to this last mildly as 'an incongruity'.[23] The burden of proof rule was seriously questioned in the dissenting judgment of Monahan, J. in *R. v. Mizzi*.[24] He put forward strong arguments to support the view that all the accused is required to do is to adduce enough evidence on the issue of insanity 'to pass the judge', in Wigmore's expression. This approach may one day commend itself in the High Court of Australia, thereby enabling it to complete the *Woolmington* revolution. That court was able to dispose of Mizzi without considering the question, though it was raised in argument.[25]

Recently Smith, J. of the Supreme Court of Victoria has said that the present rule is a harsh one. In an unreported case, *R. v. Letis*, he said this on charging the jury:

That the law should say so may strike you as a hard saying. It really involves this, that if a jury say 'It is as likely as not that this man was too mad to be criminally responsible

[23] (1957) 31 A.L.J. 255, at 256-7.
[24] Supreme Court of Vic., 1960; see Brett and Waller, *op cit*, 685.
[25] (1960), 105 C.L.R. 659.

177

but we cannot go any further than that' then they have to find him guilty of murder. The law is really saying that a conviction of murder may be arrived at because the jury find themselves unable to make up their minds as to conflicting evidence on the issue of insanity. Some people take the view that that is a very unsatisfactory state of the law; some people go further and regard it as a disgraceful state of the law, but that is what the law is at present. The only further comment that I make about it to you is this: that being the state of the law, there are the strongest reasons why you should apply your minds strongly and diligently to the evidence on this question of insanity, and try to arrive at a definite conclusion one way or the other as to whether this defence is or is not made out. Do not on any account shelter behind this rule of law that if the balance is left even you can decide the case on that footing simply by saying 'Well, the question is too difficult for us, we cannot decide it.'[26]

It is clear that in many cases in which the issue is raised the way in which the burden of proof is allocated may virtually determine the outcome of the trial. This part of the Rules has been soundly criticized outside the courts. The late Barry, J., was a constant opponent of this (and other) aspects of McNaughton. In an article published in 1939, 'The Defence of Insanity and the Burden of Proof', he joined with Dixon, J., whose views have already been mentioned, and finished his argument thus:[27]

In a striking passage Stephen has written, 'If it be asked why an accused person is presumed to be innocent, I think the true answer is, not that the presumption is probably true, but that society in the present day is so much stronger than the individual and is capable of inflicting so very much more harm on the individual than the individual as a rule can inflict upon society, that it can afford to be generous.'[28]
It is submitted that the time has come to lay aside, in respect of the defence of insanity that fear of the consequences of innovation which the history of criminal law reform has shown so often to be unfounded, and to apply the principle of Woolmington's case generally, so that society may display in the administration of the criminal law at least an equal generosity to him who pleads insanity as to him who pleads misadventure or self-defence.

The time is still coming.

'Defect of Reason From Disease of the Mind.' This requirement did not seem to cause any difficulty or provoke any discussions in Sodeman's case. It is only in the last twenty years that it has leaped into prominence, and of all of the expressions used in the Rules it is the most elusive.

Three years before Sodeman, Dixon, J. presided over the trial of Porter in the Supreme Court of the Australian Capital Territory. His instructions to the jury came to the notice of a Victorian barrister, Mr J. V. Barry (later Barry, J.) who told Sodeman's counsel about the charge.[29] The charge was published in the same volume of the Commonwealth Law Reports as the report of Sodeman's appeal.[30] In R. v. Porter, Dixon, J. said:

[26] See Brett and Waller, op cit, 686.
[27] 2 Res Judicatae, 42, at 48–9.
[28] I Hist. Crim. Law, 354.
[29] Bourke and Sonenberg, op cit, 80.
[30] (1933) 55 C.L.R. 182; (1936) 55 C.L.R. 192.

'. . . [H]is state of mind must have been one of disease, disorder or disturbance. Mere excitability of a normal man, passion, even stupidity, obtuseness, lack of self-control, and impulsiveness, are quite different things from what I have attempted to describe as a state of disease or disorder or mental disturbance arising from some infirmity, temporary or of long standing . . .'[31]

In Sodeman's case, Gavan Duffy, J. did not use similar language. He said:

Insanity simply means . . . a want of health in the mind, and everything that is a departure from the normal is insanity to a degree.[31a]

It was not taken up on appeal.

The phrase is clearly not a term of art, nor a piece of technical jargon in medical science, whatever taxonomies different psychiatrists use today. In many cases all the experts may agree that a person is suffering from a particular mental illness, but will disagree whether that illness is a disease of the mind.

The modern English cases of R. v. Charlson[32] and R. v. Kemp[33] focused attention on this expression. If 'black-out' behaviour was not characterized as a defect of reason arising from disease of the mind, then the accused could argue that it was 'no mind' behaviour, and accordingly he ought to be acquitted altogether. Devlin, J.'s view, in R. v. Kemp, bringing this sort of case within the ambit of the McNaughton Rules, received the extra-judicial support of Dixon, C.J. the following year.[34] The Chief Justice there predicted that by reasons of its consequences the view that black-out behaviour—or 'automatism', to use the most often-used expression, was not within McNaughton would prove increasingly attractive to those accused of crime. His prediction was clearly borne out in the Victorian case of R. v. Carter,[35] where Sholl, J. took the view that a plea of post-traumatic automatism (following immediately upon a blow to the head) was not a plea of insanity. The same year the New Zealand Court of Appeal, in R. v. Cottle,[36] nicely avoided committing itself to that view, or the opposing view put by Devlin, J. and Dixon, C.J.; instead it held that in each particular case the automatism was to be characterized as 'sane' or 'insane' in the light of the medical evidence. Their view seems to have commended itself to the House of Lords in Bratty v. Attorney-General for Northern Ireland.[37]

A few years after Bratty's case was decided, Sholl, J. again considered this matter in R. v. Meddings.[38] This was a case in which counsel for the accused, charged with wounding with intent to murder his best friend in a completely motiveless shooting, argued that post-epileptic automatism provided a complete

---

[31] (1933) 55 C.L.R. 182, at 188. See that judge's explanation of the expression in 'A Legacy of Hadfield, M'Naghten and Maclean', (1957) 31 A.L.J. 255, at 260. And see N. Morris and C. Howard, Studies in Criminal Law (1964), 41–2.
[31a] Bourke and Sonenberg, op cit, 71.
[32] (1955), 39 Cr. App. Rep. 37.
[33] [1957] 1 Q.B. 399.
[34] 'A Legacy of Hadfield, M'Naghten and Maclean', (1957), 31 A.L.J. 255.
[35] [1959] V.R. 105.
[36] [1958] N.Z.L.R. 999.
[37] [1963] A.C. 386.
[38] [1966] V.R. 306. See also R. v. Haywood, [1971], V.R. 755, and R. v. Pantelic (1973), 1 A.C.T.R. 1.

excuse for the violent behaviour. Sholl, J. said that the important criterion for determining whether the accused suffered from a disease of the mind, and so was raising the defence of insanity, was 'the potentiality of recurrence' of the violent behaviour. Clearly this sets aside most cases where the black-out behaviour follows a blow or a motor accident. (Epilepsy may occur post-traumatically.)

'*Know the nature and quality of the act he was doing.*' In *Sodeman*'s case, the medical witnesses said that the accused did not know the nature and quality of his act. In the High Court, Dixon, J., said that many people found the phrase 'anything but illuminating'.[39] The English judicial view was that it meant simply the physical character of the act, not its moral implications or character.[40] In the essay already mentioned, Sir Owen Dixon said that it was better put in the older cases Sir Nicholas Tindal was attempting to summarize, where 'you get the simple phrases "did not know what he did" and "a faculty to distinguish the nature of actions"'.[41] In the modern case of *Willgoss* v. *The Queen*,[42] the High Court held clearly that the physical nature view is the right one.

That case raised clearly the meaning of the verb *know*. This appears in both this and the next important limb of the McNaughton Rules, so that cognition alone is emphasized, with no mention of volition or sympathetic understanding of consequences. The whole problem of 'irresistible impulse' flows from this restriction.

In *Willgoss*'s case the High Court was invited unsuccessfully to hold that 'know' had a larger meaning, in connection with the next branch or limb of the Rules. After dealing with the meaning given to *wrong*, I shall return to *know*.

'*Know he was doing what was wrong.*' In *Sodeman*'s case, the High Court held that 'wrong' meant 'morally wrong', confirming what Dixon, J. had said when he instructed the jury in *Porter*'s case.[43] The opposite view that 'wrong' meant 'contrary to law' was adopted in England in *Codère*'s case,[44] and emphatically reaffirmed in *R.* v. *Windle* in 1952.[45] The same year the High Court decided *Stapleton* v. *The Queen*.[46] It reviewed the McNaughton Rules and the cases which preceded them and concluded that the word referred to 'right and wrong in the general sense and not lawfulness and unlawfulness'.[47]

But when the High Court heard *Willgoss* v. *R.*[48] it refused to interpret the verb 'know' with which the phrase begins in a more generous fashion. In that case it was argued that the defendant's mental condition was such that he could

[39] (1936) 55 C.L.R. 192 at 215.
[40] *R.* v. *Codère* (1916), 12 Cr. Ap. Rep. 21.
[41] 31 A.L.J. 255, at 257, quoting from *R.* v. *Arnold*, (1724), 16 St. Tr. 698 at 764, and *R.* v. *Ferrers* (1760), 19 St. Tr. 885.
[42] (1960), 105 C.L.R. 295 at 300.
[43] (1936) 55 C.L.R. 192 at 215; (1933) 55 C.L.R. 182 at 189–90.
[44] (1916), 12 Cr. App. Rep. 21.
[45] 36 Cr. App. Rep. 85.
[46] 86 C.L.R. 358.
[47] 86 C.L.R. 358 at 374–5.
[48] (1960), 105 C.L.R. 295.

appreciate the wrongfulness of his behaviour on a purely intellectual level, but that he could not appreciate or *know* it on an emotional level; he did not feel anything about what he had done. There was medical evidence to support the argument. The Court simply said that to interpret 'know' in this way was 'an attempt to refine upon what amounts to knowledge of the wrongness of the act which is not countenanced by the law'.[49]

Curiously the High Court had countenanced another refinement upon knowledge of the wrongness of the act. From the very first, one of the most potent criticisms of the McNaughton Rules was that it took no account of failures of volition, of impulses that could not be resisted. Stephen urged, on and off the Bench, that the Rules could be interpreted to allow irresistible impulse to be accommodated. In *Sodeman's* case the issue was squarely raised. The defendant's argument was again clearly based on what Dixon, J. had laid in *Porter's* case, namely that a man could be so driven by an overwhelming force or impulse to do something prohibited by the law 'that he could not reason about the matter with a moderate degree of sense and composure'.[50]

All of the four judges in *Sodeman's* case, Latham, C.J., Starke, Dixon and Evatt, JJ., seem to have accepted that argument, though it is only shortly mentioned by Starke, J. It must be noted that Dixon, J., was careful to say that to find that a man was driven by an overwhelming impulse is not necessarily to conclude that he did not know that what he was doing was wrong. He might have been able to reason with some calmness, and so know he ought not do to the act, but still felt driven to do it. Or he might have been so driven that he could not reason calmly about whether he ought to do it. The jury would have to decide which of these was in fact the accused's position, in the light of all the evidence.

The High Court continued to adopt this approach after *Sodeman's* case. The most important recent case in which irresistible impulse and the McNaughton Rules were canvassed was *Brown* v. *R*.[51] In 1959, Brown a man of 25, killed his employer four days after starting work. There was no motive for the shooting. Brown told the police that he knew it was wrong '. . . but I couldn't help myself.' In allowing Brown's appeal, the High Court said that irresistible impulse

may afford strong ground for the inference that a prisoner was labouring under such a defect of reason from disease of the mind as not to know that he was doing what was wrong. The law has nothing to say against the view that mind is indivisible, and that such a symptom of derangement as action under uncontrollable impulse may be inconsistent with an adequate capacity at the time to comprehend the wrongness of the act.[52]

The trial judge, the High Court said, had misdirected the jury by simply telling them that 'uncontrollable impulse' was a defence unknown to the law.

The Attorney-General of South Australia obtained special leave to appeal

[49] 105 C.L.R. 295 at 301.
[50] (1933) 55 C.L.R. 182 at 189.
[51] [1959] Argus L.R. 808.
[52] [1959] Argus L.R. 808 at 814.

to the Privy Council, which reversed the High Court's decision and restored Brown's conviction for murder.[53] The Council did so because it held that there must be *medical evidence* supporting the view that the defendant's mind was so affected by impulse that he was prevented from knowing that he was doing wrong, if the judge were to instruct the jury in the terms used by the High Court (set out above).[54] The Council's decision has been critically examined and accorded less than a warm welcome in the literature.[55] Its impact on the High Court, as revealed in *Mizzi*'s case,[56] seems slight. But Professor Colin Howard has said that it seems probable that the judgment of the Privy Council in *Brown*'s case will make a significant difference to the practical application of the McNaughton Rules in Australia because the possibility of a link between lack of capacity for self-control and lack of capacity to reason about right and wrong had been established,

. . . [I]t may be surmised that in most cases little difficulty will be encountered by medical witnesses in giving evidence of their belief in a link between the two.[57]

THE FORM OF THE VERDICT AND ITS CONSEQUENCES

The famous post-Hadfield statute, 39 and 40 Geo. III, c. 94, which authorized the detention of persons found not guilty on the ground of insanity during His Majesty's pleasure has its Australian descendants. Sec 420 of the Victorian *Crimes Act* 1958 is an example.[58]

The prospect of indefinite imprisonment in an ordinary prison, or at best in a psychiatric prison, has meant, in the Antipodes as elsewhere, that the defence of insanity is rarely raised, except in capital cases. Norval Morris argued, in 'Daniel McNaughton and the Death Penalty' published over twenty years ago[59] that the abolition of the death penalty as a mandatory punishment for murder would remove the real barrier to the reform of the law on insanity and criminal responsibility.

The hangman has skulked about in the background of our discussion of the McNaughton Rules . . . In the absence of the death penalty the problem of the defence of insanity is not a complex one; whilst we atavistically retain that punishment it is submitted that the McNaughton Rules modified and interpreted to incorporate some elements of irresistible impulse, to include mental defect, and with a wide meaning given to 'wrong' are the best solution to this traditional medico-legal conflict.[60]

[53] [1960] A.C. 432.
[54] [1960] A.C. 432 at 449–50.
[55] See P. Brett in (1960) 23 Mod. L. Rev. 545; N. Morris and C. Howard, *Studies in Criminal Law* (1964), 51–3; P. Brett and P. L. Waller, *Criminal Law—Cases and Text* (3rd ed., 1971), 691.
[56] (1960) 105 C.L.R. 659.
[57] *Australian Criminal Law* (2nd ed., 1970), 337–8.
[58] On the form of the verdict, see Brett and Waller, *op cit*, 713.
[59] (1953) 6 *Res Judicatae*, 304. Capital punishment for murder was abolished in New South Wales and in Victoria in 1975. It remains in force in South Australia, but no sentence has been executed for many years.
[60] Note (59), *supra*, at 336.

The development of the defence of automatism, which, if successful, must lead to an outright acquittal, is a further emphasis of the real consequences of the special verdict. There have also been instances, of which the most striking is *R. v. Jeffrey*,[61] where other defences have been raised, even though there is clear evidence of insanity; it has been ignored by the defence because of the consequences of success. This has led the Crown in Australia, in some cases, to attempt to adduce evidence of insanity under the McNaughton Rules to meet a defence of automatism or even of provocation. Clearly this has been because prosecutors have sought to safeguard the public interest by securing the detention of a dangerous man until there is expert evidence that he has recovered and is safe to be abroad. In *Jeffrey*'s case, the Victorian Full Court said quite clearly that the prosecution could not lead evidence of insanity as part of its case against the accused. That was not its task. The Victorian court bluntly rejected the opinion expressed by Lord Denning in *Bratty*'s case,[62] where he said:

The old notion that only the defence can raise a defence of insanity has now gone. The prosecution are entitled to raise it, and it is their duty to do so rather than allow a dangerous person to be at large.[63]

Barry, J. pointed out that the English *Criminal Procedure (Insanity) Act*, 1964, enacted shortly after *Bratty*'s case was decided, did not give any effect to Lord Denning's opinion that the statute made very substantial changes in the form of the verdict and in appellate procedures.[64]

At the same time, the Victorian Court agreed that if evidence which could justify an acquittal on the ground of insanity had actually been given, the trial judge should direct the jury on the issue, even though the defence had not raised the issue and had not sought a direction on it as part of the charge.[65]

*   *   *

McNaughton in the Literature

In the text of the previous part, and also in the notes to it, there are many references to Australian writing on the McNaughton Rules. Two judges in particular have made very important contributions to the learning on these Rules on the Bench and in their extra-curial writings.

Sir Owen Dixon, whose charge to the jury in *R. v. Porter*[66] had a profound opinion in later cases, revealed his views on the Rules in a paper read to a Convention of the Law Council of Australia, 'A Legacy of Hadfield, M'Naghten and Maclean'.[67] Sir John Barry's major writing on the subject, 'Insanity and the

[61] [1967] V.R. 467.
[62] [1963] A.C. 386.
[63] [1963] A.C. 386 at 411–12.
[64] [1967] V.R. 467 at 473–4.
[65] [1967] V.R. 467 at 473 and 488.
[66] (1933) 55 C.L.R. 182.
[67] (1957) 31 A.L.J. 255.

Criminal Law in Australia', was originally published in the *Canadian Bar Review*.[68] Some of that important article was reproduced on the chapter on general principles in Barry, Paton and Sawer, *An Introduction to the Criminal Law in Australia*.[69]

Among important modern essays by academic lawyers is Peter Brett's *An Enquiry into Criminal Guilt* (1963), in which Chapter V is largely on the theme of insanity. Norval Morris and Colin Howard's *Studies in Criminal Law* (1964) has an essay on 'Insanity and Automatism',[70] which covers the Australian material thoroughly.

The most recent article on the subject has the provocative title, 'Abolition of the Crime of Murder and Mental Condition Defences' and is the joint work of two lawyers (one a senior lecturer in the University of Melbourne's Department of Criminology and the other a senior and very experienced practitioner), and a doctor who is Psychiatrist Superintendent in Victoria's largest prison.[71]

Conclusion

More than 130 years after the judges gave their answers to the questions put by the House of Lords, the McNaughton Rules remain the law on insanity and criminal responsibility for a large part of Australia. Their influence on the Codes is clear, and the New Zealand provision is the Rules in legislative dress.

What is the future of the Rules? In this part of the world, as elsewhere, they have been the target of severe psychiatric and philosophical attacks. The earlier parts of this paper reveal only part of the lawyers' criticism. It has not had much impact in terms of radical change. More than twenty years ago, Australia's greatest judge wryly commented that some of the words in the advice delivered by Sir Nicholas Tindal, C.J., clearly chosen because they had 'the widest possible meaning', have been treated as 'a sacred text behind which you must not go'. In the same essay, he said of another phrase in the McNaughton Rules that Sir Nicholas Tindal

would hardly have supposed it possible that the expression would be treated as one containing words of the law to be weighed like diamonds.[72]

But that, so far, has largely been their fate. Let the last words be Sir Owen Dixon's—

The unforeseen result has, as I think, been to imprison the common law in a formula, a formula which has been misunderstood at more than one point and has deprived the common law not only of its capacity for development but even of its accustomed

---

[68] (1943) 21 Can. B. Rev. 429.
[69] (1948), 30–3. See also 'The Sodeman Case and the Defence of Insanity', (1936) 10 A.L.J. 3 and 95.
[70] Pp 37–78.
[71] K. L. Milte, A. A. Bartholomew and F. Galbally in (1975), 49 A.L.J. 173. See too N. Morris and G. Hawkins, *The Honest Politician's Guide to Crime Control* (1970), ch 7, esp 176–85. For an early psychiatric critique of the Rules, see R. S. Ellery, 'The Plea of Insanity', (1932) I. *Proc. Medico-Legal Soc. of Victoria*, 23.
[72] (1957) 31 A.L.J. 255 at 257.

flexibility of application. The growth of modern knowledge on the whole subject has meanwhile deprived the terms in which the formula is expressed of practical meaning. It is a . . . discreditable chapter of the law.[73]

---

[73] (1957) 31 A.L.J. 255 at 261. See too the last paragraph in the judgment of Barry, J., in *R.* v. *Jeffrey*, [1967] V.R. 467, at 479–80.